£14.95

D1588831

10

A

The PHYSICAL BASIS *of* RIME

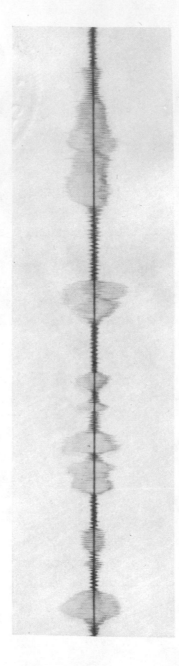

Photographic record of the first verse of Milton's *Paradise Lost*. Speaker: Professor L. E. Bassett, of Stanford University. Read from right to left.

The
PHYSICAL BASIS of
RIME

*An Essay
on the Aesthetics of Sound*

By HENRY LANZ

*"I have dissected music as a corpse,
And harmony I verified with numbers"*
ALEXANDER PUSHKIN, *Mozart and Salieri*

GREENWOOD PRESS, PUBLISHERS
NEW YORK   1968

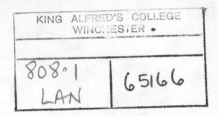

First Greenwood reprinting, 1968

LIBRARY OF CONGRESS catalogue card number: 69-10115

PRINTED IN THE UNITED STATES OF AMERICA

To
My Wife
LISA LANZ

THIS WORD [author] may spring from two roots: The one is that of a verb, dropped very much out of use in Latin, which signifies "binding words together," to wit, *auieo*. And whoso regards it well, in its first form, will clearly perceive that it shows its own meaning; for it is made of nought save the bonds of words, that is to say, of the five vowels alone, which are the soul and juncture of every word; and it is composed of them in such a manner as to form the figure of a tie. For, beginning with *a*, it turns to *u*, and then goes straight by *i* to *e*, whence it goes back and returns to *o*. . . . . And in so far as "author" is derived and descends from this verb, *auieo*, it is understood only of poets, who have bound their words with the art of music.

—DANTE, *The Convivio*, IV, 6

PREFACE

~~~~~~

THIS book is a by-product of the author's studies in logic. Some fifteen years ago, while preparing his inaugural dissertation for the degree of Master of Arts in the University of Moscow and working upon the problem of logical objectivity, the author conceived what then seemed to him the rather novel idea of extending the strategic positions of modern realism beyond the boundary line of pure logic and applying its principles to the field of aesthetics. Edmund Husserl's attack on psychology and Emil Lask's theory of "Geltung" were the philosophical sensations of the day. "Truth" got loose from psychological slavery. "Beauty" was expected to follow it. It seemed only natural that philosophy should come to regard aesthetic values as manifestations of a specific form of existence, as constituting a universe of purely objective phenomena, similarly related to or, if one wished, similarly removed from man's subjective needs and standards, just as logical values were found to be related to or removed from the consciousness of man. In search of illustrative material for this new specific objectivity the author hit upon rhythm and rime. Here he believed he had found something that could not be rationally expressed in words or definitions and yet possessed an order of its own and a high degree of communicability. They had their own laws that poets had to follow and were powerless to change. Their effect was precise and, evidently, easily transmissible from the poet to his audience. They had a complex structure and a long history of growth. In a word, they behaved like phenomenological entities of some description. What was their nature? What was the secret of their effect upon the human mind?

To answer these questions it seemed necessary to inquire into the physical nature of the sound in which they resided. And here lay a fascinating study. Unfortunately, at that time, the years 1913 and 1914, the analysis of human vowels was not sufficiently precise to justify the author's hypothesis as to the melodic nature of our speech. The vowels whose frequencies the author was able to obtain did not even approximately fit into either the diatonic or the chromatic scale. And the matter was dropped.

Much water has flowed under the bridge since then. For several years the author was not in position to continue his work. The larger part of his early manuscript has been lost during the troubled years of war and revolution. The phenomenological school meanwhile got firmly established in Germany, and secured the co-operation of such able men as Moritz Geiger, Max Scheler, and others, by whose efforts the problem of aesthetic and ethical realism has been clearly formulated and successfully solved. In its general form it no longer presents a novelty. Yet the nature of rime and of rhythm still remains an open question.

As there is no work in English that deals specifically with the theory and general history of rime, it has occurred to the author that students, of both philosophy and linguistics, may profit somewhat from an attempt to construct such theory on a purely physical basis. In the recent work of Miller and Crandall the author found a corroboration of his former views, and thus, gradually reconstructing from memory those chapters of his manuscript which dealt with rime and rhythm, and accumulating new experimental and bibliographical material, he at length believes he has succeeded in organizing his views to the consistency of a theory. The results of these long efforts are herewith offered to the public.

It would have been impossible to bring this book to a successful end without the generous assistance and effective cooperation of Professors J. G. Brown and F. E. Terman of Stanford University, who placed at the disposal of the author the facilities of their respective laboratories. It is also a pleasure to express here the debt of gratitude that the author owes to Dr. H. Fletcher, Dr. Margery Bailey, and Professors B. O. Foster, L. E. Bassett, Frederick Anderson, H. F. Blichfeldt, A. G. Kennedy, W. L. Schwartz, and H. W. Stuart for reading various parts of the manuscript. Their instruction and encouragement have been of the greatest assistance in the preparation of this volume, and many a passage stands now relatively clear as a result of their comments and constructive suggestions.

The author also desires to acknowledge the courtesy of Professor Carleton Brown for permission to reprint passages from the first sketch of "The Physical Basis of Rime," published under that title in the *Publications of The Modern Language Association of America,* Volume XLI, No. 4, December 1926.

In conclusion a word must be said in appreciation of the unfailing courtesy and skill of the Stanford University Press and its present editor, Professor W. H. Davis, whose patient assistance in solving problems of typographical detail and securing consistency throughout the work deserves hearty recognition.

HENRY LANZ

STANFORD UNIVERSITY, CALIFORNIA
December 15, 1929

CONTENTS

The
PHYSICAL BASIS *of* RIME

I

INTRODUCTION

IN the light of modern science the human word is not a mystery any longer. It allows itself to be analysed into its physical components. Physical research into the matter of speech has not merely shown that words consist of sound waves, "a succession of condensations and rarefactions in the air," but has also provided us with the means of analyzing and measuring those waves, of imitating them mechanically with a great degree of precision, and of studying them with "ruler and number." Moreover, we now possess means of producing photographic records of individual words and even whole sentences. The invisible world of sound becomes gradually more and more accessible to the eye. Many a mystery concerning the secrets of pronunciation and the mechanics of the vowel sounds has been solved. Our language has ceased to be "a kind of commonplace miracle" and "a gift of the gods." It has become a part of nature and an object of experimental analysis. The work of Rousselot in France and of Scripture in

America[1] laid the foundation of the science of experimental phonetics, and the research of recent years tends to define a still larger field of investigation that may eventually result in the formation of a new and independent discipline of "linguophysics." In this new field of research the linguist finds a real opportunity for constantly broadening the scope of analysis and a real responsibility for providing new material for investigation. One of many responsibilities of the present time is the application of physical methods to the study of poetry.

It has been remarked that our notions of poetry are based on metaphysical categories, that they are often "clothed in a loose and vague literary phraseology" and for the most part lack scientific precision. We are accustomed to think of poetry in terms of "inspiration." We define it as "the language of gods," as "that form of literature that embodies beautiful thought in rhythmical language," or as "something divine." For Plutarch poetry was a preparation for philosophy. For Benedetto Croce it is precisely the reverse of philosophy. Dante believed poetry to be "nihil aliud quam fictio rhetorica in musicaque posita"; and Lucretius went even so far as to compare it to the "sweet yellow honey with which doctors are wont to anoint the rim of the cup containing their bitter drugs." "In fact," complains Mark Liddell, "all the vagueness and bewildering confusions which attend popular conceptions and descriptions of ethical, intellectual, moral, aesthetic, and literary phenomena at some time or other enter singly or together into the discussion of this subject of poetry." The complaint repeats itself time and again. The general discontent with the traditional methods applied in literary criticism is rapidly

[1] Quite recently another fundamental work was published in this field, *Human Speech*, by Sir R. Paget (New York, 1930). I was unable to take this work into consideration here as it appeared after my book had already gone to press. But with a great satisfaction I noticed that the eminent physicist adopted the same method of musical presentation of human speech that had been used in this book.

growing, and sometimes a highly temperamental language is used for denouncing it. The enthusiasts of poetry, says one of the discontented, "find it easier to build fine sentences than to make clear to others, if to themselves, the nature of that which affects them so inspiringly."[2]

Mark Liddell offers a remedy. In 1902 appeared his *An Introduction to the Scientific Study of English Poetry*, in which an attempt is made to apply "scientific" methods to the study of poetry and to avoid as far as possible "the inherent vagueness of literary phraseology." "Our supreme question"—so Liddell formulates the methodological principle of his work —"is not how the poet happened to write his poetry, or what sort of mind or soul he had, or whence he came, or whither he went. His 'inspiration' and his 'message' are alike of no importance to us as students. But our duty is to determine what are the elements in poetry which stir our emotions and how these elements come to move us."

One may disagree with Liddell's conception of scientific or "rational" analysis. One may object that with the "scientific" categories alone it is impossible to grasp the essence of poetry; that literary categories, however vague and imperfect, are quite indispensable for analyzing poetic forms; that the task of approaching the whole of poetry with scientific methods is at present too ambitious to be successfully carried out; and that scientific analysis itself has its limits and limitations. A modern phenomenologist of the German school may justly remark that beneath the appearance of a scientific inquiry one often finds a mere falsification of facts, and that every attempt to "reduce" the genuine face value of a phenomenon to its scientific causes is illegitimate and futile. Poetry is not a physical fact. It is a phenomenon *sui generis*, and one who attempts to approach it physically or physiologically fails to understand

---

[2] E. C. Stedman, *The Nature and Elements of Poetry* (New York, 1892), page 41.

his own object. And yet all these doubts and objections, however justified, do not diminish the value of Liddell's proud resolve to approach scientifically the riddle of poetry, i.e., to examine the physical and physiological factors determining the phenomenon of poetic enjoyment. The phenomenon itself may be of a higher nature and from the phenomenological point of view not at all reducible to material causes. Yet the examination of those causes may throw some light upon the phenomenological structure of poetic forms and may help us to eliminate certain errors that come from the "inherent vagueness of literary phraseology."

What had been merely planned by Liddell on a scale too large to be practicable was successfully carried out by Scripture within the more limited field of the study of pronunciation. "The expectation of at once obtaining results concerning the laws of verse," says the author of the famous *Researches in Experimental Phonetics*, "proved to be illusory; the recorded curve of the spoken verse proved to be a problem in itself, and extensive researches had to be made before it could be understood." The physical skeleton of the individual words and speech-sounds had to be carefully studied before any further questions could be raised for discussion. Much has already been accomplished along these lines by Scripture, D. C. Miller, and their followers. Much still remains to be done. But the evidence already obtained in linguo-physics by this group of scholars brings us nearer to a solution of some important problems of the art of poetry and makes it possible to apply their conclusions to a somewhat broader scope of research.

The task of the present essay is to apply certain results of physical science to the study of rime. It ought to be understood from the outset that no attempt is made here to "reduce" the aesthetic phenomenon of rime to purely physical factors. Science claims no reductions. One who dogmatically believes in the possibility of reducing such phenomena as consciousness, beauty, or rhythm to their physical components oversteps the

4

legitimate boundaries of science and falls into metaphysics. The physicist merely claims that whatever those phenomena of "higher" levels of reality may be in themselves they have their basis and their origin in physical nature and in so far may be physically explained. Rime, "this delight for the Nordic ear," is primarily an artistic device, a poetic ornament possessing an enormous power of arousing emotion. It has its history, its philology, its aesthetic theory. All these are old and legitimate ways of approaching the question of rime, and no amount of physical insight into the matter can be regarded as a substitute for what has been already obtained in it historically, philologically, or aesthetically. And yet for a successful discussion of the numerous problems concerning the nature and value of rime a preliminary analysis of the plain physical facts on which it rests is of very great importance. Without it we are unable to explain its function in the rhythmical composition of verse or to account for its power of increasing emotional effects; without it we cannot even conceive why a repetition of identical sounds at the end of the verse lines should have a pleasurable effect at all, or why it is that in certain cases and for some particular individuals such repetitions appear to be annoying and disagreeable. Physical analysis helps us to appreciate, within certain limits, the value of rime and to be on guard against premature attacks on it on the part of those who claim to possess an especially delicate ear and "modern" taste. Thus it may have a practical significance for current poetical work in so far as it settles an old dispute among the poets concerning the advantages and disadvantages of rime. For some consider rime synonymous with poetry, and in the usual style of philosophical apriorism refuse to give the name of poetry to unrimed verse. Others on the contrary, listening rather to fashion than to the dictates of their own taste, are painfully trying to avoid rime, which they often find more difficult to do than to employ it. Both parties form their poetical ideals on an apriori basis, hastily generalizing certain cases where rime

5

appears or does not appear to be artistically effective. Instead of examining facts that may throw some light on the nature of rime and possibly explain its inefficiency in some particular case, they simply follow their momentary inspiration and then proceed to make rules for others, either exalting or denouncing it for all cases. It is time to put an end to this confusion of judgment by showing that, in its general form, the problem has no solution. This can be done only by inquiring into the physical basis of the phenomenon and examining the effect it has on mental conditions. Knowing the physical facts that lie at the basis of rime, we shall be able to explain the effect it has on our mind; and knowing this, we shall then recommend using rime when this effect is desired or abstaining from it when it happens to be in conflict with other legitimate aims of the poem.

Thus in venturing this attempt to end a century-long dispute, the author—unfortunately—is not in position to claim that, even if his explanation is correct, he is personally responsible for discovering a solution. For, in the first place, no solution is offered. One cannot claim the solution of a problem that never existed. The controversy had merely an appearance of a problem. In reality it was only a question of preference of taste, and de gustibus non est disputandum. The present study does not pretend to decide the question on either side, but merely to explain the causes of preference, i.e., why and how certain preferences are formed. On the other hand, the interpretation of the physical basis of rime that is offered here is not at all the author's "discovery"; it is only what seems to him an obvious conclusion obtained from the evidence furnished by modern physical experiments with human speech, especially from the works of D. C. Miller, E. W. Scripture, Irving Crandall, Harvey Fletcher, and Mark Liddell. As to the importance of solving a century-long controversy, I invite my reader to consider how many old disputes have been settled by science during the last two centuries without any individual efforts, just by sheer change of intellectual outlook. After

6

Newton it became senseless to dispute the number of epicycles necessary to explain the movements of the planets. After the principle of conservation of energy had been formulated no one needed to "discover" the impossibility of creating a perpetual motion machine; it was an obvious corollary to the great law. That the question of rime is still open for inquiry is simply due to the fact that no one has yet decided to look at it scientifically, i.e., to attack it from the physical side. It is one of those questions too far removed from the center of naturalistic interest, to which science has paid no attention. As soon as the question is presented in that light, the truth results of itself. The author claims only to have done something that must have been done sooner or later, to have made an attempt to apply the results of modern experimental acoustics to the problem of rime.

Herbert Spencer in his essay on *The Philosophy of Style* approached this problem from the point of view of "expenditure of energy." The importance of such musical effects as rhythm and rime, as well as word-position, sentence-building, etc., lies, he believes, in their reducing the strain of attention of the hearer or reader, i.e., in their sparing the mental energy of the recipient. They assist memory and save mental effort. Hence their aesthetic effect. To this positivistic "hence," Jespersen[3] replies: "The elementary pleasure given us by the rhythmical combinations of words generally employed in poetry is caused by the fact that it is easier for the organs to alternate strong and weak syllables, than to produce long series of syllables all strong or all weak, one after the other. But of course it will be difficult to bring under the category of the 'saving of energy' all the subtler, more musical effects produced by the harmonious alteration, especially of vowel sounds, on which so much of the highest pleasure afforded by beautiful verse depends. Here, as in the whole domain of aesthetics, there is something which, at any rate at present,

[3] O. Jespersen, *Mankind, Nation, and Individual from a Linguistic Point of View*, page 135.

escapes scientific cognition." We agree with the distinguished philologist: there is, and probably always will be, something in poetry that will escape scientific cognition. And yet this negative aspect of the situation, in terms of formal logic expressed as a particular proposition, does not exclude at least a partial affirmative: There is something in poetry that surrenders itself to science, and may therefore be "computed and measured." In fact, this "something" at present covers a vast terrain. In partial analysis of it the present volume is conceived.

II

THEORY OF RIMING VOWELS

$\mathbf{R}$IME, being a repetition of identical or closely similar[1] sounds arranged at regulated intervals, is primarily an acoustic phenomenon. Its physical analysis, therefore, constitutes a problem in the theory of sound. In the ordinary rimes, such for instance as "napping ... tapping," we shall distinguish the following three elements: (1) identity of the accented vowels $(a:a)$; (2) identity of the unaccented vowels

---

[1] It is difficult to establish absolute identity of pronunciation, partly because pronunciation is in the process of change from one generation to another, partly because it is subject to individual variations. Rousselot maintains that two successive generations probably never have exactly the same pronunciation. Scripture made a still more interesting discovery. Analyzing the vowel curves of gramophone records he found that the same vowel is hardly ever pronounced in the same way. He discovered that curves made by the same vowel display different shape, not merely from one case to another but even within a single utterance. On the basis of his numerous experiments he came to the conclusion that "a vowel is not a constant sound, but an ever-changing one" ("The Study of English Speech by New Methods

$(i:i)$; (3) identity and identical order of consonants (pp—ng : pp—ng).[2] Let us examine separately the significance of these elements.

Physical analysis of vowels.—The vowels of our speech are musical chords or, more precisely, tone-clusters in which every partial tone has its specific pitch and intensity. According to the Helmholtz-Miller[3] theory, the tone quality of a vowel, that

of Phonetic Investigation," *Proceedings of the British Academy,* 1921–1923, page 276). But as far as the riming vowels are concerned the question does not seem to present a very difficult problem. For we may simply assume that rime fails in the proportion in which the vowel tones disagree. M. de la Grasserie says: "En résumé, toutes les fois que deux voyelles finales ... n'ont plus le même sens exact soit quantitativement, soit surtout qualitative- ment, de telle sorte que ce son se trouve diésé ou bémolisé sur l'échelle voca- lique, elles ne peuvent plus rimer d'une manière complète, la rime est con- servée pour l'œil seulement, on ne peut dire cependant qu'elle manque absolument, car il y a bien partout le même son fondamental, la même note, ou pour parler plus exactement, une note très rapprochée."

If the vowels intended for rime do not exactly coincide in the charac- teristic overtone, they display the tendency to efface the difference. Rime makes them sound alike. I have asked a dramatic reader to recite the following two lines from William Blake:

> Perhaps this is all a painter can want:
> But, look yonder—that house is the house of Rembrandt!

And then after some time elapsed I asked the same reader to pronounce the following:

> 'Tis the trading English-Venetian cant
> To speak Michael Angelo, and act Rembrandt.

In the first case "Rembrandt" was instinctively pronounced to suit the sound of "want": in the other case it sounded like "cant." These observations seem to be in agreement with what philologists call "the change of sound by anal- ogy" (H. Sweet, *History of English Sounds,* §§ 177 ff.).

[2] Cf. V. Zhirmunski, *Rime, Its History and Theory,* Petersburg, 1923.

[3] Helmholtz's contributions (*Die Lehre von den Tonempfindungen,* 1863) to linguo-physics are immense. And yet the impression which is often

which makes its acoustic personality, depends on the position of the mouth cavity, which acts as a resonator reinforcing certain overtones in the speaking voice and subduing others. Of all the overtones contained in the speaking voice, the mouth cavity, when in a certain position, selects one or two particular overtones, and by sympathetic vibration brings them into promi-

produced by popular books on phonetics that he was the author of the whole movement is wrong. He was not a pioneer in the field. As a pioneer he would not have been able to produce so much. In fact, he was fortunate to have had in this particular field extremely able predecessors, both for the purely mathematical and for the experimental aspect of his work. Among Helmholtz's predecessors the name of Euler is seldom mentioned. Yet this great Swiss mathematician (1707–1783) was responsible for a number of the most fundamental discoveries in the field of acoustics which constitute an indispensable prerequisite of Helmholtz's work and are often attributed to him. It was Euler (and not Helmholtz) who, in his *Tentamen Novae Theoriae Musicae*, first provided a physical basis for discriminating the three fundamental aspects of every musical sound: pitch, which he attributes to the number of vibrations in a given time; loudness, depending on the amplitude of the vibrating particles; and quality, which—he thinks—depends on the form of the curve by which the law of density, and velocity in the pulse is defined, i.e., on the number and intensity of the component overtones. He was also, I think, the first to identify vowels as specific sound-qualities and to explain their nature by reference to the form of their respective sound waves.

Another prominent figure in preparing the ground for modern linguophysics, a real pioneer in the field, was Robert Willis, an English physicist, who on November 24, 1828, read before the Cambridge Philosophical Society his first paper "On the Vowel Sounds, and on Reed Organ-Pipes." In this long paper he stated that "vowels are mere affections of sound, which are not at all beyond the reach of human [mechanical] imitation in many ways, and not inseparably connected with human organs, although they are most perfectly produced by them." He criticized his early predecessors, Kratzenstein and Kempelen, for their futile attempt to explain the nature of the vowel sounds by reference to the form and action of the organs of speech themselves. With this profound criticism he forever condemned the purely phonetic examination of vowels as specifically human peculiarities, apart from their objective physical analysis. Musical notes, he argued, are also formed in the larynx in the highest possible purity and perfection; but who ever dreamed

11

nence, thus producing a definite quality of tone which is perceived as a vowel. This characteristic overtone remains within a certain very limited range of vibration, and is practically independent of the fundamental tone or pitch of voice. The larger part of the energy of the sound was found to be in the partials which fell within this range, no matter at what pitch

of seeking from the larynx an explanation of the laws by which musical notes are governed? These considerations induced him to lay down a different plan for his experiments, namely, neglecting entirely the organs of speech, to determine, if possible, by experiments upon the usual acoustic instruments, what forms of cavities or other conditions are essential to the production of these sounds. In other words, he arrived at the idea of synthetic vowels. In fact he succeeded in constructing a mechanical device for producing artificial vowel sounds with a reasonable degree of approximation to the natural vowels. For this purpose he used ordinary reeds so fitted into a funnel-shaped circular cavity open at the top that by changing the size of the aperture he was able to obtain different vowels "very precisely." By this ingenious method he discovered that each vowel is characterized by a specific musical tone, which was later called its characteristic frequency. Willis' explanation of the phenomenon, however, does not quite coincide with that of Helmholtz. He is the originator of the inharmonic theory.

The mathematical basis for the theory of compound sounds was provided by Fourier (1768–1830), who has shown that any vibration, however complicated, can always be analyzed into a number of "simple" vibrations whose periods decrease in the ratio of fractions: $\frac{1}{1}$, $\frac{1}{2}$, $\frac{1}{3}$, $\frac{1}{4}$, ... $1/n$ ... . Simple vibration is said to be such as proceeds in accordance with the law of the pendulum. Thus every vibration can be represented as a sum of pendulum-like vibrations (*Sinusschwingungen*). To every simple vibration with a frequency above 16 times per second there corresponds a single and simple tone. The simple tones constituting a given tone are called its partials or overtones. On the varied combination and intensity of these overtones depends the quality of the sound, or timbre. Thus, taking 100 vibrations per second as a unit, a tone whose period consists of the following partials: $\frac{1}{1}$, $\frac{1}{2}$, $\frac{1}{3}$, ... $\frac{1}{6}$ ... $\frac{1}{10}$ ... is different in quality from one which is expressed by the series: $\frac{1}{1}$, $\frac{1}{2}$, $\frac{1}{3}$, ... $\frac{1}{8}$ ... $\frac{1}{25}$, $\frac{1}{16}$ ... , although their pitch will be the same, i.e., 100 vibrations per second.

Among other predecessors of Helmholtz, mention must be made of Wheatstone, Grassman, and Donders.

the vowel was pronounced. The ear having the power of analyzing the sound waves must be able to distinguish at least those prominent components and to use them as signals for identification of each vowel.

Another theory, originally suggested by R. Willis, and more recently advanced by Hermann and Scripture, invites us to believe "that the characteristic frequencies of the vowel sounds are the natural vibrations in the oral cavities" which are excited by periodic puffs of air from the glottis quite independently of the harmonic overtones of a given fundamental. In other words, the mouth cavity, being a resonator made of a very soft material, does not exactly select a number of particular overtones already present in the harmonics of the fundamental, but rather creates new tones by responding with a definite number of vibrations to any stirrings of the air passing through it. Euler explains this effect by saying that if a pulsation be excited at the bottom of a cavity closed at one end, it will travel to the mouth of this cavity with the velocity of sound, where an echo of the pulsation will be formed which will run back again, be reflected from the bottom of the tube, and again present itself at the mouth. In this manner a specific vibration is produced whose frequency depends on the length of the tube or cavity. A cavity of this kind will respond to any stirrings of the air with the same tone. Willis points out that the mouth is a natural cavity of this kind. Hence the characteristic frequencies of the vowel sounds.

This theory, known as the inharmonic or transient theory, was at a later date revived, with considerable modifications, by M. Hermann, and has recently been supported by Scripture.[4]

---

[4] The chief reason for rejecting the harmonic theory of Helmholtz-Miller seems to lie in the fact that it was based on views of resonance valid only for metal or other resonators made of a hard material. The mouth cavity is made of a very soft, partly liquid, material with a large coefficient of friction, and the laws of resonance for soft cavities are different from those

It agrees with the Helmholtz-Miller theory in regarding vowels as tone-clusters with predominance of certain characteristic sounds—an established fact which can no longer be disputed—but differs in assuming that "no harmonic relations need obtain between the characteristic frequencies and the fundamental tone accompanying them." The tone, or tones, constituting a given vowel may very well be inharmonics of the fundamental. Both assume that the mouth cavity is tuned in a certain definite way for each particular vowel. The disagreement concerns merely the way of producing or exciting the energy of the vowel sound. Miller believes that the sound is produced by intensifying a given harmonic overtone which happens to be the nearest to the characteristic frequency of the vowel. Scripture, on the contrary, assumes no relation between the fundamental and the characteristic tones. He believes that the latter originate in the oral cavity inharmonically, deriving their energy from a series of explosive puffs of air from the glottis, these puffs acting on a system of cavities (trachea, larynx, pharynx, mouth, nose) with considerable friction, producing an effect similar to that described by Euler and Willis.[5]

Despite these minor disagreements, the modern work on sound furnishes sufficient evidence to support the belief that each vowel is a specific tone-cluster, or musical chord, whose partials have not only definite arrangement but also a definite intensity. If, knowing the exact composition of vowels, we could artificially reproduce precisely the same chord by giving

applicable to metal resonators. The process of vowel production must therefore differ substantially from the theory that compares it to the response of hard resonators to overtones (E. W. Scripture, *Researches in Experimental Phonetics*, page 110).

[5] *Transactions of the Cambridge Philosophical Society*, 3: 231–262. For modern developments consult M. Hermann's articles in *Pflüger's Archiv*, 45: 582–592; 47: 42–53, 347–391; 48: 181–194, 543–574; 53: 1–51. Also E. W. Scripture, *Researches in Experimental Phonetics*, pages 118 ff.

each component its proper intensity, we should be able to obtain a mechanical vowel very nearly corresponding to its vocal equivalent. Now, it was shown experimentally, long before the invention of the phonograph, that mechanical approximations to human vowels are quite within the range of the science of engineering.[6] Difficulty persists in our ignorance as to the exact

---

[6] A history of the experiments pertaining to the artificial vowel production may be found in Helmholtz's *"Theory of Tone-Sensations"* and in Rousselot's *"Principles of Experimental Phonetics."* Combined, they give a fairly complete account of the history of the problem; Helmholtz naturally concentrated on the early and Rousselot on the more recent developments. Nothing of very great importance can be added to their reports. Yet it may be of some interest to adduce a few facts from the early history of the question which the historical accounts ordinarily fail to mention.

In the first place, it is interesting to note that the attempts to imitate vowels by mechanical means are of much greater antiquity than is generally believed. Medieval magicians and alchemists are said to have conducted experiments in this field. Robert Willis mentions Roger Bacon, Albertus Magnus, and others who are said to have constructed machines for artificial vowel production. Some of those devices must have been mere deceptions intended to fool those uninitiated in magical mysteries. L'Abbé Mical, according to Rivarol, *Discours sur l'universalité de la langue française,* made two colossal heads which were capable of pronouncing entire sentences. His secret, however, was lost to posterity, the inventor having destroyed his mechanism "in a fit of disappointment at not receiving his expected reward from the government." The first attempt which may have a claim to a scientific character was made in Russia by Kratzenstein, who in 1780 presented the results of his experiments with artificial vowels to the Academy of Petersburg. The abstract of this prize-winning essay has been published in the *Acta Academiae Petropolitanae* (volume 21). Kratzenstein succeeded in producing a number of vowels by means of an ingenious construction for which no explanation was offered, except that experience had shown it to be well adapted to the production of the sounds in question. Another early attempt of a similar nature has been described by Kempelen in a separate treatise: *Le Mécanisme de la parole suivi de la description d'une machine parlante* (Vienne, 1791). The next decisive step toward a successful solution of the problem was taken by Robert Willis, who in 1828 made public the results of his experiments with

intensity of various components. In a rough manner one may easily obtain a mechanical approximation of any vowel, and even of some of the consonants, by holding the right pedal of a piano and speaking loudly into the mechanism of the instrument; if the experimenter holds his lips fairly close to the strings, by sympathetic vibration the strings will repeat the sound.

Thus each vowel represents a musical chord in which each component sound has a specific intensity.[7] Among variously

reeds and their application to pipes and cavities of different and varying magnitude.

Helmholtz's experiments in this field are well known. After Helmholtz a number of ingenious improvements have been made by various investigators, among whom W. H. Preece and A. Stroh deserve much more attention than they have actually received on the part of our historians (Rousselot allots only a few lines to both of them). They have devised a machine upon which were fitted disks whose peripheries were cut in exact copy of the curve produced by their synthetic-curve machine, previously constructed on Fourier's principle. These curves were then transmitted by vibration to the receiving diaphragm of a phonograph. A number of combinations of curves had been cut on the circumferences of the disks, representing each vowel sound with certain variations of the partials, as experience determined. By revolving the disks, sounds were produced fairly resembling the vowel sounds of the human voice. The vowel sound *ah* was the easiest to reproduce by this method. They tried to explain this peculiar preference of their machine for *ah* by assuming that *ah* is obtained when all the partials are equally represented, from the first to the eighth, the easiest effect obtainable under the circumstances (*Proceedings of the Royal Society of London*, 28: 358–367).

From the modern contributions to the problem the most important are by Sir Richard Paget, "The Production of Artificial Vowel Sounds," *Proceedings of the Royal Society of London*, 1923; *Vowel Resonances* (International Phonetic Association, 1922); J. Q. Stewart, "An Electrical Analogue of the Vocal Organ," *Nature*, 1922; and E. W. Scripture, "Report on the Construction of a Vowel Organ," *Smithsonian Miscellaneous Collection*, Volume 47.

[7] Soon after Helmholtz had published his *"Theory of Tone-Sensations"* (1863) the results of his vowel analysis were confirmed by Jenkin and Ewing

16

intoned partials, however, there is in each vowel one characteristic overtone to which falls the larger part of the energy of the sound. Professor Miller testifies that the partials lying within a characteristic region of resonance of the mouth cavity often contain as much as ninety per cent of the total energy of the sound. This means that the human ear must be able to perceive the characteristic overtone of each vowel as a distinguishable sound, and only our habit of associating it with the rest of the vowel chord makes us unaware of its particular presence; in the process of hearing it becomes fused with other partials and appears in a disguised form of an individual vowel timbre. Thus, according to Bevier,[8] the most decided characteristic component for the identity of the vowel *a*, as pronounced in the word "father," is the overtone, or overtones, whose frequencies of vibration fall between 1,000 and 1,300 vibrations

(*Transactions of the Royal Society of Edinburgh* [1878], 28:745–777). Since then a vast amount of material has been accumulated in this field. The same year M. F. Auerbach published his "Untersuchungen über die Natur des Vokalklanges," (*Poggendorf Annalen*, Volume 8, comp.). Omitting the minor papers by Koenig, Doumer, Eichhorn, and Lahr, we shall mention only the most important works in the field. In 1890 M. Pipping, in Finland (then Russia), opened a series of important papers by publishing an article on "Hensen's Phonautograph." This was followed by "Ueber die Theorie der Vokale," *Acta Societatis Scientiarum Fennicae*, Volume 20, 1894, and *Zur Lehre von den Vokalklängen* (1895). At the same time, between 1890 and 1893, Hermann published his articles in the *Pflüger's Archiv*. Between 1890 and 1897, R. J. Lloyd published his papers on "Speech-Sounds, Their Nature and Causation" (*Phonetische Studien*). In America A. M. Bell wrote his "Phonetics" (*Science*, 1890), and *Speech Tones* (Washington, The Volta Bureau, 1893). From the Bell Telephone Laboratories a number of most important works have appeared recently (Crandall, Fletcher). The vast amount of evidence presented by all these writers in favor of the overtone theory of vowels establishes at least the main points of the doctrine beyond any reasonable doubt.

[8] L. Bevier, "The Acoustic Analysis of the Vowels," *Physical Review*, 1900.

17

per second, i.e., approximately at D♭ of the fifth octave: "this is the main resonance of the mouth when formed to utter this vowel, and remains remarkably constant no matter what the fundamental pitch may be," i.e., quite independently of whether the vowel is pronounced at a low or a high pitch. According to Miller the eight standard vowels of the English language have been found to contain the following characteristic tones:[9]

Vowel	As Pronounced in the Word	Low Characteristic Frequency	High Characteristic Frequency	Musical Equivalent
ä	father	910	. . . .	$D_5♭$
aw (ô)	raw	732	. . . .	$G_4♭$
ō	no	461	. . . .	$B_3♭$
ōō	gloom	326	. . . .	E_3
ă	cat	800	1,840	$A_4♭ + B_5♭$
ā	hate	488	2,461	$B_3 + E_6♭$
ĕ	pet	691	1,953	$F_4 + B_5♭$
ee (ē)	meet	308	3,100	$E_3♭ + G_6$

From this table[10] we see that some vowels are characterized by only one region of resonance, while others have two characteristic frequencies. As spectra of different chemical elements consist of a number—which sometimes is very large—of lines that have a fixed position in different parts of the light spectrum, similarly vowels are characterized by more than one specific tone. As we say, each vowel is a complex

[9] The numbers given in this table very closely correspond to those recently obtained by I. B. Crandall in the Bell Telephone Laboratories.

[10] There is every reason to believe that these figures are very accurate. But this high degree of accuracy was attained only on the basis of a long list of difficult experiments and mathematical triumphs that preceded it. The first experiments made by Willis with resonating tubes and cavities yielded but very imperfect results, which can be seen from the fact that for the short English ĕ he gave C of the sixth octave.

cluster of tones which have a constant position in the scale of musical tones. Each component overtone within a vowel is completely characterized by two factors: its frequency and its amplitude of vibration. Both may be expressed in numbers. Accordingly each overtone, as far as our purposes of vowel description are concerned, is completely fixed by such a pair and may be plotted upon a chart in which two perpendicular lines have been chosen as the axes of a rectangular Cartesian system of co-ordinates, the frequencies being measured along the horizontal and the amplitudes along the vertical lines. Such charts representing relative amplitudes of the different frequency components are called acoustic spectra. Dr. Fletcher in his *Speech and Hearing* gives spectra of eight vowels. His charts are of special interest as they represent the most recent and most accurate measurements. With his permission they are here reproduced on pages 20 and 21.

These charts give a very clear visual representation of our theory. They visualize the inner structure of each vowel, and lay bare to our view the secrets of their acoustic personalities. We observe that a short *a* as in "tan" is characterized by a fairly strong development of a large number of overtones, whereas in *ōō* nearly all but one appear to be subdued to almost a zero. Long *a* as in "tape" displays an unusual poverty of overtones, whereas short *i* shows a very large number of fully developed tones. In *ee* we clearly perceive two regions of resonance, whereas in *äh*, as in *ōō*, the characteristic frequency absorbs the larger portion of the energy of the sound. But in every vowel there are one or two overtones which stand out more prominently than all the others. Those powerful overtones are then considered characteristic of the vowel. It must be borne in mind, however, that their frequency numbers do not represent absolute musical values. Their musical equivalent, as given above, is their mean value. The numbers, too, represent the mean frequencies obtained by analyzing a large

19

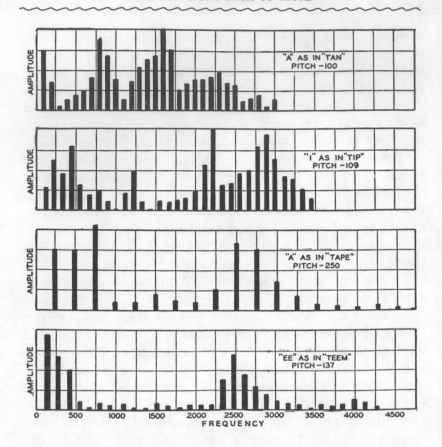

number of cases where the same vowel was intoned. Evidently there are as many different shades in pronouncing *a* as there are different shades of red or green color; *a* in "father" is considerably different from *a* in "part."[11] There are reasons to believe that even within one and the same word there are slight variations of the sound quality which depend probably on the position of the head, on the slight differences in the opening

[11] Irving B. Crandall, "The Sounds of Speech," *Bell System Technical Journal* (1925), page 26.

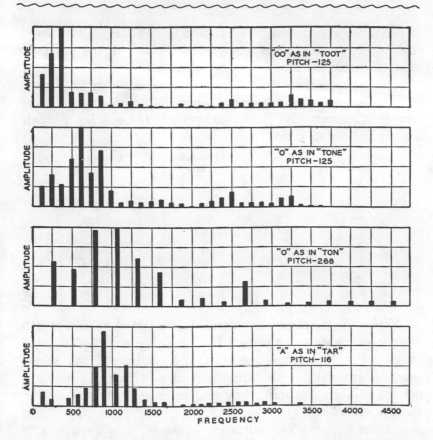

of the mouth, on resonance conditions in the pharynx, intensity of voice, etc. Yet as long as the characteristic partial falls within a given region of resonance—for *a*, according to Bevier, between 1,000 and 1,300 vibrations per second—the vowel sounds the same. Therefore a number given above for each particular vowel does not represent a definite tone of a tuning-fork but a certain limited region of tones within which the vowel can be practically identified as such. We may conceive, Liddell suggests, "of these frequency constants as central points in qualitative bands [regions] on each side of which the quality

21

of the given vowel shades off until it finally merges into some other quality. When we arrange those bands in the order of their characteristic frequencies we shall have something like a vowel-tone spectrum, the qualities themselves being analogous to color hues shading into one another."[12] Arranging our eight vowels in the order of their characteristic frequencies, Liddell has the following table:

Vowel	As Pronounced in the Word	Characteristic Frequency
$\bar{oo}$	gloom	326
$\bar{o}$	no	461
aw $(\hat{o})$	raw	732
$\ddot{a}$	father	900
$\breve{a}$	mat	1,840
$\breve{e}$	pet	1,958
ey $(\bar{a})$	they	2,461
$\ddot{i}$ $(\bar{e})$	be	3,100

When the characteristic overtone of a vowel has about 326 vibrations per second it sounds like *oo* in "gloom." When the frequency of vibrations increases, the quality of the vowel changes, gradually approaching that of *o* in "no." Thus *oo* is not absolutely characterized by 326 vibrations per second; the number of vibrations may be 320 or 350 and the vowel still sound like *oo*. For our purposes, however, it is important to bear in mind that whenever a vowel is actually pronounced, its shading tends to become perfectly definite; for of the whole region of possible characteristic tones only one at a time can take place. For *oo* it may have any number of vibrations, say, between 310 and 340, i.e., within these limits we do not perceive any variations in the quality of the *oo* sound. If it goes

[12] Mark H. Liddell, *The Physical Characteristics of Speech Sound*, page 17. To this group belong all those vowel changes which Henry Sweet characterizes as "parasite developments due to a following *r*" (*History of English Sounds*, §§ 905, 946).

beyond the limit, it may still retain its general characteristic quality, but it will be an *oo* as pronounced by a German or a Frenchman. On the other side of its mean frequency, i.e., when the number of vibrations per second is decreasing, the quality of the vowel will gradually approach the Russian *oo*. But in each particular case, of course, only one definite number of vibrations can take place; that is, in actual speech a vowel contains a definite tone, identical with some particular tone of the tuning-fork, which gives to it its individual quality.[13]

When we speak, these sounds produce a gentle accompaniment to our speech which only lacks the unity of a musical phrase in order to become a melody. It is a continuous flow of subdued musical sounds, a sort of "infinite melody" in the Wagnerian sense, which is gently whispered into our ear by the vanishing vowels. In a very precise and not at all metaphorical sense our vowels produce music. And the specific beauty of a language depends largely on the purity and variability of vowels which when set in motion may produce highly varied musical effects. Our ear seems to be very sensitive to these musical effects; for we easily distinguish what is musical or unmusical in prose and poetry and even in ordinary speech. The slightest deviation from the standard sounds, as for instance in foreign accent, offends our ear.

If we agree to neglect the disturbing influence of consonants, we may be able to represent the musical content of a spoken phrase or verse in the common musical signs.[14] The

[13] "For each vowel there is a different shape of the interior of the mouth. The lower jaw can rise and fall; the lips can be rounded and protruded or straightened and held back. . . . . The changing shapes of the interior of the mouth are the causes of the distinction between vowels" (B. Dumville, *The Science of Speech*, page 27).

[14] This method of presentation has been already used by me in my article on "Physical Basis of Rime" (*Publications of the Modern Language Association of America*, Volume 41, No. 4, December, 1926). In Sir Richard Paget's

analysis of the following lines from Wordsworth may serve
as an illustration:

> Hail, Zaragoza! If with unwet eye
> We can approach, thy sorrow to behold,
> Yet is the heart not pitiless nor cold:
> Such spectacle demands not tear or sigh.

The vowels of this fragment, when pronounced, contain the
following melody.

Below is given the musical transcription of the first stanza of
Gray's "Elegy." If by some appropriate physical device we
were in position to intensify the characteristic overtones of
every vowel, we might be able to hear the melody directly at

recently published work on Human Speech the reader will find a more detailed justification for this method. The frequency constants for short *u, o, i,*
and *er* are taken from the tables furnished by I. B. Crandall (Bell Telephone
Laboratories).

24

its source. By playing it on the piano or some other musical instrument, one may obtain but a rough and very imperfect reproduction of it. But even if we used tuning-forks, which give the purest sound, almost free from overtones, we should obtain only an approximation of the real process.

There are three main reasons why musical signs cannot correctly represent the melody contained in the vowels.[15] In the first place, a vowel is not a single tone but a chord. Although one tone predominates in this chord and is much stronger than all the others taken together, yet in reality it remains a chord and a very complex one, too. Neglecting the other tones in our musical representation we distort the nature of the melody involved, which in fact is not only melody but harmony.

[15] It must be borne in mind that the melody contained in the vowels has nothing in common with the so-called "intonation," or change of the fundamental of our voice as we speak. About intonation, see Verrier, *Essai sur les principes de la métrique anglaise,* I : 94 ff.

Secondly, the mouth is not so rigid an instrument as a piano, or even a violin. Every time it is tuned to pronounce a particular vowel, it has to change very rapidly its position from the preceding one. In the process of speech the mouth never rests in any given position. It is constantly in motion. A vowel takes time to be pronounced. However short, this fragment of time covers a period of many tens, sometimes hundreds, of vibrations. During this period the mouth is not at rest. And since every slightest change of position modifies the shape of the air wave, the vowel never sounds in the beginning as it sounds in the end of the period. Analyzing the vowel curves of spoken words, Scripture,[16] indeed, found that the shape of the waves changes from instant to instant. The effect is similar to that of the Hawaiian guitar, where the correct tones are taken on a glide. Similarly, in pronouncing vowels the mouth just touches upon the characteristic overtone, holds it for a comparatively few vibrations and then glides over into adjacent vowel qualities. This, however, does not kill the melody; it only renders it impossible of correct representation. The tunes played on a Hawaiian guitar can never be written down precisely as they are played. Nevertheless they retain their tuneful quality and are undoubtedly musical.

The third factor of incorrectness in our tables is concerned with the impossibility of attaching an exact musical value to any characteristic frequency. Although in every particular case the vowel is pronounced in a perfectly definite way, yet we are ignorant as to the precise value of its characteristic frequency. We only know that it lies within a certain limited region of tones. In other words, we can never be sure as to the absolute identity of two *a*'s pronounced in succession. One time it may contain precisely D♭ as the characteristic tone; the next time it

[16] E. W. Scripture, *Researches in Experimental Phonetics*, chapter iii, "Qualitative Analysis" (Carnegie Institution, Washington, 1906), pages 43 ff.

may be pronounced on the tone half-way between Db and C♯, or even at C, and the ear will still perceive it as *a* as long as other characteristic frequencies remain relatively constant. In other words the mouth is an instrument that very easily gets out of tune without our noticing it.[17]

Though we are unable to represent exactly, still less play, the music contained in the vowels of our speech, the music nevertheless is there and in a very definite form. It is a very strange music, which reminds one of those fantastic sounds, probably suggested by one's own imagination, which one may occasionally hear in a moving railroad car when one listens intently to the monotonous noise of the rolling wheels. It is an abstract musical vision that never exists for our consciousness as a distinct, individual perception but is blended with other sound perceptions, producing what is commonly called the musical value of a verse. Every poem, apart from its meaning, has a characteristic musical appearance, the physical cause of which lies largely (though not exclusively) in the arrangement of overtones associated with the individual vowels. *The musical value of a verse is a function of that arrangement.*

When a succession of two chords, or even tones, is repeated several times it acquires for us the significance of a musical phrase. No matter how strange the combination may sound it has an aesthetic value, in so far as it brings forth and formulates certain emotional response. That is the reason why a frequent recurrence of the same vowel, or a successive repetition of two or three vowels, produces a strong "melodious" effect in poetry. For so is formed a fragment of melody; and, since with every melody is associated a certain emotional content, the vowels impart their emotional peculiarity to the stanza, or sometimes

[17] There is still another element of error that must be mentioned: the characteristic frequencies of the unaccented vowels are not so distinct as those of the accented ones.

27

to the whole poem in which this combination occurs. The poem appears to have a definite "mood," and we are accustomed to call such poems "musical," not even suspecting that the word conveys much more than a vague analogy.

An irregular repetition of the same vowel is called assonance. Remarkable assonances we find in Shakespeare. For example:

> And like unl*etter*'d cl*er*k, still cry "am*en*"
> To *every* hymn. . . . .

or:

> Making their t*om*b the w*om*b wherein they gr*e*w.

In the first fragment we have a remarkable performance of vowel sounds: " . . l*etter*ed" introduces a musical phrase , which is inverted in "cl*er*k ... am*en*" and imperfectly repeated in "*every*," with the last *er* but vaguely perceived in the quality of *r*. Such is the structure of the first extract as it appears through the magnifying glass of physical analysis. The second passage may be similarly analyzed.

One may find an ample number of beautiful examples of assonance on every page of Shakespeare. In the space of the fourteen lines of Sonnet LXXXIII, I have counted seven different forms of assonance. Less numerous are cases where a certain musical phrase dominates larger fragments. Such, for instance, is the case with the opening stanza of Gray's *Elegy* (see p. 25), where the opening melodic phrase appears in an inverted form at the beginning of the second line, "The c*ur*few t*oll*s . . . . The l*o*wing h*er*d," and the whole fragment is dominated by an *er* ... *o* melody . Very rich in melody is the well-known passage from Coleridge's "Love": "I played a soft and doleful air," etc. Shelley often unites his vowels by various forms of melodic arrangement:

28

Life of life! thy lips enkindle
With their love the breath between them;
And thy smiles before they dwindle
Make the cold air fire; then screen them
In those looks, where whoso gazes
Faints, entangled in their mazes.

Child of Light, thy limbs are burning . . . .

The vowel melody introduced by the opening line, "Life of life! thy lips enkindle," is repeated to the last *i* in the beginning of the second stanza: "Child of light, thy limbs, etc." . . . . The vowels *i, i, ee* dominate the whole poem; long *i* occurs 13 times in the first two stanzas, while *o* appears four times, and *e* all together twice. When long *a* appears it introduces a new melodic form which is well perceived by the ear, owing to the rhythmical symmetry in which it lies imbedded: "*Faints,* entangled in their *mazes.*"

In modern poetry we often find cases where certain vowels, or even groups of vowels, dominate larger rhythmical units. Read, for example, Father Manning's "At Even":

Hush ye! Hush ye! My babe is sleeping.
Hush, ye winds, that are full of sorrow!
Hush, ye rains, from your weary weeping!
Give him slumber until tomorrow.
Hush ye, yet! In the years hereafter,
Surely sorrow is all his reaping;
Tears shall be in the place of laughter,
Give him peace for a while in sleeping.

The first two syllables introduce the melody , which occurs again and again throughout the poem in the direct ("until," "your weary," "surely"), as well as in the inverse form ("him slumber"). Short *u* occurs 16 times in the space of the twelve lines which constitute the poem. Different

29

varieties of *i*-sound, such as "ye," "winds," "sleeping," etc., occur 44 times, while short *e* occurs only 4 times. This remarkable predominance of the *u* ... *i* melody gives a peculiarly
monotonous touch to the poem, quite in accordance with its
nature as a cradle song.

In other languages still more attention is paid to various
forms of assonance. L. Becq de Fouquières finds in 366 verses
of Racine over 250 verse lines connected by different forms of
vowel melody. Grammont quotes hundreds of lines from various poets with inner harmonies very delicately constructed, such
as La Fontaine's:

> Après qu'il eut brouté, trotté, fait tous ses tours.

Goethe's verse is, for the most part, built on the contrast of
vowels; yet he is a master of assonance. For instance:

> Schon fühl' ich meine Kräfte höher,
> Schon glüh' ich wie von neuem Wein,
> Ich fühle Mut, mich in die Welt zu wagen,
> Der Erde Weh, der Erde Glück zu tragen,
> Mit Stürmen mich herumzuschlagen, ...

In the space of five lines we find here ten *u*-sounds, which in
the first three lines form an *Anfangsreim*.

In modern Russian poetry, which is highly experimental,
one often finds less conventional and more elaborate forms of
vowel melody, based on two and even three different vowel
sounds rhythmically arranged, such as Balmont's:

> Я победил холодное забвенье,
> Я каждый миг исполнен откровенья.

The number of illustrations could be indefinitely enlarged.
But those already given suffice to show that poets, consciously
or unconsciously, often arrange vowels into well-ordered
groups. The aesthetic effect and the emotional efficiency of

30

such groups lie in their musical significance. Those groups are fragments of melodies distinctly perceptible to the ear in the quality of the vowel sound—perceptible with a high degree of accuracy, for the difference of a hundred vibrations per second sometimes creates a totally different vowel. Yet those fragments are not yet melodies. Melody requires a reference tone which is called key. Thus the expression, "melody of vowels," is still somewhat vague and exaggerated.

Having reached this point of the treatise we can see the physical reason why a succession of vowel sounds may have an aesthetic value. For we know that physically every vowel group forms a musical fragment; and every musical fragment, especially if repeated, may cause an emotional response. Yet it is difficult to see what can possibly shape those fragments into real musical phrases that have a semblance of melodic unity. Prose also contains a succession of vowels; and in prose, too, may occur occasional combinations of vowels that are repeated a number of times. Just as a matter of accident it is quite possible that vowels of a prose fragment form a symmetrical distribution in which certain sounds are repeated at regular intervals. I opened at random Mr. Douglas Ainslie's translation of Benedetto Croce's *Aesthetics*, and after having read about half a page I found the following remarkable case of assonance:

> ". . . . since it appears that the first purpose
> limits and impedes the second . . . ."

The vowels of this phrase have an interesting arrangement. The assonance of "first purpose" is imbedded in two symmetrical groups: *i* ... *i* ... *ee*, *i* ... *i* ... *ee*. In poetry it would be considered a remarkable juxtaposition of vowels. Here it is quite accidental. But is it just the fact that it is accidental that deprives it of any aesthetic significance? And are the quoted illustrations from various poets beautiful just because they are intentional? What is it that makes poetry so sensitive to the

31

slightest differences in the arrangement of vowel sounds? What is it that justifies application of the word "melody" to certain phonetic groups, while the same groups, if transferred to another environment, produce no musical effect whatsoever? To answer those questions means to uncover the mystery of rime. But before going any farther we must consider the physical and psychological nature of melody.

What is melody?—Melody rests upon the harmonic affinity of tones. A physical theory of harmonic relations was worked out by Helmholtz and later perfected by Victor Goldschmidt. It may be briefly and popularly stated as follows:

The tones used in music are not gathered at random, but are so selected that they reveal among themselves a very simple mathematical relation. In the first place, they are divided into octaves, i.e., into sections of notes having n, $2n$, $3n$, etc., vibration per unit of time. For instance, if a string is tuned for C with 264 vibrations per second, the next higher C, its octave, has 528 vibrations per second. Each octave, in turn, is divided into seven steps, which constitute a run and which all stand in a simple, rational relation to the first tone, which is called fundamental. This relation is expressed by the series:

$$1 \quad 9/8 \quad 5/4 \quad 4/3 \quad 3/2 \quad 5/3 \quad 15/8 \quad 2$$

which means that, whatever the vibration number of the first tone, the second tone in the run has $9/8$ of that number, the third $5/4$, and so on. The tones so arranged are called the diatonic scale. They are not arbitrarily chosen, but constitute a harmonic series which has its natural basis in the system of the overtones accompanying every musical sound. They are not derived, as is commonly believed, by dividing the octave into twelve equal steps, called half-tones; for the distances between various tones of the scale are not equal. The fourth interval in the scale (between F and G) is $3/2 - 4/3 = 1/6$, while the

32

first (between C and D), also regarded as a full-tone interval, is only $9/8 - 1 = 1/8$. Thus the tones of our scale are not equidistant. They are not formed from each other by elementary division, but are all derived from the fundamental by a simple operation which Goldschmidt calls "complication."[18]

It is a well-known fact that simple musical tones do not exist in nature. When a string begins to vibrate, both its halves vibrate independently at a double rate producing precisely the octave of the tone given by the whole string. This octave can be very clearly heard, for instance on a grand piano, if after striking a note we press the string in the middle. Similarly, the third part of the string vibrates independently at a rate three times that of the whole. If the vibration number of the whole string is C, its third part vibrates at the rate $\overline{G} = 3C$, which gives a tone beyond the limits of an octave. Transposing this tone an octave lower, i.e., between C and 2C, we obtain $G = 3/2C$, which gives us the middle or dominant tone of our diatonic series, $3/2$. Other tones of the diatonic scale are similarly derived from the fundamental. What is the psychological effect of such physical organization of the diatonic scale?

Listening to a musical sound we never perceive a single note, but a whole chord. If C is intoned by the voice or any other musical instrument, we can clearly detect G in its sound; E is heard less distinctly, though quite audibly even without the assistance of any tone-intensifying device. Thus natural concomitants of C are G and E, both in harmonic relation to C. Our ear, therefore, is by nature trained to hear harmonic concomitants. It is quite possible, as Goldschmidt suggests, that it becomes biologically adapted to the conditions of harmonic hearing. Man hears G whenever C is intoned. A transition from one to the other appears, therefore, quite natural to him.

[18] Victor Goldschmidt, *Ueber Harmonie und Komplikation*, Berlin, 1901.

And in fact this transition—the interval of the fifth—is the foundation of all melodic motion. Melody, then, naturally rests on harmony. For we are prompted to take one tone after another (succession of tones; melody), because immediately before that we heard them together (simultaneously, in a harmony).

An important further fact, therefore, is that, for some unknown reason, *as soon as the second note of the interval is actually taken, or even heard, a strong impulse is born in our mind to return to the original tone. This impulse is the real origin of melody.* It may be immediately satisfied in the most primitive way by a direct return to the tonic; or else the motion may be executed by means of another intermediate note, or notes, that lead the voice back to the original tone. In the latter case a *feeling of suspense* is produced that modifies the original craving for return. This craving can be intensified and varied in many different ways, producing innumerable melodies, from the sweetest Italian tunes to the most fantastic intuitions of a Scriabine.

From the physical point of view melody is the relation of affinity among a given number of successive tones. On the subjective side this relation stimulates in each particular distribution of tones a peculiar tendency or desire to come back to the original tone. Psychologically, therefore, melody is to be defined as a *variety of desire*, a longing or craving. It is not, I am aware, an expression of some heterogeneous desire, such as love, longing for God, or moonlight, or what not, which the composer—such is the popular belief—is supposed to transmit to us. He does not transmit anything except his immediate and *perfectly unique desire to move from one tone to another (musica est scientia bene movendi).* The manner in which a desire is expressed in consciousness is called "feeling" or "emotion." We are aware of our own desires only through the medium of our emotions. Therefore, from the psychological point of

34

view melodies represent a specific class of emotions, a class peculiarly connected with tones.

It is well known that our visual and auditory sensations are accompanied by slight emotional effects. Certain colors and sounds, especially in contrast to others, appear pleasing; others, on the contrary, affect us in an almost painful way.[19] In a melody, owing to the instinctive impulse to reach the end of it, i.e., to return to the original tone, the emotional effect associated with each coming sound is greatly intensified. Every coming tone appears now in a definite emotional relation to the original or fundamental tone; that is, the whole movement is dominated by the sensation of tonic, or sense of key. This psychological affinity of tones as heard sounds appears to be an image (*Abbild*) of their physical relation as vibrations. What in the physical world appears as a system of harmonically related numbers is vaguely reflected in consciousness in form of an emotional affinity of tones. In using the word "emotional" here, I do not mean to suggest that melodies stir up and express standardized emotions of love, hate, joy, or anger. *No other "emotions" are expressed by melodies except those which are produced by the tones themselves, owing to their ability to please or to offend the ear.* They may, in a way, be vaguely comparable to the emotions of love, reverence, or joy, for our methods of describing emotions are very inadequate; but they cannot be identical with those, because their physical origin is entirely different. Musical emotions are all based on the psycho-physical fact that when we hear a harmonic deviation from a given tone we feel a peculiar tendency to go back to the original. Every melody starts and ends with the tonic. "The tonic note," says Helmholtz, "as the connecting core of all the tones in a regular constructed melody, must be heard on the first part of a bar, and also at the close, so that melody starts

[19] E. W. Scripture, *The New Psychology*, page 306.

35

from and returns to it." In other words, melody is the experience of a peculiar tendency to repeat the same tone after several others have been taken. The fundamental tone which forms the center of melodic motion brings unity into formless succession of tones, and is commonly called tonic, or key. Unless one feels and perceives the relation of every coming tone to that original center, one cannot hear the melody, just as a savage taken to a modern opera will perceive the succession of tones without being able to organize them into a melody. Key, therefore, is both physically and psychologically the organizing principle of the melodic motion. The unity of melody is based on it.

At present we can no longer accept Helmholtz's analysis without some modifications. Modern developments in music tend to show that melodic and harmonic effects may be produced without a definite tonality, i.e., without reference to a constant fundamental tone. Scriabine often ends his compositions in chords that have no relation to the tonic. Hindemith seldom indicates tonality in his compositions; in fact, they have no tonality. In the "Studies in Black and White" by N. Slonimsky, recently published in *New Music,* the right hand plays on the white keys only, the left hand on the black keys. The composition is peculiarly consonant, for only consonant intervals—thirds, sixths, and occasional fifths—are used. Tonality, under the circumstances, is not merely absent but actually impossible, for obvious reasons.

Helmholtz's analysis, therefore, may still be regarded as correct with regard to the origin of melody. But the historic development of music has brought about forms where actual return to the tonic is indefinitely postponed. To this in poetry correspond blank verse and free verse. Yet the fundamental idea of the great German scientist still remains valid: A transition from one tone to another does excite an emotional response. Moreover, it has been recently shown by psychological experiment (Lipps-Meyer Law)[20] that the fundamental tone in any scale based on octave division has the property of being preferred over all other tones as the melody ending. Professor P. R. Farnsworth in his recent article on "A Modification of Lipps-Meyer Law"[21] has shown that with the tones E and G in the scale of C, and even with the interval of the seventh (B), is associated a certain amount of melodic satisfaction when those tones are used to end a melodic sequence. Yet the fundamental preference rests with the tonic. As a rule, any end of a melodic sequence excites some emotional response; but the end in a tonic is decidedly pleasurable. In this property of causing pleasure lies its distinction. A modern musician may deliberately object to what he calls the sentimental sweetness of conventional endings and may end his melodies in any other tone; but his melodies will not have a pleasing quality. Art, of course, is not obliged to produce exclusively pleasurable effects. Even painful effects may be intensely artistic. And the artist is, therefore, perfectly justified in producing indifferent, or even painful, emotional effects. He may specialize in such effects, if he wishes. Sweetness and pleasantness are out of fashion in modern art. And, indeed, it is true that one may artistically enjoy even a painful sensation. Yet the fact remains that if, in music, the artist wishes to produce a conventionally pleasing sensation, he must end his melody in the tonic note. Similarly a poet, if he wishes to introduce the element of conventional pleasantness into the melody of his verse, must use rime.[22]

[20] Max F. Meyer, *The Musician's Arithmetic*, University of Missouri, 1929. See also Professor Meyer's article in the *American Journal of Psychology*, 14 (1903): 195 ff., 456–478.

[21] *Journal of Experimental Psychology*, Volume 9 (1926).

[22] I know that the latter two statements will meet with opposition on the part of some modernists in art. Feeling, however, that the opposition may be

It has already been pointed out that with a given fundamental the number of tones available for melodies is limited. Our diatonic scale is so built as to fit into our system of harmony. The simplest harmonic modulation, which is the foundation of all our music, is given in the following sequence of chords:

We have here three major chords, which, with respect to the first, are called fundamental, subdominant, and dominant chords. The tones of the major chord, as we already know, are all contained within every single tone as its harmonic partials. They form the most consonant harmony because their constituents do not produce any beats. Let us write those chords in letters:

C F G
E A B
G C D
C F G

Examining this group we find that all tones of our diatonic scale are here represented:

C D E F G A B C

---

simply a result of misunderstanding, I wish to add a few words of more or less personal explanation.

I do not in the least feel inclined to doubt the legitimacy of the modern in art which may be properly characterized by the musical term "dissonant." Dissonance in color, form, or music may well be enjoyed artistically. But I feel that "artistic enjoyment" and "pleasure" are two different things. Tonality is a source of pleasurable emotions. Those who discard tonality are deliberately unwilling to drink from that source. It does not mean that their attitude is in any way less legitimate than that of a classical composer. But the difference cannot be obliterated by the legitimacy of their position.

Thus our diatonic scale is practically a combination of three major chords. Its significance lies in the fact that it furnishes all the tones which are necessary for the construction of the harmonically simplest musical pieces. It is the storeroom for all major harmonies. In order to obtain a similar storeroom for minor harmonies we need semi-tones. This necessitates our *chromatic scale*, which provides *all* the tones needed for our harmonic system.

It is interesting to observe that our vowels fit very precisely into this harmonic system. Physical analysis of vowels has shown (see above, page 12) that every time a particular vowel is pronounced its characteristic tone falls within the same limited range of tones. The range of variations is not large, yet sufficient to produce a difference of a full tone and even more. This means that we can never be sure that the same vowel is pronounced in exactly the same way. We can only study its mean value. And here we find the interesting fact that if we arrange our vowels in a certain way according to their mean characteristic (low) frequencies *they form two runs, each within the limits of an octave, which fit almost precisely into our chromatic scale.*

Let us consider the following vowels: $\bar{oo}, \bar{o}, \bar{a}, \breve{u}, \bar{er}$. Their mean frequency constants (according to Miller and Crandall) are: 326, 461, 468, 574, 641, which form the following ratios with the lowest one (326):

$$1 \quad 1.41 \quad 1.49 \quad 1.70 \quad 1.97$$

These numbers are very near to the required values

$$1 \quad 7/5 \quad 3/2 \quad 5/3 \quad 2$$

which are all contained within the limits of our chromatic scale within the distance of one single octave. The disagreement is very small, and psychologically may be easily neglected, as it falls largely beyond the range of least perceptible difference.

Another run obtains between the vowels *ŭ, ĕ, ŏ, ă, ăh*, and corresponds to the ratios

$$1 \quad 5/4 \quad 4/3 \quad 3/2 \quad 2$$

which is still more remarkable as the series is contained within the limits of our diatonic scale:

$$1 \quad 9/8 \quad 5/4 \quad 4/3 \quad 3/2 \quad 5/3 \quad 15/8 \quad 2$$

Thus the whole series of English vowels, with the exception of *i* and *ee*, is a combination of two harmonic runs. Both excluded vowels, *i* and *ee*, are defined by their high characteristic frequencies, which, probably, constitute a fragment of a third run. High frequencies, however, for the normal ear are too vague to allow an extensive development into a consistent run.

It is very possible that each language develops a system of vowels that may be similarly arranged into scales with mathematically harmonic structure. It is also probable that the vowels are, in the process of development, so selected as to form a melodious run, and that each language tends to produce a harmonically consistent system, i.e., to exclude all sounds which do not fit into a harmonic system of some order. All this, however, remains to be investigated. At any event, English reveals a highly consistent system of vowel sounds. In musical notation their mean values constitute a system of two runs of perfect harmonic consistency and high melodic value:

We must not forget that these runs represent the mean values obtained from a large number of cases when the same vowel was pronounced by different persons. It shows that the mouth, acting as resonator, tries to adapt itself to the melodic conditions expressed by those scales. For the most part its attempts fall very close to the ideal. Rime, and especially inner rime, which we must now proceed to discuss, plays an important part in this process of adjustment.[23]

Inner rimes.—If a melodic deviation from a well-perceived musical tone may cause in our mind a feeling of alienation and a desire to go back to the original tone, there are reasons to believe that an indistinct musical tone, such as is perceived in the sound of vowels, has the same effect, only in a smaller degree. The phenomenon of assonance corroborates this view. There is a great deal of satisfaction connected with the return to the same vowel, especially after certain definite intervals. It has been noticed, however, that consonants exercise a considerable influence on the quality of the vowel sounds, so that the same vowel sounds differently in different consonantal environments. For a poetic ear a vowel followed by a different consonant probably sounds out of tune. Repetition of a vowel accompanied by the same consonant affords a greater musical satisfaction. Such combinations of assonance with alliteration, if they occur within a single verse line, are called inner rimes.

There is another feature characteristic of inner rime. Plain assonance may be quite irregular. In Gray's "Elegy," which affords a good example of assonance, we find a definite musical phrase (*ur ... o*) begun, but not brought to an end. We miss the

[23] For the philologist rime has a specific value for the study of the history of pronunciation. The question as to how certain sounds used to be pronounced in olden times can often be cleared up by reference to rimes. See H. C. Wyld, *English Rhymes from Surrey to Pope;* also K. Bauermeister, *Zur Sprache Spensers auf Grund der Reime.*

satisfaction of returning to the original tone. Inner rimes, on the contrary, are as a rule melodically complete. They are brief melodies within the verse. Thus *ur* ... *o* ... *ur* would be a rime. At the same time it is melody; for it returns to the original tone. Such lines as Edgar Allan Poe's:

Hear the mellow wedding bells,

contains a brief but completed melody in which the overtone characteristic of the vowel *e* is repeated three times in succession. After this tone strikes our ear in "mel-," and then shifts over to "-low," a slight impulse is born in our mind, as in every melodic deviation, to return to the original tone. And we receive a slight, almost imperceptible satisfaction when the next syllable takes us back to the original tone *e* in "wedding." The whole movement has now the character of a musical phrase. The melodic effect is similar to the transitions from sol and do and to sol again. It may be objected that such a phrase is musically too simple and primitive to be seriously considered as an object of aesthetic enjoyment. Yet on the basis of those two intervals Wagner built up a melody that served as the fundamental leitmotif of a whole opera. I have in mind the leitmotif of *The Flying Dutchman* which, in the key of F, reads:

It consists of an effective repetition of the two simplest musical intervals, the fourth and fifth. There are only three tones involved in this melody, which make its musical skeleton:

Considering that the last F is an octave of the first we may assume that melody practically consists of two musical tones,

F and B♭. Precisely the same notes, with the exception of
"-ing," are contained in

> Hear the mellow wedding bells

Disregarding "-ing," which, being an unaccented syllable, does
not essentially alter the general effect, and substituting an
octave for the last syllable, "bells," as rhythmically the most
important, we obtain:

which with a large degree of approximation represents the
musical phrase contained in those words. It reminds one very
closely of the music of *The Flying Dutchman* motif. Apart
from the rhythm the two melodies are practically identical.
This is not at all a vague poetic analogy, for the melody is actually there. It accompanies the sound of those words whenever
uttered. The comparison shows that melodies contained in
certain groups of vowels are by no means musically so different from what we ordinarily hear, nor so melodically absurd
as to afford no musical satisfaction. On the contrary, the melodies contained in the uttered words are sometimes quite pleasing
and very simple. An essential prerequisite of a pleasing effect,
however, is that the words, or syllables, should form a rime.
For only in rime do we find the conditions of musical melody
fulfilled: (1) the vowels are pronounced in exactly (or at least
very nearly) the same way, because the consonants following
them are identical; and (2) the musical phrase introduced by
the vowels receives a definite melodic structure—it ends with
the same tone with which it began.

Reading the score of *The Flying Dutchman* one finds the
transition from F to B♭, which forms the initial stage of the

43

fundamental leitmotif, dominating the whole opera. Whoever has heard the music remembers the frequent and often unexpected outbursts of the interval of the fourth:

which always indicates the approach of the Flying Dutchman. In certain sections it is rhythmically repeated at regular intervals without being finished, and thereby produces the impression of an approaching catastrophe. This fragment, F, B♭, appears as a flash of sound in the beginning of a number of musical phrases, binding them together into larger rhythmical patterns. The artistic effect of it is very similar to that produced by inner rimes which bind two- and sometimes three-verse lines together; such, for instance, as the well-known words from the "Raven":

> While I nodded, nearly napping, suddenly there came a tapping,
> As of someone gently rapping, rapping at my chamber door.
> " 'T is some visitor," I muttered, "tapping at my chamber door."

Or that from Goethe's "Hochzeitslied":

> Da pfeift es und geigt es und klinget und klirrt,
> Da ringelt's und schleift es und rauchet und wirrt,
> Da pispert's und knistert's und flistert's und schwirrt.

Inner rime often occurs in popular sayings, such, for instance, as German *"ganz und gar," "schalten und walten,"* or English: "in every time and clime," "cash and carry," etc. In Shakespeare we find numerous illustrations of such brief riming of two, sometimes three, words. For instance: "From fairest cr*ea*tures we desire incr*ea*se"; "Make war upon this t*y*rant, T*i*me"; "How many a holy and obsequious t*ear* Hath d*ear* religious love stol'n from my eye," etc. To the same category belongs the charm from Shakespeare's skilful repetition of the

44

same word, as in: "a sum of sums"; "and in fresh numbers number all your graces"; "Then can I grieve at grievances foregone," etc.

A still simpler melodic form of assonance is produced by a successive repetition of the same vowel, corresponding to the musical form:

Musically such a phrase is too monotonous to possess artistic value. Yet approximations to this form are sometimes applied in musical compositions, as for instance the "Smith melody" in Wagner's *Das Reingold* which consists almost entirely of one note:

The monotony of such repetitions in the melody of verse is covered by variations introduced by accompanying consonants, especially if those consonants like *r* or *l* are in themselves embryonic vowels. The classical illustration of such mono-tonic inner rime is contained in the opening line of Horace's ode, "Monumentum":

Exegi monument' aere perennius

A symmetrical distribution of consonants among closely similar vowels, e-*r*-e *p*-e-*r*-e, gives a peculiar charm and the rhythmical swing to the whole passage.

Many composite words, especially in Old Germanic and Anglo-Saxon, were formed following this simple melodic scheme, according to which one part of the word appears like an echo of the other. Such are, for instance: "wordhord," "eardgeard," "warothfaroth," "sunderwonder," etc. Many of

45

our words at the present time show a similar musical (not philological) structure, such as "torpor," "murmur," "neglect," "remember." Others seem to have been formed on a more complicated F-B-F basis. Thus, "horizon," "phenomenon," and especially proper names, such as "Ariadne," "Adrianus," "Napoleon," etc.

Assonance and alliteration seem to have had much stronger influence upon the process of formation of our present stock of words than is generally admitted. The melodic element in the history of philological forms has never been sufficiently investigated. Yet there are reasons to believe that a great many of our word stems originated from a simple repetition of one consonant, or one syllable, according to the scheme of Latin "memoria," and Greek βάρβαρος.[24] For we know that many words which at present have no reduplication prove to have originated from consonantal reiteration, such as modern English "further" from Anglo-Saxon "fyroran." Primitive duplications have a tendency to disappear, and it is hardly possible to determine their limits. At any rate in the infancy of language they must have played a very important part. For if we trace certain roots far enough we find consonantal reiteration in cases where it would hardly be suspected. English "go," for instance, is related to German "gehen," which in "Gang" retains its ancient duplication of Anglo-Saxon "gan-gan." Through German "gehen" another consonantal duplication can be ascertained in the Greek κιχάνειν. German "nagen" shows no alliteration in its present form; yet through English

[24] Related to Sanskrit ... barb ... ("to rove," "roam"), according to Holbrook, *Aryan Word-Building*, page 63. This derivation, however, is doubtful. Iwan Müller suggests relation to Sanskrit "balbala-karoti" ("er spricht stammelnd aus"). However that may be the word shows a riming reduplication in the root, and belongs to the class of what Brugmann calls "reduplizierte Nominalbildungen" (*Handbuch der Klassischen Altertumswissenschaft*, herausgegeben von Iwan Müller, II, 1, page 207).

46

"gnaw" it appears to be related to the Anglo-Saxon "*gnagan*," which shows definite consonantal iteration.[25] Russian "*brat*" has lost every trace of the original duplication still retained in the second *r* of its English equivalent, "brother," which points to the Greek φράτηρ, a member of the same φράτρα (clan).[26] "Sit" sounds like an alliteration even in the German "*sitzen*," still more in the Old Germanic "*sizzan*" or Greek ἕζεσθαι. Even "house," which is a place for "hiding," can be reduced to alliterative form through Anglo-Saxon "higan," and possibly through Greek κιχάνειν (to reach, implying destination).[27] Knowing that many primitive languages form their words by repeating the same sound twice, we have reason to believe that in the infancy of our language, at a time probably preceding the formation of our common Indo-Germanic roots, a similar tendency existed. The hypothesis is corroborated by the fact that our children, who in many respects repeat in their individual development the process of phyletic growth, are very fond of forming words by simple reiteration of the same sound. Such words as "mamma" and "papa," "dad" (Sanskrit "*tata*," Russian "*tyatya*") and "sis" are now rare, and represent exceptional cases of linguistic atavism; but in the infancy of language, probably, a large number of words were formed according to the principle of simple reiteration, i.e., on the basis of inner rime. Güntert also shows that many words of Aryan extraction have been modified by analogy from riming associations, such as "*gravus*" from "*grevus*" after "*ravus*." Thus we may assume with a great degree of probability that

[25] Holbrook, *op. cit.*, page 237.

[26] *Ibid.*, page 64. A considerable material pertaining to the influence of rime upon word-building has been accumulated by H. Güntert, *Ueber Reimwortbildungen im Arischen und Altgriechischen*, 1914.

[27] E. Sweet expressed the opinion that "the primitive uninflected words or 'roots' of language were probably dissyllabic" (*History of English Sounds*, § 188).

47

rime has been an important factor in the development of our language.[28] What is at present a mere ornament seems to have been originally a vital force. By repeating the same consonant the word is divided into regular rhythmic sections. By repeating the same vowel a primitive musical effect is introduced into the structure of words. In classifying various types of reduplication Brugmann introduces a group of what he calls "*sonantisch beginnende Wurzeln*," that is, such as have no other reason for reduplication except euphony, i.e., verbal melody. For example, ἀραρίσκω, ὀροφεῖν, ἀλάλκε, ἐνεγκεῖν, etc. It is evident that the tendency thereby is to repeat precisely the same vowel. Knowing how difficult it is for the mouth cavities to reproduce exactly the same system of overtones constituting an individual vowel, we can appreciate the educational importance of such repetitions throughout the history of linguistic development. The institution of inner rime appears to be a great readjustment department in the administration of linguistic forms.

End-rime.—We have so far investigated only very brief melodic phrases which result from the sound of one or two vowels. We have seen that if a vowel is pronounced and then the next syllable strikes a different overtone, the mind evidently retains some more or less definite feeling of melodic relation between them and a tendency to return to the original. Hence the satisfaction that we obtain from inner rimes. How long can this impulse last? In other words, how large can the

---

[28] Compare G. Sarrazin, *Der Einfluss des Accents auf die Entwickelung des englischen Vokalismus*, 1890. It may be of interest to mention in this connection that primitive languages sometimes make use of assonance (inner rime) for grammatical purposes. According to Peschel, "soll im Yakutischen das Suffix *l-r*, welches den Plural ausdrückt, zwischen *l* und *r* denjenigen Vokal aufnehmen, der in der Hauptwurzel steht: also achalar Väter, aber ocholor Kinder, äsälär Bären, u.s.f." (Th. Ziehen, *Vorlesungen über Aesthetik*, 1 : 249.)

48

period between the beginning and the end of a vowel melody be to be appreciated as such?

I believe that this question cannot be answered in general terms. A trained poetic ear may notice assonance far beyond the limits of one verse, while an ordinary person has difficulties in noticing it even in an immediate proximity. Different nationalities display different degrees in their ability to appreciate assonances. If we may believe C. F. Richardson, the assonance in some Spanish poems "would not be noticed, without explanation, by one English ear in a thousand." Ticknor considers "futile the attempt to transfer Spanish assonance into English or German, for the Teutonic ear does not apprehend it, like Castilian." This is no doubt an exaggeration. There is no reason to believe the Teutonic ear so hopelessly dull. Yet there is a difference in the extent of application of assonance in the Germanic and the Romanic languages. In Old French, for instance, we find plenty of illustrations of verse lines coupled by means of terminal assonance, such as:

> Carles li magnes mar vus laissat as porz;
> Tort nus ad fait, nen est dreiz qu'il s'en lot,
> Kar de vus sul ai bien vengiet les hoz'

while in English such things are rather exceptional. After the period of alliterative verse English language goes over to perfect end-rimes.

Apart from individual variations, both between persons and nations, there is another psychological factor to be considered in estimating the capacity of the mind for keeping longer vowel melodies. This new factor is rhythm. Assonance is easily detected, even by an untrained ear, if it is rhythmically stressed, i.e., if it takes place at the end of certain rhythmical units. Such assonances can be heard across several verse lines. The phenomenon of end-rime supports this view.

For rhythmical reasons the last accented vowel in ə verse

49

line, forming a demarcation line between two rhythmic series, stays prominently in the mind and consequently modifies the perception of the following vowels in the same way in which the first stressed tone in a melody modifies the perception of the next coming tones. In other words, as has been several times suggested in the literature on rime,[29] the last vowel in a verse line acts in a manner similar to that of the keynote in a melodic motion. What in the traditional philological views on rime was suggested as an analogy, from the point of view of physical analysis proves indeed to be very near the truth. As human vowels contain definite musical tones, the deviation from the last vowel in the verse line which is rhythmically stressed must act melodically, i.e., must stimulate a desire to return to one of the previously remembered tones. As the sound of the last accented syllable is rhythmically stressed, it dominates other sounds, and we have a greater musical satisfaction in returning to it than to any other vowel previously uttered. Our ear seems to detect a faint shadow of melodic motion on the background of the spoken vowels and involuntarily selects one of them for a key. This is not a vague comparison any longer. It is a fact. For our speech, be it in prose or in verse, is really, and not at all metaphorically, accompanied by musical motion. And the phenomena of assonance and inner rime prove conclusively that an immediate return to the original tone after a brief deviation is psychologically effective, which shows that our ear is sensitive to the brief melodies produced by the vowel sounds. Those two facts established, why should we hesitate to explain the phenomenon of end-rime on the same basis?

Yet we shall guard ourselves against the danger of old analogies. The fact that rime is related to melody does not in the least justify the assumption of a mystical common center,

[29] J. P. Dabney, *The Musical Basis of Verse* (1901). Compare also Paul F. Baum, *The Principles of English Versification*, page 172.

50

owing to which, according to Dabney, "the spirit drops back for anchorage to the simple starting-point — the soul center —the spiritual keynote." References to the ultimate "resting place," to the great "C major of this life" are good only to obscure the issue. What is profound in poetry does not help us to understand the nature of poetry. It is not comparison that interests us, but the germ of truth which lies in the comparison. Rime is similar to the keynote in a melody, not because, as Dabney suggests,[30] the first word of a rime, such as "face" for instance, corresponds to the dominant and prepares the ground for the "perfect cadence," such as "chace" (for musically there is no "dominant" here), but because together with other vowels it physically contains or defines a melody. Nor does melody involve a keynote "because in the tonic chord, or triad, ... we have the only perfect cadence producible in music"—for we do not believe any longer in an Aristotelian fashion that perfectness obliges—but simply because physical analysis proves melody to be based on the harmonic affinity of tones with the keynote as its physical basis.

What we have found is not a poetic comparison but a psychophysical fact. We have found in both, rime and melody, the same law operating under different conditions. Melody moves from one tone to another, and then to the first again, directly through the medium of musical tones. Rime executes through the medium of words a motion similar to that of physical sounds which consist partly of musical tones. This at once explains the similarity and indicates the difference. Rime is related to melody in so far as the satisfaction derived from it is based upon the return to the original tone, a satisfaction

[30] Dabney, *The Musical Basis of Verse*. Compare also Colin McAlpin, *Hermaia*, page 150, where the author writes: "Music in the making is therefore to be found in the soulful attitude of the poet; in the inner sentiment or keynote of his art." Phrases like this only obscure the issue.

51

which is apparently well perceived even though psychologically it is given to us through the medium of words. This is what both have in common and what sufficiently accounts for the origin of the emotional effect possessed by both. Yet at the same time rime is different from melody in several other respects. And these differences ought not to be ignored or covered with vague analogies.

The first difference that we may note concerns the position of the tonic within the melody. In a musical phrase the key is generally given in the first accented part of the opening bar. This is necessary in music because the task of the composer is to create from the outset a longing for return. In poetry, on the contrary, the music of vowels does not, as a rule, belong to the intention, or conscious effort, of the poet. It is an involuntary by-product of other factors. Psychologically any vowel in the verse line may, or may not, serve as a tonic. In fact, in the infancy of poetry an uncertainty and confusion prevailed as to where the riming syllables should be located. In old poetry we often find them organized into brief musical phrases within the verse line, such as:

> Ich minne, sinne lange zit:
> versinne Minne sich,
> wie sie schône lône mîner tage.
> Nu lone schone: dîst mên stât:
> vil kleine meine mich,
> niene meine kleine mîne klage.

Quite often alongside of the inner assonantal forms we find overlapping rimes, when an identical syllable, and often an identical word, ends one line and begins the next following one, such as:

> Sumer, nu wil din ge*walt*
> *walt* den anger und die *heide*
> *beide kleiden:* dast dien *kleinen* vogelen not.

Gradually those riming formations begin to be more definitely localized, as shown by the following:

> Wie gerne ich mit froiden *waere*,
> *waere* unfroide niht so *wert*.
> Nu ist dem richen un*maere*:
> *maere* ist swer ir ze rehte *gert*.

In the process of this historical localization one thing seemed to be certain from the outset: only accented syllables could rime. The reason for this is obvious. Only accented vowels have a definite musical physiognomy. The unaccented ones are not sufficiently clear to serve as the starting-point of a melodic motion. Moreover, even a superficial inspection of the old texts with uncertain or variable rime-schemes reveals the fact that rimes gravitate toward rhythmically important places. This, again, is not difficult to explain. Beauty of the musical effects contained in a rime attracts attention and, therefore, can be conveniently utilized for metrical purposes. We shall dwell upon this subject at some length in the chapter on "Rime and Rhythm." At present, we are only interested in the question: Where are those rhythmically important places located?

In music it is the beginning of each bar that receives a rhythmical stress. In poetry any part of a bar, which is called "foot," may have a stress: we have dactyls, and anapests, and iambi, and others. Why it is so, I do not know. We here simply admit the difference as a fundamental fact without venturing any explanation of it. It is probably this peculiarity of poetic rhythm which deprives the initial vowel of its leading significance. Moreover, musical rhythm is more natural, and therefore much less regular. There are no prescribed rules as to the length of a musical phrase. Whereas in poetry, with the exception of modern free verse, we have regular recurrence of larger rhythmical units, such as verse, couplet, or stanza. Of these three the verse is particularly important.

Nearly all poetry is divided into regular periodic waves which receive almost universal recognition in writing and printing. It is customary to allot a separate line for each wave. This division is so characteristic that many are inclined to identify poetry with it, and regard free verse—which, in fact, is nearer to music—as merely a rhythmic prose. This peculiar, and rather artificial, arrangement makes the last foot (bar) of each line of special significance. It indicates the end of a rhythmical phrase. Thus the melody of vowels finds its natural unit of measure in the length of a verse line. Rhythms in poetry and in music are in this respect quite different.

This difference reflects upon the position of rime within the verse. In music the tonic, the function of which corresponds to that of rime, is to be found ordinarily somewhere in the beginning and right at the end of a musical phrase. Imitating the structure of musical phraseology some modern poets attempted to rime the first with the last syllable of each verse, or—more frequently—the first words of each two successive verse lines. Such experiments are by no means new. We find them in great abundance in old poetry. Two verses from a song by Walther von der Vogelweise may serve as an illustration:

> *Ein* klosenaere, ob erz vertruege? ich waene er *nein*.
> *Daz* und ouch me vertrege ich doch dur *etewaz*.

This is from the musical point of view the most natural arrangement. Yet, though musically consistent, such or similar arrangements were soon given up as rhythmically ineffective. There is a well-defined melody in every line of this kind. But it is not easily detected because it is rhythmically misplaced. We forget the musical physiognomy of the initial vowel long before we reach the end of the line. That the device is purely experimental and artificial may be seen from the fact that the distance between the riming words *"ein ... nein"* in the illustration above is in some instances so absurdly large that it cannot possibly be detected by the ear, and has therefore no musical significance whatever. In Gottfried von Neisen, for example, we find a ballad consisting of five stanzas, each of which begins and ends with the same word, such as:

> *Bar* min herze ie bernde wunne,
> daz was swenne ich sach ir wunnelichen schîn
> unde ir ougen sam der sunne
> dur mîn ougen liuhten in daz herze mîn.
> dar nâch wart mir leit in kurzen stunden.
> owe Minne wunden.
> wie hast du sus dich mîn underwunden
> daz ich sender siecher bin noch froiden *bar*.

Here the significance of *"bar ... bar"* is of a purely intellectual nature. It is an artificial ornamental device to be admired by the refined lovers of poetry as an additional difficulty for the poet to overcome, but without any musical meaning. Absurdity of such complicated riming devices shows that there is no natural limit where musical phrases of this kind should either begin or stop.

But if the poet selects, not the beginning, but the end of a line as the starting-point of his melodic motion, then—owing to the rhythmical importance of the final accented vowel—its musical physiognomy is better remembered than any of the others and can easily serve as the starting-point of a musical phrase. Thus rime may be placed anywhere. But in order to be appreciated, or even noticed (if the phrase is long enough), it must begin with a vowel which is easy to remember. Such an easily remembered vowel is not the first, but the last accented vowel in the verse line. This latter stays for a while in the foreground of that portion of consciousness which in the process of speech is allotted to acoustic impressions. A deviation from that musical center is, according to the general laws of musical hearing, perceived as a disturbance and accompanied by a slight

55

feeling of expectation. This feeling evidently persists for some time until at the end of the next rhythmical unit, i.e., at the end of the next line, the same vowel is repeated. If it is repeated, the energy of expectation finds a discharge. And as a rule every normal discharge of energy produces a pleasing effect. Besides every process of expectation, no matter how insignificant, is slightly unpleasant. When the expected note comes, the unpleasant sensation is removed. And that ever intensifies the feeling of satisfaction. Thus there are several psychological causes that contribute to the ultimate effect. But the physical reason is one, and it is the same which is found in melody: one tone is selected to dominate the melodical motion, be it in a musical phrase or a rimed verse, and every other tone is then taken in relation to that fundamental tone.

Why a deviation from a given tone (provided it be rhythmically stressed) excites a desire to return to it, may serve as a subject for psychological speculation. Here it is simply claimed as a fact. Every one knows by experience that when one begins to sing or whistle one cannot arbitrarily break up the melodic motion on one of the middle notes without doing violence to his own emotions. In singing a melody one has a peculiar desire to go through with it and bring it to its natural end, i.e., back to the tonic note; in other words, to finish it in the same key in which the melody was started. If the melody is broken in the middle, one is left more or less strongly dissatisfied, and ordinarily within a very short time will unconsciously resume singing or whistling until the melodic phrase is brought to its natural end. It has been shown that a similar situation lies at the basis of rimed poetry.

Possible objections.—It is here convenient to answer a few possible objections.

1. First, I have to expect the most obvious objections arising from my readers' failure to hear any of the melodies

that I am speaking of. It may be you have an exceptionally refined ear or too rich an imagination—they may ironically remark—which makes it possible for you to hear melodies where ordinary people hear nothing but words; we are certainly unable to perceive any of the overtones that you are speaking about. Neither am I, I am obliged to admit. Between hearing and perceiving there is a great deal of difference. We hear many sounds which we do not perceive as individual sounds; they are psychologically fused with other stronger sounds and are perceived as the sound-quality or timbre of these sounds. Yet timbre is something that we undoubtedly hear, and objectively it consists of nothing else but fainter sounds. Take those sound shadows away and you will destroy something that you undoubtedly hear. You will destroy all vowels. For, not hearing overtones, you will not be able to hear vowels. This may be so — my readers will probably reply. Yet, as you say, we hear those overtones not as individual sounds but as timbres. And melody is certainly not a relation of timbres but precisely of individual tones. How can tones which are not perceived as individual tones determine a melody? How can they stimulate our emotions and produce pleasurable effects? To this I answer by asking a similar question in return. How can harmony be determined by a system of overtones that are never perceived by ordinary people as individual tones? They are also fused with the fundamental and perceived as the latter's timbre. Without considerable effort and mental strain we are unable to hear directly even the first two overtones. And yet there is hardly any doubt now that the system of overtones determines our practical harmony, stimulates our emotions, and is perhaps largely responsible for the very existence of music. Precisely the tones which are not perceived are creative of musical pleasure. Now in vowels the characteristic overtones are much more prominent than in many other musical tones. We have already pointed out that, according to Miller,

57

they absorb sometimes as much as 90 per cent of the total energy of the sound. Under such conditions it is remarkable that we do not perceive them as individual tones. Only our habit of associating them with the rest of the vowel quality is responsible for our failure to hear them distinctly. It is therefore rather an "imagination" that we do not hear them. We cannot fail to hear a sound which, at the moment, absorbs 90 per cent of the whole sound energy.

2. Another objection may be raised by musicians. It may be pointed out that the key in the melodic motion of vowels does not necessarily coincide with the tone contained in the last accented vowel. The key in which, for instance, the above-given melody corresponding to "Hail, Zaragoza" seems to move, is G♭ major, whereas according to our interpretation the first and the last bar should be regarded as composed in the key of D♭, while the two middle ones ought to move—from the musical point of view quite absurdly—in the key of B♭. Such an objection, however, can be raised only by a person who has completely misunderstood the meaning of my argument. I have already pointed out that the conception of key could not be simply transferred from music to poetry; it must be rather substantially modified in several respects. The technique of musical composition, of course, does not apply to the natural music of vowels, which is not "composed" by anybody. What I believe to have demonstrated is, not the technical coincidence, but the identity of the physical basis of two comparable phenomena. The phenomenon of rime appears to be reducible to something with which we are more familiar—to melody. But far from proclaiming a complete technical identity (which would be but little short of a miracle) between rime and the key in a melody, I merely maintain that rime fulfills a function similar to that of the key, in that it introduces a reference point to which all other vowels in the verse are melodically related. In music, too, key is a reference point to which all other tones are related. Yet

there is an essential difference in the arrangement of tones. In music all tones constituting a melody are harmonically arranged. In verse, however, they follow each other to a very large extent without any technical scheme, and only at the end return to the same tone with which they have started. The emotional satisfaction derived from returning to the original tone is there, but the constant reference of all tones to this common center is lacking. In our diatonic scale we constantly feel the presence of the key. In our vowel-scales—as in many scales applied in modern music—the key becomes plastic and changeable. This does not mean, however, that it is entirely lost. It just depends on each particular arrangement.

Let us for a moment forget the linguistic origin of the two vowel runs given above and consider them from the purely musical point of view. I invite the reader now not to listen to my, or to anybody's argument, but to the music of those runs, playing them time after time on the piano. Let us argue musically for the time being. What do we find? We find the interesting fact that every tone constituting those runs may function as the key of several melodic developments. In other words, those runs do not define a key within our harmonic system. Melodies built up from such material may be written in different tonalities. I can write several phrases, musically quite sensible though brief, all built up from the material furnished by the *oo-ō-ā-ŭ-er* scale

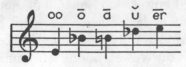

and yet each phrase is in a different key. For example:

Key of E major (*ōō*)
(*Tannhäuser*;
G is omitted)

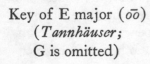

59

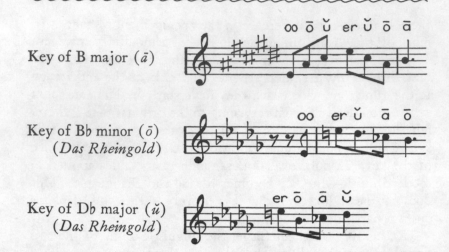

Key of B major (*ā*)

Key of Bb minor (*ō*)
(*Das Rheingold*)

Key of Db major (*ŭ*)
(*Das Rheingold*)

This is quite in agreement with the fact that any vowel can be used to form a rime which defines and not merely follows the key.

3. It may further be justly objected that rime is not based exclusively on vowels; it requires a complete identity of sound at the end of two verse lines. What is the function of consonants in producing that identity? Why are such rimes as "tree" and "street," which satisfy the conditions of melody, for $\overline{ee}$ is identical, nevertheless considered monstrous? If our theory were correct the identity of consonants in rime would be quite superfluous. For the melodic phrase is brought to completion by the last accented vowel. Consonants do not contribute anything to the melody of languages. They are just noises, from the musical point of view only disturbing and certainly unpleasant. But why are the vowels alone not sufficient to form a perfect rime?

The next chapter attempts to answer all these questions. So far we have considered only one element of rime: identity of the accented vowels, which indeed appears as the most important. Now we have to consider two other factors mentioned in the beginning of this chapter: (1) identity and identical order of the consonants; and (2) identity of the unaccented vowels.

But before we go any farther one more suggestion must be ventured which aims, it will be said, at rehabilitating an international reputation. Among the various languages English is often branded as the least musical, while Italian and Spanish are popularly considered best adapted for musical purposes. In touching upon such a delicate question one is in danger of being favorably or unfavorably prejudiced in regard to a certain language by what may be termed linguistic patriotism. Putting aside all patriotic considerations I shall attempt to discuss the question on purely objective grounds. To judge a musical work by the amount of sweet pleasure it gives to the ear is a symptom of unpardonable dilettantism. A musician must possess other criteria and standards for criticism beyond his personal enjoyment. Similarly the musical qualities of a language cannot be judged on the basis of the acoustic impression it is apt to produce upon a foreign ear. The mere sweetness of sound—as, for instance, in Italian—is not sufficient to decide in favor of a particular language. One of the most important factors in the musical structure of a language is its variety of vowel sounds. It is impossible to produce a great masterpiece of music on the seven strings of the Hawaiian guitar. There are, as I am informed, not knowing the language myself, only seven vowels in Italian, whereas there are over twenty-three different vowels in English.[31] For this reason as far as melodic opportunities are concerned the English language stands to the Italian in the same relation as the grand piano to the Hawaiian guitar. The variety of vowels presents to the

[31] O. Jespersen in his *A Modern English Grammar*, 1:414–439, gives twenty-five different vowel sounds in English. Henry Sweet gives twenty-three vowels for each period, OE, ME, and LE (*History of English Sounds*, page 405).

English poet such musical opportunities as can never be found in any other language, except perhaps in the ancient Greek. If expression, and not sweet beauty, is the pivot of art, there is certainly much more to express and to create on the basis of twenty-three than on the basis of only seven vowels. This accounts perhaps for the fact that, in spite of the scarcity of rimes in the English language and other unfavorable circumstances, England has created one of the richest poetical literatures in history.

III

THEORY OF RIMING CONSONANTS

IT has been remarked many times that
both alliteration and assonance belong to the same category.
One is a repetition of consonants, the other that of vowels.
"One occurs at the beginning of a sound-group, the other at
the end, that is all." Alliteration, assonance, and end-rime are
merely different expressions of the same thing.[1] Repetition lies
at the bottom of all three. Yet is that really all? Repetition
is merely an external form; it does not explain anything. It is
itself a problem that needs explanation. What is the reason
for the repetition? Is it the same in all three cases?

If we ask the question in this form we see at once how inadequate the traditional reply is. Repetition of vowels in an
assonance is of melodic origin. The vowels are repeated to
form a melody. But consonants are not tones. They are noises,

---

[1] Charles F. Richardson, *A Study of English Rime* (Hanover, 1909),
page 22.

and do not belong to the melodic scheme of the verse. Why do we have to repeat them in rime? If rime is melody, it ends with the last accented vowel. All the rest is irrelevant. "Remember," then, is just as good a rime for "temper" as it is for "ember." If it is not good enough, there must be some other reason for it. Melody cannot account for the deficiency; for, from the melodic point of view, all three rimes are equally perfect. What is the function of consonants in rime?

If we wished to be partisans of our melodic point of view, we could attempt to explain the function of consonants on the same melodic basis, by reference to what Henry Sweet calls "vowel parasitism."[2] It is indeed true that consonants have a modifying effect upon the quality of neighboring vowels. In the history of language the diphthongs and often the simple vowels undergo certain specific changes in consequence of the influence exercised upon them by preceding or following consonants. Sweet calls them parasitic developments, the vowel sound being changed, as it were, at the expense of its consonantal associates.[3] Generalizing upon evidence obtained from a large number of observations in many different languages, this distinguished philologist comes to the conclusion that eventually "every consonant modifies the preceding vowel more or less.

[2] Henry Sweet, *History of English Sounds*, §§ 159, 427.

[3] The influence is mutual. In Russian the front vowels and the now silent *i* (soft sign) communicate their character to most preceding consonants, so that nearly every consonant has a double pronunciation. On the other hand, "the fronted consonants again in their turn influence a preceding sound. . . . . It is certain that a considerable number of vowel changes are due entirely to the direct influence of the immediately following consonant, for if that vowel is not fronted by a following consonant, as sometimes happens, the vowel remains unmodified. In these Russian changes we have the key to the Germanic vowel-mutation or 'umlaut' " (Sweet, *op. cit.*, §§ 142–145). The laws governing the vowel-mutation as well as other changes derived from consonantal environment have been known to philologists since the days of Grimm. But exact physical measurements have been made only recently.

Thus in English the *i* in 'fish' has not quite the same sound as in 'hiss.' "[4] Not merely the quality but also the quantity of a vowel changes in consequence of its consonantal environment. Stops, especially voiceless stops, have the tendency to shorten.[5]

These philological observations have been quite recently corroborated by physicists. We have seen that vowels have been measured by physicists. The identity of a vowel sound was found to depend upon the relative loudness energy of its various components, from which, as a rule, one or two absorb the larger part of the energy of the wave train. The loudest component of a vowel—be it remembered—is called its "characteristic frequency." We have seen that the characteristic frequencies are independent of the fundamental tone, i.e., remain relatively constant no matter at what pitch the vowel is intoned. Yet being independent of the fundamental the characteristic frequency depends on a good many other factors. It was shown in the first chapter that each vowel is characterized, not by a fixed overtone, but by a certain limited region, or band, of resonance. Its characteristic frequency is not absolutely but only relatively constant. This may be explained by saying that *a*, for instance, retains its identity for ordinary audition even if the number of vibrations be decreased, say, to 750 as against its normal 910 as long as all other partials remain relatively constant. Crandall has shown that *a* in "part" differs from that in "father" by more than 300 vibrations per second. Yet all we

[4] Sweet, *op. cit.*, § 163. In French phonetic literature the question is discussed at length by P. J. Rousselot. In his *Principes de phonétique expérimentale* he distinguishes three aspects in which consonantal environment may influence the vowels (pages 370–371): "Le tracé que nous venons d'étudier suggère trois observations importantes: (1) La voyelle interconsonantique devient naturellement plus courte que la voyelle isolée ... (2) Le commencement de la tension ... ne répondent pas à un même degré de l'action musculaire ... (3) Le caractère de la tenue est sensiblement modifié."

[5] Sweet, *op. cit.*, § 114.

notice is just a slight difference in the quality of *a* due to its "parasitic" relation to *r*. There are all sorts of gradations possible between the English and American pronunciation of "half." When a native of Indiana—to use Liddell's illustration—substitutes the low-frequency *e* for *ae* in cases where the vowel precedes an *r* followed by a vowel, as when pronouncing "barrel" like "beryl," the context of conversation enables the hearer to catch the meaning. In the course of linguistic development our vowels were subject to marked variations. Our present *a* in "make" was at one time pronounced as *ae*. The Western pronunciation of "water" is quite intelligible to the Eastern ear, although the short *o* (high-frequency *o*) is the standard vowel for this word.[6] Now if a vowel with a characteristic frequency lying on the border of *ae* is still identified as *a*, how much less noticeable are the variations that are caused

---

[6] Having studied many such variations throughout centuries of development, Liddell comes to the following conclusion: "Two sets of consonants for the same vowel can exist side by side in the same generation without destroying the conceptual intelligibility of the words containing those tones as long as tones in question fall within neighboring bands of the vowel spectrum. The speech habits of the majority establish the norm, and the other is forgotten." Influence of consonantal environment upon the quality and quantity of vowels has been an object of careful study in comparative philology. Among the most prominent scholars in the field we have already named Grimm, Sweet, and Mark Liddell. To these must be added a number of minor investigators: E. Brugger, "Zur lautlichen Entwickelung der englischen Schriftsprache im Anfange des 16 Jahrhunderts," *Anglia*, Volume 15; Gottfried Hackmann, "Kürzung langer Tonvokale im Alt-, Mittel-, und Neuenglischen, Studien zur englischen Philologie," *ibid.*, Volume 10; K. Luick, *Untersuchungen zur Englischen Lautgeschichte* (Strassburg, 1896); Charles L. Eastlake, "Changes in the Pronunciation of English," *Nineteenth Century* (1902), 52:992–1001; B. W. Wells, *Development of O. E. Long Vowels*, 1884; "History of the *a*-Vowel from Old Germanic to Modern English," *Transactions of the American Philological Association* (1882), 12:68–88; "The Vowels *e* and *i*," *Transactions of the American Philological Association* (1886), 16:133–64; "The Sounds *o* and *u* in English," *ibid.* (1887), 17:47–77.

by the difference of forty or fifty vibrations per second. Such slight differences may be produced by various circumstances, one of those being the consonantal environment in which a given vowel is imbedded. When we pronounce *a* with the mouth ready to utter *th* afterward, the resonance conditions of the mouth cavity must be slightly different from those which obtain when we intend to utter *r* afterward. Therefore *a* in "father" and *a* in "part" have different frequency-constants. But rime requires complete coincidence of sound. The nearer the approximation, the purer its melody.

Indeed, history of rime corroborates this view. The oldest rimes known to us disregard consonants. We shall soon discuss this question more in detail. For the present it will suffice to mention that the early French poets did not hesitate to rime "*vol*" with "*og*," or "*-on*" with "*-os*," as for example:

> Sanct Pedre sols veinjar lo vol,
> estrais lo fer que al laz og,
> si consegued u serv fellon,
> la destre aurelia li excos ...

Tertullian, the earliest rimer known to us from the Christian world, combines "*coeli*" with "*orbis*," and "*docebit*" with "*nimbi*." And we do not have to search for such monstrosities; in *De Judicio Domini* they occur almost regularly, the poem being written in assonantal rimes. History shows that perfect end-rime develops from imperfect vowel-rimes by a long process of gradual stratification. From the physical point of view it is like tuning a musical instrument. It took centuries to perfect the vowel melodies, to get our poetry in tune. Musically speaking such primitive rimes as Old-Germanic "*wisman*" and "*gizam*," or Tertullian's "*coeli*" and "*orbis*" actually are out of tune. For the frequency constants of the riming vowels are different. Crandall has measured the difference for "father" and "part," and found it quite considerable. The two *a*'s are

67

melodically different because they are pronounced in the neighborhood of different consonants. According to Crandall *a* in "father" has 955 vibrations per second, while in "part" it has only 630. Harvey Fletcher in his recently published *Speech and Hearing* gives a number of oscillograph records of the vowel *a* preceded by different consonants. The wave-curve in each particular case displays marked differences.[7] That shows that not merely those consonants which follow a vowel, but also those which precede it, modify its characteristic frequency. The wave-form of *la* and *ga* being different, their riming values appear to be slightly out of tune. At this point philology corroborates a purely physical discovery. There are certain languages, such as Russian for instance, in which consonants preceding rime are required to be identical, *if no other consonant follows the rime*. In other words, in Russian *la* and *ga* do not rime. Physical analysis gives the reason for such a limitation: their frequency constants are different, and to a sensitive ear they sound out of tune. In English we are obliged to tolerate this little harshness for technical reasons similar to those which force us to tolerate modern pianos which are deliberately made out of tune, because otherwise playing on the piano would be rendered impossible. Riming words in English are comparatively so few that an additional limitation concerning the purity of sound would probably be disastrous.

Rimes which barely satisfy the conditions of phonetic identity are called "sufficient rimes"; those which introduce an additional element of euphony above what is barely necessary to make rime "sufficient" are called "rich rimes." Thus "imprest ... rest" is a rich rime. Such rimes are musically the most perfect ones, because the identity of the consonantal environment physically guarantees the identity of the vowel sound. Different consonants put the vowels slightly out of tune.

[7] Harvey Fletcher, *Speech and Hearing* (New York, 1929), pages 33–44.

68

Yet all this argument probably applies only to certain consonants and in the immediate vicinity of the riming vowels. There is no evidence whatsoever that the consonants which are farther removed from the basic vowel, such as *b* in "remember," should influence the latter at all. The question, therefore, still stands unanswered: What is the significance of consonants in rime? Some of them may modify the characteristic tone of the preceding vowel. But those are in the minority. What is the function of all others? What is their general meaning for the rime? To answer this question we have first to consider the physical nature of consonants and then to draw our conclusions accordingly.

Physical nature of consonants.—While vowels are a variety of musical tones, consonants, according to Helmholtz, are various kinds of noises produced by the tongue, lips, and larynx. Noises are air-trains of irregular formation. Recent investigations into the matter, by Paget and Crandall, have proved that *every consonant shows the presence of a faint and usually very high characteristic frequency of its own.*

As far as *r* is concerned, the opinions of the experimenters disagree: some regard it as a consonant sound, others are inclined to consider it a vowel. Crandall found that there is no sharp transition point between the preceding vowel and the subsequent *r*-sound. Yet, apparently, the *r*-characteristics are best displayed toward the end of the record. They contain a well-defined and comparatively low characteristic frequency, which makes some experimenters believe that *r* is a variety of vowel sounds.

The liquid *l*, and the nasals *m*, *n*, and *ng*, are commonly regarded as semi-vowels. They show a remarkable adaptability to the subsequent vowel in the behavior of their characteristic frequencies. Their amplitudes are on the whole smaller than the amplitudes of the affixed pure vowel sounds, "but some of

69

them are surprisingly large." "The high frequency characteristics of all four sounds lie between 2,400 and 2,900."[8]

All other consonants are in the nature of drum sounds—brief characteristic noises that separate one vowel tone from another. Their duration is very small. The mean duration of the voiced consonants, according to Crandall, is 0.14 second; of the unvoiced consonants, 0.05 second.

Function of consonants in the melody of verse.—In the melody of verse consonants function as time-beaters. They are means of stopping and starting vowels. Being of a drum-like nature they serve the purpose of separating the vowel tones into more or less regular time intervals. They help create rhythm.

Now the more similar the repeated elements, the more effective is the rhythm. *La-la-la-la-la* is a more rhythmical group than *ta-na-va-sa-ka*. That is why we instinctively use it for singing without words. Therefore the drum effect of an identical consonant may be easily heard at a distance of several syllables. Alliteration acts like a powerful drum in the melody of verse. It emphasizes for us the brief musical phrases within the verse, and helps us to count the syllables; applied at the end of each line it announces the completion of the fundamental time interval—the verse. Therefore the aesthetic effect of alliteration is quite different from that of assonance. It is of rhythmical origin.

In a modern orchestra there are several different kinds of drums. To produce a marked rhythmic effect only one at a time can be used. That is musical alliteration. In our English language there are sixteen different consonant sounds which, apart from the semi-vowels *r, l, m, n, ng,* can be applied to

[8] Crandall, "The Sounds of Speech," *Bell System Technical Journal,* 1925, page 31.

produce various rhythmical effects. Those effects, however, are possible only if one consonant at a time is used. This is the rhythmical music of alliteration. Both assonance and alliteration combined produce the actual melody of verse. For melody without rhythm is impossible, or at least highly ineffective. This seems to me to be the reason why a repetition of a vowel alone at the end of a verse line, if it is accompanied by different consonants, produces an impression of something incomplete, unfinished, and even dissonant. Imperfect rimes affect us as discords.

What is discord in poetry?—As far as I know Jean Hytier was the first who, on the basis of modern poetic practice, attempted a systematic classification of accords and discords in human speech. As his ideas, though not original,[9] are very characteristic of modern poetic technique and afford a convenient terminology for a theory of imperfect rimes, I shall discuss them at some length. The time and effort needed for the study of the minute distinctions that he introduces are amply recompensed by the results attained.

Hytier defines an accord as "a repetition of a simple sonorous element" (*la répétition d'une sonorité simple*). Two different kinds of accords are distinguished and carefully analyzed: accords of consonants, and accords of vowels. Each kind in turn is subdivided into three groups with respect to the position of the repeated consonant or vowel. Identical consonants may precede different vowels, such as (substituting English illustrations for French):

> To these rare moments turbulent weeks entrust
> The peace that vivifies, the calm from risk.
>
> —AXTON CLARK

[9] For a long time they have been practiced by modern poets.

71

Or identical consonants may follow different vowels:

> What has the brain that it hopes to last lo*nger*?
>
> . . . .
>
> The groping, the break of her voice in a*nger*.
>
> . . . .

—L. UNTERMEYER

This kind of a consonantal accord accompanied by a vowel discord is a very common form in English, though very exceptional in French. Most visual rimes belong to this category: "noon ... son," "war ... star," "prove ... love," etc.

Or identical consonants may be placed before and after different (oftener after identical) vowels:

> . . . . the mind re*c*eives
> Serenely grave assuagement; and a coo*l*
> And gracious solitude endures, a*l*oof,
> One silent hour with meditative ea*s*e.

—AXTON CLARK

Or:

> But forms of clay are lightly broken;
> They will lie shattered and forgotten in a dingy co*r*ner.

—JEAN S. UNTERMEYER

Similar subdivisions are easily obtained for the vowel sounds. Thus Hytier arrives at the following:

TABLE OF ACCORDS

Simple Accords				Double Accords	
Of Consonants		Of Vowels			
$r\bar{a}$	ray	$l\bar{a}$	lay	$r\bar{a}$	ray
$r\bar{o}$	row	$r\bar{a}$	ray	$r\bar{a}$	array
$\bar{a}r$	air	$\bar{a}l$	ale	$\bar{a}r$	air
$\bar{o}r$	ore	$\bar{a}r$	air	$\bar{a}r$	fair
$r\bar{a}$	ray	$\bar{a}l$	ale	$r\bar{a}$	ray
$\bar{o}r$	ore	$r\bar{a}$	ay	$\bar{a}r$	fair

It is easy to see from the table above that rime obtains as a special case of accord: a double accord of consonants and vowels results in a rime; cross-sonorization of consonants and vowels (*ra ... ar*) make an imperfect rime, such as *"tuera ... Nisard"*; or "cool ... aloof."

One of the most characteristic features of modern poetic technique, according to Hytier, is a widespread use of discords. Discord is defined as an acoustic effect based on the difference of sonorous elements (*un effet sonore fondé sur la différence des sonorités*). A classification of discords may be obtained by analogy with the table of accords:

TABLE OF DISCORDS

Simple Discords				Double Discords	
Of Consonants		Of Vowels		Of Consonants and Vowels	
ra	ray	*ra*	ray	*ra*	ray
la	lay	*ro*	row	*lo*	low
ar	air	*ar*	air	*ar*	air
al	ale	*or*	ore	*ol*	soul
ra	ray	*ar*	air	*ra*	ray
al	ale	*ro*	row	*ol*	soul

The part played in poetry by such discords is far more important than is commonly believed. Consider for instance the effect produced by an unrimed line in a group of rimed lines. The effect is very peculiar. It was known to the Italian poets even before Dante. "There are some poets," Dante says, "who sometimes do not make all endings rime in the same stanza. They weave into their stanza one line unaccompanied by rime, which is called the key." Thus we see that not merely a special name existed in Dante's time for discords, but the line which was in discord with others was deemed so important as to be regarded as the key-line of the stanza. Milton has a fine ear for dissonances even when he does not sing in blank verse. In "Lycidas," for instance, a number of discords irregularly scattered throughout the poem greatly contribute to the mournful effect of the elegy:

> Yet once more, O ye laurels, and once *more*
> Ye myrtles brown, with ivy never sere,
> I come to pluck your berries harsh and crude,
> And with forced fingers rude
> Shatter your leaves before the mellowing year.
> Bitter constraint and sad occasion dear
> Compels me to disturb your season due;
> For Lycidas is dead, dead ere his prime,
> Young Lycidas, and hath not left his peer.
> Who would not sing for Lycidas? he knew
> Himself to sing, and build the lofty rhyme.
> He must not float upon his watery bier
> Unwept, and welter to the parching *wind*,
> Without the meed of some melodious tear.
> Begin, then, Sisters of the sacred *well*
> That from beneath the seat of Jove doth spring . . . .

Modern poetic technique makes an extensive use of discords. Instead of rimes we often find application of vowel-discords, such as:

> Qui me le dit qu'en ce mom*ent*
> Dans la pleine epaisseur du m*onde* ...
>
> Ils replongent d'un bond m*ol*
> Dans le limon etern*el*.
>
> —JULES ROMAINS

Or in English:

> Let the boy try along this bayonet-bl*a*de
> How cold steel is, and keen with hunger of bl*oo*d[10]

[10] Among the modern American poets Untermeyer appears to be the master of discord. In his "Roast Leviathan," discords are intermingled with rimes, both being used on an equal footing: "day," "away," "*see*," "upon," "sun," "just," "*risen*," "dust," "*begins*," etc.

74

Here the contrast of vowels is strongly emphasized by the identity of consonants. Thus *a* and *o* seem, psychologically, more different, i.e., their difference attracts our attention, when they are accompanied by the same consonants, as in "road ... raid," or "blade ... blood." The effect is precisely the reverse of rime, and, since rime is based on harmony, its reverse may properly be called discord. In view of our former discussions the term is more than a mere analogy.

Significance of the order of consonants in rime.—Now we are prepared to answer the question that was raised in the beginning of this chapter: What is the significance of consonants and their order in rime?

When, at the end of a verse line, the accented vowel forms an assonance with the preceding line, while the consonants or the unaccented vowels turn out to be different, a discord obtains between the first verse and the second. As a contrast to the preceding assonance the disagreement appears to be more striking. When in a blank verse all lines end differently, we do not notice the disharmony of endings. But when part of the ending agrees in sound, and satisfies our sense for melody, every little disagreement that follows receives a stress. If one line ends with "temper" and the next with "cataclysm," the musical nature of the words remains entirely outside of the sphere of attention. But if one line ends with "temper" and the other with "remember," our ear detects at once the difference between the two. We say, then, that *b* and *p* form a discord. Thus imperfect rimes may be properly regarded as a special case of poetic discord. And as such they appear to be fully legitimate. For in both music and poetry dissonance is a legitimate element in composition.

The question now arises why a consonantal discord appears to be rather unpleasant. The unpleasantness evidently comes from the broken rhythm. The last accented vowel ends the

75

melody of a comparatively large group of words. The sensation of relief associated with the close of a melody gives a rhythmical stress to the verse end. The terminal consonants, if they are identical with those of the preceding line, announce the end of a rhythmical unit, as it were with a drum; the rhythmical tendencies mutually assist each other. But if the consonants are different, they make us feel that the line is still going on. *The final drum signal is missing,* and we are left under the impression that the last vowel made, so to speak, a false alarm, and that the real end has not come yet, that the motion is still continuing. The situation results in a conflict between two rhythmical tendencies: one, arising from the accord of vowels, emphatically demands an end of a rhythmical series; the other, originating from the discord of consonants, rejects this end and keeps the verse line flowing. The conflict awakens in our mind an unpleasant sensation. In other words, with the melody of vowels closed we expect the end of a rhythmical series to take place. If the consonants are identical, they produce an alliteration (which is rhythmical) and our expectation is gratified. If they are not identical, they form a consonantal discord, their contrast receives an emphasis, the rhythmical series continues, and our expectation is frustrated. An unfulfilled expectation is as a rule unpleasant. Hence the peculiar feeling of dissatisfaction or irritation that usually associates itself with imperfect rimes.

The mental reaction, however, appears to be subject to individual variation. What is irritating and unpleasant to one, seems highly stimulating and agreeable to another. In fact we shall see that imperfect rimes may occasionally become an object of deliberate cultivation. Evidently there is something in an imperfect rime that appeals to our aesthetic sense. It is not difficult to see what this something is. With the help of physical analysis we have succeeded in dissecting the phenomenon of end-rime into two heterogeneous factors. One part of it is melodic in its nature: it gives us a musical satisfaction to hear the melody of vowels closed at the end of the verse. The other part is rhythmical in its nature. The drum effect of terminal consonants adds a new touch to the melodic effect of the vowels. But each of those effects separately is quite justified. The effect of the end-rime is naturally stronger, because it is a combination of two separate effects. But each effect separately is not entirely destitute of artistic value. Therefore an imperfect rime is not necessarily a bad rime.

Yet there is a strong feeling against imperfect rimes, especially in English poetry. It is generally taken for granted that an imperfect rime is a bad rime. In suggesting that rimes which are at present incorrect might have been perfect at the time they were written, H. C. Wyld says: "It is scarcely possible to conceive a conspiracy among poets to spoil their verse by adopting bad rimes. . . . . It seems reasonable, then, to argue that when a certain class of rimes recur in the poetry of an age there is an apriori presumption that these rimes were 'good' and satisfactory to the ears of the poets and readers of that age."[11] This is not always true. For Mr. Wyld's tacitly admitted premise—that imperfect rimes are *eo ipso* bad rimes —has not always been shared by the poets.

If this were true, that is, if imperfect rimes were unconditionally objectionable, a very serious blow would be given to our fundamental point of view. For—our opponents might argue—if rime rests on the music of overtones, it must be completed with the sound of the last vowel. What difference does it make, from your point of view, they may say, whether the consonants are identical or not? We should expect at least a certain amount of satisfaction from the coincidence of terminal vowels alone without any regard for consonants. And yet the

[11] H. C. Wyld, *Studies in English Rhyme from Surrey to Pope* (1923), page 10.

77

satisfaction fails to obtain; any change in the identity of the ending is resented by us as a blunder. Contrary to what you have been trying to prove, the melody of vowels alone is evidently not appreciated. In fact, it is rather unpleasant. Poetry on the whole discards rimes which are not strictly identical.

Now apart from other considerations, the main point in my defense is that such rimes do actually occur in various languages, not merely as a matter of accident but as an object of deliberate cultivation. The tradition that forbids imperfect rimes was not always so faithfully followed as it is now, and even now it is by no means universally accepted.

Imperfect rimes in popular poetry.—The popular poetry of all languages contains numerous illustrations of imperfect riming which in some cases is even more effective and beautiful than the mathematical exactness of our classical rimes. Whose pedantic sense would object, for instance, to the following popular lines?

> When a pretty little *boy*,
> A young merchantman so gay,
> With my lollipops and *toys*,
> Of Duke's place I bore the sway.
>
> . . . .
>
> A few years pass away,
> And a young man soon I grows,
> When around in London streets,
> I chant away "Old clothes."
> "Clo sale—clo sale—*clo*—"
> I raise aloud the cry,
> And as I pass *along*,
> How the pretty damsels sigh!

This is the most common type of imperfect riming which rests entirely on the melody of vowels without considering the consonants at all (*"boy ... toys"; "clo ... along"*). It may be called "apocopated" rime, as it cuts off the ending and leaves the alliteration either completely out or unfinished.[12] One can find plenty of illustrations of this type in Negro songs. Consider, for example:

> Railroad Bill mighty bad *man*,
> Shoot dem lights out o' de brakeman's *hand*.
> It's lookin' for Railroad Bill.

Or:

> Some rides in buggies,
> Some rides in *hacks*.
> Some rides in hearses,
> But they never come *back*.

In imitation of popular Germanic poetry Goethe makes use of apocopated rimes in his famous "Song of the Flea" (*Faust*, 2211):

> Es war einmal ein Koenig,
> Er hatt' einen grossen *Floh*,
> Den liebt' er gar nicht wenig,
> Als wie seinen eigenen *Sohn*.

Another type of imperfect riming may be properly called "assonantal" or "embryonic" rime. For, as we shall see later, it is probably the oldest form in which the vowel melody first appeared and from which our end-rime developed. In this case both the accented and the unaccented vowels form a very close assonance, while the consonants are changed, as in the model above: "temper ... remember." In popular poetry we find many illustrations. In D. Scarborough's collection of Negro folk-songs, *On the Trail of Negro Folk-Songs*, we find the following examples:

---

[12] Jules Romains calls this kind of rime *"la rime par augmentation ou par diminution"* (*Petit traité de versification*, Jules Romains et G. Chenneviére, page 61).

> Here I stand
> All ragged and *dirty*.
> If you don't come kiss me,
> I'll run like a *turkey*.

Or:

> I went to John Seley's hospital;
> The nurse there she turned me around.
> She turned me around, yes, so *slowly*,
> An' said, "The poor girl is sleepin' in the ground."
> I was walkin' down Walnut street so *lonely*,
> My head it was hanging so *low*.
> It made me think of my sweetheart,
> Who was gone to a world far *unknown*.

Such primitive coupling of words by means of terminal assonance occurs very frequently in Russian proverbs:

> Trood *kórmit*, a lenj *pórtit*.
> (Work feeds, but laziness spoils.)

Or:

> Semj raz *otmér*, odin *otréz*.
> (Seven times measure, once cut.)

It is evident that the primitive ear derives a great deal of satisfaction from the melody of vowels without any regard to the accompanying consonants. At any event, the satisfaction derived from the melodic element of a verse or a phrase is sufficient to attract the attention of the poet and to make him use it for aesthetic purposes without regard to the correct distribution of consonants.

Imperfect rimes in the old poetry.—For the Germanic poets of the eleventh or twelfth centuries it seemed quite proper to bind *"quam"* with *"man,"* or *"wisman"* with *"gizam."* Even Hans Sachs found it possible to rime *"aufblasen"* with *"übermassen"*:

80

Wie hat er dich so gross aufblasen,
Hochmutig gemach übermassen.

The older versions of English ballads make constant use of such imperfect endings, which are just as charming as the infirm lines of Pre-Raphaelite madonnas. In the early copy of "The Boy and the Mantle" we read:

He had a sute of silke
About his middle *drawne;*
Without he cold of curtesye
He thought itt much *shame.*

. . . . . .

He plucked out his potever,
And longer wolt not *dwell,*
He pulled forth a pretty mantle,
Between two nut-*shells.*

In the *Chanson de Roland* it is terminal assonance, not perfect rime, that serves as the basis for the arrangement of verses into stanzas. Every stanza has its own accord: *en* or *o* or *a,* etc.:

Quand Rolanz veit la contredite gent,
Ki plus sunt neir que nen est arremenz, ...
        (-*enz* 8 times)
Quant paient virent que Franceis i ont poi
entr'els en unt e orgoil e cunfort;
dist l'uns a l'altre: "li emperere ad tort."
li algalifes sist sur un ceval sor,
brochet le bien des esperuns a or,
fiert Olivier deriere enmi le dos;
le blanc osberc li ad desclos el cors. ...
        (-*o* 8 times)

Here *os* appears as an assonance among a number of *or*-endings. Speculations concerning a possibly different pronunciation of words at that time cannot help us to reconstruct the foregoing

81

into perfect rimes, particularly from the French point of view. We can find many groups of assonances in the *Chanson* that cannot by any means be interpreted as perfect rimes, such as: *"Marsilies ... agalifes"*; *"Garmalie ... maldite"*; *"oreilles ... milie"*; *"ire ... paienime"*; *"vivres ... primes"*—all based on *i*-accord with irregular consonantal environment.

It is difficult to decide whether this form of rhythmically constructive assonance was an invention of the troubadours or an adaptation, and a development, of some earlier, perhaps less regular, forms of similar composition. In any case, employment of assonance for rhythmical purposes can be traced to the early Latin church poetry. Coelius Sedulius, for instance, employs it regularly in his hymns:

> Solutus omni corpore
> > Jussus repente surgere
> > Suis vicissim gressibus
> > Aeger vehebat lectulum.
> Tunc ille Iudas carnifex
> > Ausus magistrum tradere,
> > Pacem ferebat asculo
> > Quam non habebat pectore.

Or, a still more elaborate assonantal design:

> A solis ortus cardine
> Ad usque terrae limitem
> Christum canamus principem,
> Natum Maria virgine.
> Beatus auctor saeculi
> Servile corpus induit,
> Ut, carne carnem liberans,
> Ne perderet, quos condidit.
> Clausae parentis viscera
> Coelestis intra gratia,
> Venter puellae bajulat
> Secreta, quae non noverat.

82

Some of Sedulius' vowel schemes are highly elaborate and obviously intentional, such as: *"limitem ... principem"* (i ... i .. e, i ... i ... e); *"liberans ... viscera"* (i ... e ... a, i ... e ... a); *"pastoribus ... omnium"* (o ... i ... u, o ... i ... u); etc.

Sedulius was a follower and a pupil of C. Vettius Aquelinus Juvencus, who in his *Evangelica Historia* often employs inner assonances and Leonine rimes. But the beginnings of assonantal monotony in Christian Latin can be traced to the time of Tertullianus in whose—if it is his—*De Judicio Domini* we find clusters of Leonine rimes arranged on the basis of vowel monotony:

> Resumptisque su*is* homines adstare figur*is*
> Arida sic vacu*is* redduntur semina terr*is,*
> Et penitus fix*is* putrescunt mortua sulc*is*
> Nonne animatur et hinc reparatis culmen arist*is,*
> Atque iterem viv*is* flavescunt fortia gran*is,*
>
> . . . .
>
> Igneus his vigor est, rutilantia corpora, coel*i*
> Vis divina micat, hinc totus murmurat orb*is,*
> Hinc trepidans penitus, vel quanta est, terra remug*it,*
> Parturiens homines, quos reddere jussa doceb*it*
> Omnes mirantur, turbantur denique nimb*i.*[18]

The latter group of five lines ending in *i* is especially significant. For the inner rimes are here missing. The rime effect rests entirely with the end assonance. That is something that we never find in classical Latin. In Tertullian's poem this arrangement is not a matter of accident, for we find it consistently followed through the larger part of the poem, which consists of nine chapters. If it had not occurred at such an early stage

[18] *Patrologiae Cursus Completus,* 2:1147. O. Dingeldein has shown that imperfect rimes were theoretically known to Quintilian and Cicero, who both discuss this phenomenon under the name of *"similia."* (Dingeldein, *Der Reim bei den Griechen und Römern,* page 9.)

83

of rime history, it might be regarded as a degeneration of Leonine rime into terminal assonance. But unfortunately this hypothesis is entirely untenable, as at that time the Latin rime was just beginning its career. Where did it come from? It is difficult to believe that Tertullian should have invented it. And he could not possibly derive it from classical sources. The only reasonable explanation is that he got it either from the popular Latin of his day, of which no remnant is preserved to us, or from the northern barbarians of some description. At any rate Old French assonance of the tenth and eleventh centuries was not an invention of those days. It must have existed long before that time and have been retained, evidently as a reflex, in the Church-Latin.

Professor V. Zhirmunski of the University of Leningrad gives an interesting illustration of embryonic rime from the Old Italian. In a certain "Hymn to the Sun" which is ascribed to St. Francis of Assisi he points out the following lines:

> Laudato si, mi signore, per sora luna e le stelle,
> I celu l'ai formate clarite e belle.
> Laudato si, mi signore, per frate *vento*
> e per aere et nubilo et sereno et omne *tempo,*
> per le quale a le tue creature dai sustenta *mento.*
> Laudato si, mi signore, per sor *acqua,*
> la quale è multo utile et humile et pretiosa et *casta.*
> Laudato si, mi signore, per frate *focu,*
> per lo quale enallumini la *nocte,*
> ed ello è bello et jocundo et robusto et *forte* ...

Here *"vento"* and *"tempo," "nocte"* and *"forte"* form a good example of embryonic rime, the effect of which is very near to perfect rime, just as in our problematic "temper," "remember." *"Acqua"* and *"casta"* retain nothing but assonance.

It seems that imperfect rimes occur in all languages. We find them even in Latin. As we have already seen, medieval

Latin poets make an extensive use of rime which, at times, is highly imperfect, such as:

> Me receptet Sion illa,
> Sion David, urbs tranquilla,
> Cujus faber auctor lucis,
> Cujus portae lignum crucis,
> Cujus claves lingua *Petri,*
> Cujus cives semper *laeti,*
> Cujus muri lapis vivus,
> Cujus custor Rex festivus.

The fragment is evidently constructed on the basis of feminine disyllabic rimes. And as such, *"Petri"* and *"laeti"* constitute an imperfect assonantal rime; for *e* and *ae* evidently were regarded as riming vowels, as Augustin frequently rimes these vowels. Anselm of Canterbury rimes *"singularis"* with *"virginalis,"* *"almis"* with *"ramis,"* *"suspice"* and *"lumine,"* *"ordinem"* and *"hominem."* In Latin the imperfect rimes may properly be regarded as "rich" rimes in the sense that they accomplish more than is formally required of a rime. In the following lines from Alphalus (tenth century),

> Gemnis micantem fulgidis
> Gestat coronam luminis

-dis and *-nis* alone would have been sufficient to produce a riming effect; but the poet extends his assonance to the two preceding syllables: *u-i-is* and *u-i-is*. A. de Saint Victor rimes *"dexteram"* with *"vesperam."* As monosyllabic rimes, all those cases would be perfect. But the accent in all those words does not fall on the end. They must therefore be regarded as either feminine or even dactylic rimes. And as such they are not perfect. From the modern point of view *"fulgidis"* and *"luminis"* cannot be regarded as perfect rimes unless the accent falls on *-is*. Professor Foster has pointed out a large number of im-

perfect rimes in Propertius which are evidently intentional, because sometimes the meaning is strained to suit the sound.[14]

Imperfect rime in Old Russian.—What has just been said about the imperfect rimes in Latin throws some light upon the interpretation of Russian epos. Russian heroic epos was for a long time considered rimeless. It is strange that such an obvious mistake could have persisted. Zhirmunski was the first to point out that at least one-third of all existing verse lines of the *"bylina-epos"* are connected by various forms of embryonic rimes. Those rimes remained unnoticed, or rather disregarded, only because they have not complied with the standards of modern perfect riming. They largely belong to the class of imperfect rimes similar to the Latin *"fulgidis"* and *"luminis,"* such as *"práhvoye ... lévoye."* Judging from the point of view of the modern pronunciation, the latter couple does not constitute a rime, because the last accented vowels: *ah* and *e,* do not rime. But we must not forget that bylinas were not recited but chanted. The relative value of the unaccented syllable, therefore, was greater (the accent coefficient becomes smaller in singing), and it had a full riming value; that is to say, in chant it was sufficiently accented to afford a rime.

Those embryonic rimes in the Old Russian evidently were the products of spontaneous generation. For they arise largely from the grammatical parallelism of construction. Such rimes based on grammatical parallelism often appear even in prose. It has been suggested that they may have come to Russia from Byzantium. But if that were true we should expect them to appear in the books which were directly influenced by the Greeks; and yet we find no traces of rime in "The Chronicle," while we do find it in the popular ballads and historical

[14] B. O. Foster, "On Certain Euphonic Embellishments in the Verse of Propertius," *Transactions of the American Philological Association,* Volume XL, 1910, pages 34–35.

sagas, where, on the Byzantine hypothesis, we should least expect it to appear. It is interesting to note that in prose the rime often appears in a strange form closely similar to modern Russian "rhyphmoids."[15] Zhirmunski gives an interesting illustration of the imperfect rime from the medieval Russian prose:

Иде же сечен бысть младый **хвраст,** ту рассечен лежаше храбрых **возраст;** и иде же режем бываше младый **прут,** ту растерзаем бываше птицами челвеческий **труп.** И неблгодарен бываше о сем **торг;** сопротивных бо полк со оружием прискакаше **горд.** Исходяще же **нужницы,** да обрящут си **веницы,** за них же и не хотяща отдаху своя **зеницы.** Текущим же на лютый сей добыток **дров,** тогда готовляшеся им вечный **гроб.**

Imperfect rimes in modern poetry.—The preceding paragraphs have, I think, sufficiently demonstrated that the melody of vowels alone, without consonants, is sufficient to produce a noticeable artistic effect. Primitive poetry (unless it is alliterative) pays no attention to the identity of consonants at all. Evidently the melodic effect of rime is more easily appreciated than its rhythmical function. But it is not exclusively old poetry that makes use of imperfect rimes.

It must be borne in mind that in our aesthetic judgment as to what constitutes "good" or "bad" rime much depends on our loyalty to a long-established tradition. In itself "temper ... remember" contains nothing that could offend our artistic sense. As an inner rime it would be, probably, considered quite successful. If it accidentally occurred in a blank verse, it would produce an effect very similar to that of a rime. For the lines connected by those two words would constitute a musical phrase with F as the key. Such assonance is melodically pleasing. And yet it shocks something in us. I am convinced that this something is our sense of tradition more than anything else. Apart

---

[15] See below, page 91.

from a violated tradition there is nothing shocking in the combination "temper ... remember." It is just the fact that it might pretend to be called "rime," while it should not be so called, that offends us. Let it then be called something else, endassonance, for instance. It is effective nevertheless. In fact, in disregard of the rules of conventional prosody, modern poetry once more pronounces such imperfect rimes legitimate and aesthetically acceptable. I say "once more," because we saw that the tradition that forbids imperfect rimes was not always faithfully followed and even now is by no means universally accepted.

Modern art delights in returning to primitive forms. In our modern painting, music, even architecture, we observe a marked tendency to retrospection, a reaction against perfect symmetry, and an expressed desire to utilize the primitive simplicity of form. In the name of expressiveness Gauguin repudiated the tradition of "beautiful taste" and went to the Tahitian Islands to study what appeared to him the magic simplicity of primitive art. After him primitivism became a fashion and was almost universally accepted. Roerich goes to study the archaeological treasures of the ancient Russian tombs, and in the remnants of the Varangian civilization finds an inexhaustible source of inspiration for his own mystic paintings. Bakst concentrates on the study of Cretan civilization, and performs a remarkable transfusion of ancient, pre-historic blood into our modern life by reviving pre-historic styles and fashions in our costumes. Quite innocent of the historic origin of modern dressmaking, our fashionable ladies are unconsciously imitating the style of ancient flappers, finding it much more rational and considerably more beautiful than romantic corsets and bashful long skirts. This is one of the effects of our modern artistic primitivism which, through Bakst, has worked its way into general acceptance.

In poetry, this retrospective logic of modern art found its

expression partly in the new movement against rime, and partly in the recent tendency toward simplification of the riming process. Embryonic, i.e., purely melodic, assonantal, and apocopated rimes have been recently revived in modern poetry.[16] Contemporary French poets tend to revolutionize the traditional system of French versification in several respects. Revolutionization of rime appears to be merely one of the issues in this "great technical anarchy" (*grande anarchie technique*). The classical rules are violated in modern French poetry so frequently that the poets' disregard for them can no longer be considered a mere license; for with many poets licenses become rules. Out of the chaos of individual experiments new principles begin to arise. In the place of rime we find the system of accords and discords practiced with such a premeditated persistence that it can no longer be ignored as a fad.[17] Jules Romains makes an extensive use of imperfect rimes. In his treatise on versification he not merely approves of imperfect rimes but even attempts to give an exhaustive classification of them.[18] Among his numerous illustrations we find such interesting specimens as:

---

[16] As a matter of exception one may find imperfect rimes in the classical and romantic poetry. H. Olovsson counted 515 cases of inexact rimes in 8,392 verses of A. Musset, which makes 6 per cent of the entire number. The same percentage, on the average, he finds in Baudelaire. Gautier displays a still more marked inexactitude, covering 8 per cent of the entire number of rimes (625 in 8,174). See H. Olovsson, *Étude sur les rimes de trois poétes romantique*, page 136. Among the older English poems there are many rimes whose apparent imperfections must be accounted for by difference in pronunciation, such as Wyatt's "health" and "self" or "swolne" and "bemoan." Not all of them, however, can be disposed of in such a convenient way.

[17] Jean Hytier, *Les Techniques modernes du vers français* (1926), page 47: "Le système des accords est un principe nouveau; c'est en lui que réside la modernité de la nouvelle technique."

[18] Jules Romains et G. Chenneviére, *op. cit.*

> Pour toute la multitude
>
> .   .   .   .   .   .
>
> Ni stupeur ni amertume.

Or:

> Il pointe un homme noir d'où gicle de la voix
>
> .   .   .   .
>
> Oh! je t'aime déjà, comme un nouveau devoir.

Another interesting variety is:

> Le merchand de julep
> Chassé de l'archipel ...

which Jules Romains calls *"rime renversée,"* and which consists of the same vowel accompanied by inverse consonants:
-lep ... -pel.

Modern German poets are experimenting along similar
lines. J. R. Becher makes an extensive use of apocopated and
assonantal rimes, such as:

> O süssester Traum, der streicht wie Sommer lind!
> Doch bald musst du wohl mehr sein als ein *Ahnen.*
> Da blüht er auf wie kleinster Duft von Wind.
> Ein Engel durch der Leichen Schlucht sich *bahnend.*
>
> Dein Tag—: er wölbt! Die Stadt birst *Geläut.*
> Die Sonne Fluss erbraust in jeder *Strasse.*
> Gemäuer hoch spriesst goldner Strahl—*Efeu.*
> Fanfarenmünder Halleluja *blasen.*

In German such experiments do not appear to be entirely new.
Friedrich Nietzsche in his poems often applied consonantal discords. Even in classical poetry they are not entirely lacking.
Thus Goethe rimed *"diesen"* and *"schliessen,"* *"entstanden"*
and *"Galanten,"* *"Neige"* and *"Schmerzenreiche."* The *"Wal-
purgisnachtstraum"* is full of such imperfect rimes:

FIDLER

Das hasst sich schwer, das Lumpenpack,
Und gäb' sich gern das *Restchen;*
Es eint sie hier der Dudelsack
Wie Orpheus' Leier die *Bestjen.* . . . .

PUCK

Tretet nicht so mastig *auf*
Wie Elefantenkälber,
Und der plumpst' an diesem *Tag,*
Sei Puck der derbe selber.

Wieland rimes *"beladen"* with *"waten,"* which is melodically less appropriate than our problematic "temper" and "remember."

In modern Russian poetry we observe a conscious and systematic effort toward reviving the primitive, embryonic rime with a view to extending the limits of rime and making our ear again sensitive to the effective melodies of terminal assonance. There is perhaps no other language where the experiment proves to be so successful as it is in Russian. Owing to the nature of a highly inflectional language and to richness of consonant combinations there are easily obtained in Russian phonetic approximations which may be properly regarded as pseudo-rimes. They are, first of all, very fascinating technically. Where perfect rimes are too easily obtained they lose a great deal of their artistic charm. They cease to interest the poet, to whom it quickly becomes commonplace to follow the same paths over and over again. Thus in modern Russian poetry occurred a reaction against what is called rime puritanism, and a strong movement arose among the ultra-modern poets in favor of substituting a more or less complete assonance for the regular rime. There was even a special name created for such rimes. They are called "rhyphmoids."

Alexander Block is largely responsible for the growing popularity of rhyphmoids. "In the poetry of Al. Block," says Zhirmunski, "imperfect rime ceases to be an attribute of a special system of versification; the method is extended to all poems as a legitimate device on equal footing with ordinary rimes." Here we find such combinations as *"gonit ... koni"*; *"vecher ... veter"*; *"bystry ... iskry"*; *"glubi ... lubim"*; *"koopol ... slooshal"*; etc. Boris Pasternak in his interesting novel in verse hardly employs any other combinations but rhyphmoids. In his search for strange and difficult assonances he succeeds in bringing into melodic unity ideas and images which otherwise would probably never occur to the poet's mind. The music of words, in his case, appears to be productive of exotic logical material. Helping the poet to discover strange and unusual passages from one word to another, such rimes often result in daring intellectual adventures. An interesting effect is obtained by P. Oreshin in his poem, "The Whirl" (1919). The hardship of the revolutionary time is here contrasted with the enchanting reminiscences of the past. In the heavy, broken motion of the lines describing the present one perceives the tragic steps of history, the march of a generation passing with dirges and sobs to the burial of their ideals. The strange music of the broken rimes seems to re-echo the dreadful groans of hunger, hardship, and despair. And as a contrast to this, splendid chords of perfect riming accompany the stanzas dedicated to the past, making it seem surrounded with the magic mist of reminiscence. Here the quality of the terminal assonance performs a definite function in the composition of the verse.

In English imperfect rimes are very exceptional. In normal English verse they occur only as approximations to perfect rimes, and not at all as an independent device. It is true, we often find such pairs as "splendor ... render" (Shelley), which I believe is not phonetically quite correct; or "dwelling ... Ellen" (Campbell); "Dishonor ... left on her" (Hood); and "sister ... vista" (Poe). But all such cases are licenses which are explained by either local pronunciation or a certain phonetic liberalism on the part of the poet. The tendency is to limit such licenses instead of extending their application; and this in spite of the fact that English poets are never tired of repeat ing Chaucer's complaint about the "scarcitee" of "rym in England." Shakespeare jokingly remarks that he "can find no rime to 'lady,' but 'baby'," which would be in the nature of imperfect rime. But he never applied it. Elizabeth Browning's imperfect rimes are probably due to her deficiency in hearing. Only William Blake seems to employ imperfect rimes deliberately and comparatively often:

> Then every man, of every *clime*,
> That prays in his distress,
> Prays to the human form di*vine:*
> Love, Mercy, Pity, Peace.

He occasionally binds "east" with "ceased," "wide" with "delight," "lambs" with "hands," "reason" with "teasing," etc.

Among the modern poets we occasionally find whole poems with deliberately imperfect rimes, such as, for instance, Axton Clark's "The Silent Hour":

> Now softly rain brings in the early dusk,
> And round columnar eucalyptus *trees*
> The drops and darkness mingle in a mist
> That thickens vaguely over drooping *leaves.*
>
> The patter playing on the friendly *roof,*
> And the hasty dripping, heavier from the eaves,
> Merge with the ground-bass of the canyon *brook,*
> Uninterrupted, in long symphonies.
>
> To these rare moments turbulent weeks entrust
> The peace that vivifies, the calm from risk.
> Spreading like earth in rain, the mind re*ceives*

93

> Serenely grave assuagement; and a *cool*
> And gracious solitude endures, *aloof*,
> One silent hour with meditative *ease*.

In Humbert Wolfe's "Kensington Gardens," "many stanzas are saved in this way from banality or sweetness." Imperfect rimes help us to avoid what Tennyson described as the "weary sameness" of rimes. And yet such experiments are very scarce in English. We meet occasionally with monosyllabic, i.e., masculine imperfect rimes, as shown by the quoted Clark sonnet; but the bisyllabic, i.e., feminine, imperfect rimes are almost completely absent from English.

Now there arises an interesting question: why is it that imperfect rimes are so liberally used in some languages, such as Russian, and are obviously and systematically avoided in others? Is it just because the Russian temperament, as is commonly believed outside of Russia, tends toward anarchy and disharmony? But why then does the same tendency appear in French and Spanish poetry? Or is it perhaps a certain conservatism of Anglo-Saxon character that makes English and American poets adhere more loyally to the established tradition? Ticknor in his *History of Spanish Literature* gives still another explanation. He believes that it is futile to attempt to transfer imperfect end-assonance to either the English or the German tongue, because the Teutonic ear does not apprehend it with the same facility as the Spanish ear. But do we really have to ascribe the difference to the peculiar inability of the English ear to perceive the finer nuances of vowel melody? Is this explanation plausible in view of the fact that English is no doubt the richest language as far as vowel nuances are concerned? The English ear discriminates with ease vowel nuances which are entirely lost in other languages. We have seen that there was a time when such imperfect assonances were liberally employed in English too. Saintsbury calls it a fore-echo of rime. At present it is changing into a faint after-echo, perceivable even in English poetry. Imperfect end-assonance, if skilfully employed, is by no means negligible, and the English ear is evidently by no means dull in perceiving it.

Apart from such psychological speculations as to differences in the national mind or the national ear, speculations which I believe are not quite safe, is there not something in the nature of the languages themselves that accounts for the difference?

Rôle of unaccented vowels in rime. — In order to find whether there is any difference between the English and the Russian enunciation of accented vowels, a number of experiments were arranged with Dorsey's phonelescope. This apparatus consists of a receiving horn ending in a diaphragm which receives the vibrations. These vibrations, then, are transmitted, by means of a bow and ribbon, to a small mirror attached to a spindle. The mirror is so fixed that it can vibrate about the three principal axes without changing the position of the source of light. When a ray of light is directed toward the mirror, a simple optical lever is obtained, the short arm being the radius of the spindle and the long arm the distance from the vibrating mirror to the screen. For photographic purposes, instead of a screen, a revolving cylinder is used, which revolves within a case supplied with a thin opening. When the cylinder is set in uniform motion a photographic plate pasted on it registers the vibrations of the diaphragm. Although this apparatus is not reliable for the observation of finer details, it is quite sufficient for showing certain rough peculiarities of the sound, such for instance as the difference in amplitudes between accented and unaccented vowels.

Further experiments were arranged with the oscillograph such as described in Appendix I. The results obtained from the phonelescope in the matter of relative accents were entirely corroborated by the oscillographic records.

First, a word was selected which is the same in both Russian and English: *"contrást."* An English and a Russian speaker were asked in turn to pronounce this word into the receiver, with the admonition to each that he should speak normally and without any affectation or strain. In order to prevent any psychological influence each was kept ignorant of the real purpose of the experiment. The result indicates clearly that the difference between the accented and the unaccented parts of the word in Russian is larger than in English. The records made are shown in the plate facing this page.

Individual words, however, cannot serve as a safe basis for generalization. It is difficult to retain normal, conversational rhythm when the same word is pronounced several times in succession. Besides, the choice of words introduces an undesirable subjective factor. To avoid these difficulties experiments were made with photographing whole phrases. The opening line from *Paradise Lost* was photographed as contrasted with a line from *Boris Godunov.* A contour line has then been

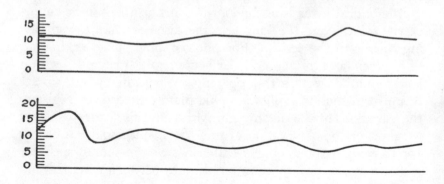

taken from the photographic record with fluctuations of amplitudes representing the accented and the unaccented syllables in each verse. It shows that English verse flows smoothly without showing marked differences between the accented and the

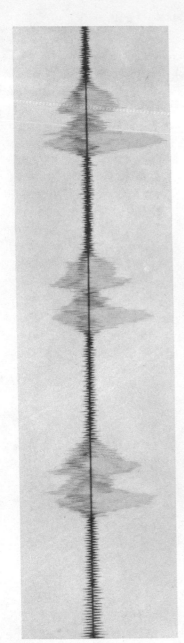

Record made by English speaker

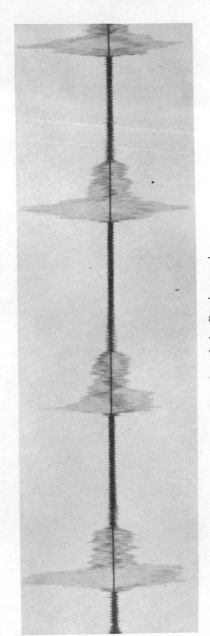

Record made by Russian speaker

unaccented vowels, while the curve representing the Russian phrase rises and falls quite considerably.

Now, those diagrams seem to corroborate what, I think, is vaguely felt by everybody who knows both English and Russian. The difference between the accented and the unaccented syllables in Russian is considerably more pronounced than it is in English. Thus -ows in "arrows," for instance, absorbs much more of the accent energy than -oo in Russian "yedoo." Therefore "arrows" and "marries" cannot even approximately form a rime, while "yedoo" and "yeda" are likely to be used for an imperfect assonance. Let us call the ratio of loudness (amplitudes) between accented and unaccented syllables *the accent coefficient of the group*. We have then:

$$\frac{a}{u} = C$$

where *a* is the average amplitude of the wave-train of the accented vowel, *u* the same of the unaccented vowel, and *C* the accent coefficient of the group of the two syllables. On the basis of the foregoing diagrams we may say that the accent coefficient of the English language is, on the average, smaller than in Russian, its value in some cases approaching 1, which is the accent coefficient of a spondee. The larger the accent coefficient, the less distinct becomes the unaccented vowel. And, of course, the more indistinct it is, the less significant it becomes musically. We may therefore conclude that the relative loudness, and consequently the musical value, of an unaccented vowel in a verse foot is inversely proportional to the accent coefficient of the group:

$$u = \frac{a}{C} .$$

If $C = 1$, the relative value of the unaccented vowel becomes equal to that of its accented companion (spondee), and

97

feminine rime becomes impossible. If C is less than 1, u becomes larger than a, which means that the second vowel obtains a preponderant position in the group, and the accent is transferred to the end, i.e., the feminine rime is changed into a masculine one.

The larger C is, the easier it is for the poet to disregard u and with it the relative musical value of the unaccented vowel, which is evidently proportional to the value of u. This accounts for the remarkable success obtained by modern Russian poets along the line of imperfect riming in Russian poetry, and for the reluctance of English poets to apply similar methods.

It may be objected that the existence of the imperfect rimes in modern French upsets all these demonstrations. You have admitted, our critics may argue, that the modern French poets make an extensive use of imperfect rimes. And it is evident without any physical measurement that the accent coefficient in French is very small, much smaller than in English,[19] French disyllabic words being mostly in the nature of spondees. In "*garçon*" it is difficult to determine where the accent is to be located, on the first or the second syllable; for both are pronounced with equal force. The accent coefficient of this word, then, according to your scheme equals 1. And yet imperfect rimes do occur in French.

To this I answer that my opponents misconstrue the issue. We are at present discussing disyllabic (feminine) rimes. And in French disyllabic rimes do not occur except in name. What the French prosodists call feminine rimes are acoustically masculine rimes only with a mute (feminine) ending, such as "*-aille—broussaille ... tressaille*." Thus the French language is not merely quite consistent with the foregoing argument but proves its validity more forcibly, because it actually excludes

[19] Compare Verrier, *Essai sur les principes de la métrique anglaise*, 1:40.

disyllabic rimes. The accent and the rime in French verse are always at the end.

As far as English riming is concerned, the relatively small accent coefficient explains, of course, merely the existing reluctance, i.e., the psychological reaction of the English mind to the phenomenon of imperfect riming. It does not, however, exclude imperfect rimes from the range of poetic possibility. In English the accent coefficient is on the average smaller than in Russian. Yet it is probably, at least in a good many cases, not so small as to exclude all chance of success. The question can be decided only on the basis of extensive poetic experimentation. Unfortunately there is a regrettable scarcity of experiments along those lines; English and American poets prefer to give up rime altogether rather than return to the ancient method of imperfect riming. Obviously, further experiments along the lines suggested by Axton Clark, Humbert Wolfe, and others may ultimately prove to be of great value.

It is understood, of course, that not every imperfect assonance is available for poetic purposes. Imperfect rimes must be applied with great discrimination. Modern Russian technique produced means of covering the discords of unaccented vowels by various forms of consonantal accords whereby ingeniously deceiving combinations are often created that sound almost like perfect rimes; for instance, "*bezmolvny ... volny*"; "*radosti ... starosti*"; "*skosite ... kosti*"; etc. In such languages as German and English, where longer words have secondary accents, and which still retain certain traces of distinction between long and short syllables, a great deal of attention should be paid to the accent coefficient in every particular case. Edgar Allan Poe rimes "sister" with "vista." Here -*ter* and -*ta*, which are quite different in their absolute values, are reduced almost to the point of identity because of the large accent coefficient. But the same accent coefficient would probably be insufficient to reduce the difference between -*ter* and -*ty*; therefore it would be difficult and clumsy in English to rime "sister" with "misty." Yet with a sufficiently large accent coefficient, perhaps, any residue can be made musically irrelevant. Russian, in fact, presents numerous illustrations of this kind.

Now it is easy to make a guess as to the significance of the unaccented vowels in rime. In disyllabic, feminine, rimes there are two pretenders for the tonic, i.e., two vowels that might be selected to serve as the key in the melody of vowels. If those are equally accented ($C = 1$), feminine rime becomes impossible. If the accent coefficient is not sufficiently large, the second pretender (unaccented vowel) still retains some of its melodic rights for serving as a key. This tendency may or may not be gratified. If it is not gratified, an imperfect rime obtains which, like most musical compositions, has decidedly only one key. If the pretense of the unaccented vowel is gratified, then a perfect rime obtains which, like some of our modern musical compositions, has two keys. In verse such duplicity is less paradoxical than in music, for the second key has but little weight; it is merely a musical satellite of the first. We have seen that modern poetry in many languages disregards it completely. Old poetry based on embryonic rimes was able to get along without it very well. The identity of the unaccented vowel is, from the musical point of view, not at all obligatory. History of rime corroborates this statement.

Identical rimes.—It remains for us to answer one more question. If rime rests on melody, and derives its artistic effect from the anticipated return to the same sound, why is it that a repetition of the same word is considered a poor rime? If it is the sound that counts, why should the identical word interfere with the artistic pleasure derived from the identical sound? It would seem that we cannot possibly select a better and more complete return to the tonic than precisely the sound of the same word repeated.

100

In dealing with this problem it is important to point out again that identical rimes do actually exist. Of course they are excluded from the riming dictionaries; for it requires no art to find such a rime—just repeat the word at the end of the next verse! We have seen that ancient poetry (Latin, Hindoo) did not entirely ignore this method. In fact, it is one of the forms of embryonic rime. Modern poetry is still more liberal with identical rimes. Suffice it to mention Poe's "Raven," where repetition of the same word at the end of each stanza is retained throughout the poem as its riming scheme:

> . . . . vainly I had sought to borrow
> From my books surcease of sorrow—sorrow for the lost Lenore—
> For the rare and radiant maiden whom the angels name Lenore—
> Nameless here for evermore.

Yet it seems to me that such rimes are unsatisfactory precisely from the acoustic point of view. For it is not the repetition of sound in such rimes that primarily attracts our attention but the repetition of meaning. Interference of meaning with the work of musical keys has a bad effect on the music of words. Perception of verse-melody vanishes in view of the logical apperception. Repetition of meaning, being a more or less unusual form of expression, attracts our attention and kills, for the moment, the sense of melody. Consider, for instance, Lessing's "Die Schlaffende Laura":

> Sie schlief, und weit und breit
> Erschalten keine Nachtingallen,
> Aus weiser Furchtsamkeit
> Ihr minder zu gefallen,
> Als ihr der Schlaf *gefiel,*
> Als ihr der Traum *gefiel,*
> Den sie villeicht jetzt *träumte,*
> Von dem, ich hoff'es, *träumte.*

What is aesthetically striking in these lines is neither the rhythm, nor the repetition of sound, but precisely the repetition of the meaning, which would produce exactly the same effect if it were used in prose. We forget about the rime effect in view of the intellectual emphasis on "*träumte*." And indeed, it is sometimes difficult to tell whether the author intended to produce a rime or a figure of iteration. Amy Lowell, for instance, seldom employs rime. But in "The City of Fallen Leaves" for almost a page she rimes "leaves" with "leaves":

> Leaves fall,
> Brown leaves,
> Yellow leaves streaked with brown.
> They fall,
> Flutter,
> Fall again.
> The brown leaves,
> And the streaked yellow leaves,
> Loosen on their branches
> And drift slowly downwards.
> One,
> One, two, three,
> One, two, five.
> All Venice is a falling of autumn leaves.

What is it? A rime, or simply the figure of repetition? If different words were used, the effect would have been decidedly a musical one. But here the musical effect is killed by the emphasis on meaning. Or take another illustration from Carl Sandburg's "Prairies":

> I tell you there is nothing in the world,
> Only an ocean of tomorrows,
> A sky of tomorrows.

Although it is not at all accidental that the identical words appear here at the end of the verse line, yet their appearance

102

there is not necessitated by melodic considerations. That they form a vowel melody in addition is of secondary importance, and is hardly noticed in actual reading. As rimes they escape our attention.

That identical rimes are logical rather than musical repetitions is clearly shown by the logical effect which such rimes produce. There are certain poetic forms, such as the triolet, for instance, for which repetition of identical words is essential. It is interesting to note that in such cases our identical rimes result in a strict reproduction of the whole phrase. And it is quite obviously the repetition of the whole phrase that attracts our attention as the characteristic feature of this particular form.

Thus repetition of the same meaning spoils the musical effectiveness of rime. That is partly the reason why the so-called rich rimes are considered bad in English, and why analogous grammatical forms are not recommended for rimes in French: "quant au sens, les mots rimant entre eux doivent être aussi différents que possible."

Résumé.—Let us look back over the path we have traversed, and recapitulate. On the basis of the foregoing, *rime may be defined as the unity of key in the melody of vowels as perceived through the tone quality of the whole ending.* Accented vowels, musical tone-clusters, are the chief factor in rime: the return to the same vowel at the end of a rhythmical series makes a musical phrase of that series. The consonants and the unaccented vowels are of secondary importance; they may or may not be identical. History knows numerous cases, whole systems of versification, in fact, where the return to the same vowel sound ends the rime, and where neither the consonants nor the unaccented vowels are considered at all. The accented vowel sound constitutes the whole of the rime's adventure, as far as the melody of verse is concerned. The significance of consonants seems to be of an entirely different nature. They help us to arrange verse into rhythmical groups. The greatest artistic satisfaction is evidently found when those two factors are combined. But the degree of their combination differs for different linguistic groups and historical epochs. The purity of rime appears to be, not at all an absolute aesthetic value but a highly variable factor; it is always relative to the conventional standards of a given epoch.

IV

CONCERNING THE ORIGIN OF RIME

THE preceding discussions throw some light upon the long-debated question as to the origin of rime. At least they afford an opportunity to analyze the question itself and to see in which sense the question may and in which it may not be answered.

Double view of the question.—What is the origin of rime? It seems to me that in the literature on rime two entirely different aspects of the question are hopelessly confused. What does the question mean? Does it mean that we are asking about the particular time and place where rime was originally invented and from which it migrated to other countries? Among modern scholars the feeling prevails that in this form the question cannot be answered. "We assume it as self-evident," says O. Dingeldein, "that rime could not have originated as a perfect product from the head of some Zeus-versificator, but must have gradually evolved from embryonic nuclei." We cannot lay hand on one particular literary document and say: here is the origin of rime. We cannot even trace the early paths of rime within any particular literature we know. It has been justly remarked that rime lies so deep in human nature and in human language that it is as little worth while to discuss the origin of rime as that of dancing or singing. On the basis of ample evidence Richardson comes to the conclusion that "rime, broadly defined as similarity of stressed sounds in significant places in verse . . . . was certain to appear, and did appear, independently in many places, before and after the time when classical quantity was recognizable."[1]

Or does the question imply that rime in its perfect form is, as a rule, preceded by some less developed, embryonic forms and that we wish to know what those forms, in general, are? If by "origin" we mean the causes from which rime develops in many different places, i.e., linguistic factors which tend to produce rime, then the question appears in a wholly different light and may be answered with a considerable degree of precision. In other words, it is admittedly hopeless to inquire into the literary sources of rime. But it is quite possible to study its natural causes. Let us consider the question in both its aspects.

Various hypotheses.—Speculations on the historic origin of rime have been numerous and sometimes highly ingenious. For a very long time the opinion prevailed, especially in England, that rime was introduced into Europe by "Goths and Huns," and was therefore of an unworthy, barbaric origin. This theory survived in England as late as Mitford's time. At a somewhat later date it was wholly discarded in favor of the so-called hymnological hypothesis. According to this view,

[1] As to the origin of the word "rime" the reader may consult Karl Borinski, *Die Antike in Gothik und Kunstheorie*, 1:47.

which for some time was almost universally accepted, rime originated in the medieval Latin in connection with the choral singing in the early Christian churches, and from there gradually penetrated into the vernacular dialects. "Rime," says Duffield, one of the greatest authorities on hymnology, "seems to have made its way into the literature of the modern world through the Latin hymns."[2] According to Duffield the oldest hymn, and—since classical Latin practically knows no rime—the oldest document in Latin in which rime is employed intentionally and throughout is the hymn to the Martyr Agatha composed by Damasus. It is the same Saint Agatha who by the kind of torture inflicted upon her impressed Anatole France so profoundly that he gave a characteristic extract from her story:

Dum torqueretur beata Agatha in mamillas graviter dixit ad judicem: "Impie, crudelis et dure tyranne, non es confusus amputare in femina quod ipse in matre suxisti? Ego habeo mamillas integras intus in anima quas Domino conservavi."

This "grave" incident was destined to play an important part in the history of world literature, as it was evidently the first historic event to be recorded in rime. I am giving it therefore in full (from Duffield):

Martyris ecce dies Agathae
Virginis emicat eximiae,
Christus eam Sibi qua sociat,
Et diadema duplex decorat.

Stirpe decens, elegans specie,
Sed magis actibus atque fide:
Terrea prospera nil reputans
Jussa Dei sibi corde ligans.

[2] Samuel W. Duffield, *The Latin Hymn-Writers and Their Hymns* (1889), page 44.

Fortior haec trucibusque viris
Exposuit sua membra flagris,
Pectore quam fuerit valido
Torta mamilla docet patulo.

Deliciae cui carcer erat,
Pastor ovem Petrus hanc recreat,
Laetior inde magisque flagrans
Cuncta flagella cucurrit ovans.

Ethnica turba rogum fugiens,
Hujus et ipsa meretur opem:
Quos fidei titulus decorat,
His Venerem magis ipsa premat.

Jam renitens quasi sponsa polo,
Pro misero rogitat Damaso,
Sic sua festa coli faciat,
Se celebrantibus ut faveat.

Gloria cum Patre sit Genito,
Spirituique proinde sacro,
Qui Deus unus et omnipotens
Hanc nostri faciat memorem.

If this hymn really belongs to the Pope Damasus, it must have been composed in the fourth century. But rime frequently, though not systematically, occurs also in earlier hymns.

Apart from the perfect end-rime, there are other forms of rime to be found in the early Christian poetry. Coelius Sedulius, also of the fourth century,[8] in his *"Elegia,"* a poem of

---

[8] The *Dictionary of Christian Biography* places Sedulius in the fifth century, remarking, however, that very little is known concerning him. The *Patrologiae Cursus Completus* gives the year 392 as the date of his birth. Sedulius was of Scotch origin (Scotus Hiberniensis), and thus properly belongs to the history of British literature.

some hundred and ten lines, chooses to discuss the principle of salvation and the effect of incarnation in a very peculiar poetic form, where the first half of the hexameter line regularly repeats by epanalepsis in the last half of the pentameter:

> *Primus ad ima ruit* magna de luce superbus
> Sic homo, cum tum*uit, primus ad ima ruit*
> *Unius ob meritum* cuncti perire minores
> Salvantur cuncti *unius ob meritum.*

By this method the poet succeeds in producing a very artificial figure, which possesses, however, a marked singing quality, approaching the nature of a refrain.

The beginnings of Latin (Christian) rime can be traced still farther back to the end of the second century, to the days of Tertullian (160–230). In fact, a fully developed inner rime is consistently used by the latter in his *De Judicio Domini:*[4]

[4] If we can trust the tradition which ascribes this poem to Tertullian (see: *Tertulliana Opera Omnia, Patrologiae Cursus Completus*, Volume II). This, however, is doubtful in view of Tertullian's dislike and mistrust of poets. He was not merely antagonistic to the popular poetry of his days which, if we judge from the testimony of Irenaeus, was of a very low caliber, but eventually made fun even of Homer, mentioning (with an evident satisfaction) the story related by Ennius that "Homer remembered that in one of his previous incarnations he had been a peacock." In his *De Anima* Tertullian says that he "cannot believe poets, even when they are wide awake." In view of such an uncomplimentary attitude toward poetry and poets it is rather improbable that the aged montanist would write a large poem in rime. Yet, Tertullian's or not, *De Judicio Domini* is a literary fact dating, in all evidence (Migne), from Tertullian's time.

Th. Ziehen (*Vorlesungen über Aesthetik*, page 250, footnote) mentions Commodius' *Instructiones Adversus Gentium Deos, c.* 250 A.D., as one of the earliest documents of rimed poetry in Christian Latin. The evidence above adduced shows that rime existed in Christian poetry long before the time of Commodius. O. Dingeldein regards Commodius and Augustin as representatives of fully developed rimed verse (*Der Reim bei den Griechen und Römern*, 1892, page 3).

Quis mihi ruricol*as* aptabit carmine Mus*as*?
Et verni rose*as* titulabit floribus aur*as*?
Aestivaeque graves matur*as* messis arist*as*?
Quis dabit et tumid*as* autumni vitibus uv*as*?
Quisve hyemi placid*as* semper laudabit oliv*as*?

. . . .

Et lux unde nov*o* praefulserit aurea mund*o*,
Quisve hominem laet*o* posuisset fingere lim*o*,
Unde genus vacu*o* potuisset crescere saecl*o*;
Et quae vivendi popul*o* sit multa cupid*o*,
Quaeve creata mal*o*, moriendi quaeve propag*o*,

. . . .

At the end of the first millennium the great interchange of poetic traditions between the West-European North and South becomes evident. That the influence was deep and by no means one-sided is best shown by the fact that the Old Germanic and Anglo-Saxon alliterative verse reflects back upon the medieval Latin. In the Hymns of the "Venerable" Bede (673–735) we can trace only an approximation to alliteration. But in some later hymns, such as *"Cantemus Omni Die Concenentes Varie,"* alliteration is freely used.[5] An interesting illustration of alliterative Latin verse is quoted by Grimm:

Sic mandat ipse maximus magister summi filius.
Ast cui felices fertili glebas foecundat germine
Illum laetantem cumulat fructus laboris centuplex.[6]

If the cultural intercourse was so strong as to influence Latin verse by the elements of "barbarous" tradition, how much stronger must have been the opposite impulse. There is a great deal of evidence pointing to the fact that rime penetrated the

[5] Duffield, *The Latin Hymn-Writers*, page 363.
[6] W. Grimm, *"Zur Geschichte des Reims"* (Berlin, 1881–1884), *Kleinere Schriften*, 4:322.

vernacular literatures from the church. In some cases the evidence seems to be fairly complete. We know definitely that the first specimen of rimed verse in German literature was Otfried's *"Evangelium Harmonie."* His reason for adopting rime is said to have been his hatred "of what he called the obscene songs of the laymen, i.e., the popular epic ballads. . . . . As these still preserved the alliterative measure, Otfried could not have marked his opposition to them more effectively than by introducing a poetical form hallowed by the example of the great hymn-writers of the Latin church."

On the basis of this evidence the hymnological hypothesis seemed for a while to be firmly established. Wackernagel in his *Geschichte der deutschen Nationalliteratur* believes it to be "beyond doubt" that "Otfried learned the art of riming from the Latin hymns." And yet it was possible to believe this only as long as rime was construed to mean nothing but perfect end-rime. There is, however, a great deal of evidence pointing to the existence of various forms of imperfect rime a long time before Otfried. Why, then, should the Latin tradition be the only one that influenced Otfried? It seems to be hardly probable in view of the unusual skill with which Otfried deals with various forms of rime, some of which never existed in Latin.[7] Where did he obtain those forms?

---

[7] Wilhelm Grimm, *Zur Geschichte des Reims*, page 318 (*Kleinere Schriften*, Volume 4): "Woher hat Otfried die feinen, aber nicht erdachten Gesetze, womit er leicht und sicher, als folge er nur de Ueberlieferung, den rührenden Reim, den erweiterten, den doppelten, den ungenauen und den angehäuften behandelt, Gesetze, die nach und nach verschwanden, weil man sich von ihnen keine Rechenschaft zu geben wusste? Gewiss nicht aus den Lateinischen Hymnen, in welchen sie nur zum Theil und unvollkommen beobachtet sind. Noch eine andere Frage. Wenn Otfried den Reim lateinischen Dichtern entlehnte, so war er auf vollen Gleichklang angewiesen, der zu seiner Zeit bei jenen schon durchgesetzt war, warum ist er davon abgegangen? Was berechtigte ihn zu einer solchen Freiheit?"

Wilhelm Grimm seems to have been the first to attribute fundamental importance to the study of imperfect rimes. On the basis of an overwhelming amount of evidence collected with painful persistence and astonishing patience, he came to the conclusion that many forms of rime existed in the Germanic folklore long before Otfried, and that the latter must have known them alongside the Latin forms.[8] "Different shades of imperfect rime," he says, "into which it developed can be clearly observed in Otfried; the deviation from perfect rime is often quite insignificant."[9] Not only the imperfect but also the identical—*rührender*—rime, which consisted of two identical words with different meanings, was often used as an ornamental device before Otfried's time. Grimm found more than ten different forms of embryonic rime in the old Germanic poetry. It would be too tedious to go here into the detailed description of those forms. Suffice it to point out that on the basis of Grimm's evidence the hymnological hypothesis can no longer be defended.

There is another way of attacking the hymnological hypothesis, a way also indicated by Grimm. It seems that in the classical Latin rime was not such an exceptional thing as many are inclined to believe. It is sufficient to mention the two lines from Horace's *Ars Poetica* quoted by Hegel:

> Non statis est, pulchra esse poemata: dulcis sunto,
> Et quocunque volen, animum auditoris agunto.

Grimm produces hundreds of verses from various Latin authors which prove the existence of rime in classical poetry be-

---

[8] Wilhelm Grimm, *Zur Geschichte des Reims*, page 318: "Wie abweichend auch Otfrieds Auffassung war, so ist doch hoch wahrscheinlich, dass er, ungeachtet seiner Abneigung vor der Weltlichen Volksdichtung, nicht bloss herkömmliche Redensarten und Sprüche daraus beibehielte, sondern auch die ganze äussere Form, mithin auch den Reim."

[9] *Ibid.*, page 322.

yond any doubt. Especially often occurs the so-called Leonine rime, which is an inner assonance that divides a verse, usually in hexameter, into two parts, thereby emphasizing the effect of the caesura, such as Lucretius'

> Toto res tener*as* effert in luminis or*as*?

or Virgil's
> primus humum fodi*to*, primus devecta crema*to*.

Bi-syllabic rimes, perfectly developed occur not infrequently in Lucretius. Grimm produces a large number of illustrations, of which I select only two:

> Nunc age, res quoniam docui non posse creari
> de nilo neque item genitas ad nil revocari . . . .

and:
> His tamen et supra quos diximus inferiores
> partibus egregie multis multoque minores . . . .

The list of similar illustrations may be extended indefinitely. But those already adduced are quite sufficient to support Grimm's conclusion. He says: "The Leonine rime in its numerous varieties appears among the Roman classics, and already in Lucretius, as something based on a well-established tradition, and cannot be regarded as a new invention. The Latin speech with its melodious inflections often forced it into existence, and even if there had been a tendency to suppress it that would have been difficult to do. . . . . Of course, no one will support the view that rime could have remained unnoticed; I am rather inclined to think that it was not merely tolerated but to a certain extent even cultivated, though never systematically followed."[10] In view of all this evidence it is now difficult to believe that rime originated in the church hymns. It evidently was in existence a long time before the appearance of Christianity.

[10] *Ibid.*, page 295.

113

Byzantine rimes.—Hymnological hypothesis has recently found further support from the scholars engaged in the study of Byzantine history and literature. It is highly improbable that rime originated in Latin poetry, Christian or pagan. For Roman literature from beginning to end was influenced by Greek patterns, and the influence of Constantinople upon the cultural life of Europe lasted till the time of the conquest (1453). After the fall of Rome, Western Europe was thrown into a hopeless state of social and political anarchy that lasted for several centuries. Constantinople remained the only center where the traditions of ancient culture were preserved and further developed for the benefit of future generations. In painting, the Byzantine technique furnished the foundation for the work of our Western pre-Raphaelites. In music, the remarkable achievements of the Byzantine choral singing served as the basis for our diatonic system of harmony. Rome has never shown much genius or interest for art. It would, therefore, be contrary to all we know about the spirit of Rome if we assumed that such a fundamental artistic category as rime had been originally invented and introduced by the Romans. In all probability they just followed the example of the Greeks in this as in practically everything else except law.

Edmond Bouvy, in his dissertation (*Poètes et mélodes, étude sur les origines du rythme tonique dans l'hymnographie de l'église grecque*) presented to the Faculty of Letters of the University of Paris in 1886, makes an attempt to connect the origin of rime with the development of tonic versification which found its way into Byzantine poetry from the time of Synesius of Cyrene, a descendant of a very old pagan family, educated in Alexandria in the spirit of neo-Platonic philosophy, and in later years introduced to the doctrine of Christianity. His hymns are regarded by Bouvy as the first experiments of tonic versification, although those that I was able to inspect seemed to be written in the meter and style of classical poetry, display-

114

ing, indeed, an unusual wealth of assonances. Synesius lived in the fourth century.

But the strongest impulse rime received from the pen of the most brilliant poet of the whole Byzantine period, Romanus the Melode, who lived in the sixth century. Professor Vasiliev in his *History of the Byzantine Empire* says:

> The hymn writers were gradually getting away from their original practice of imitating classical meters and developed their own peculiar meters, which had nothing in common with the older forms and were considered as prose for a long time. It is only in comparatively recent times that these meters have been partly explained. The hymns of this period contain various types of acrostics and rime. Unfortunately, the religious hymns of the fourth and fifth centuries are known very little; the history of their gradual development in this early period is therefore obscure for us. And yet this development, it is quite apparent, had been vigorous. While Gregory the Theologian, in most of his poetical hymns, followed the antique meters, the works of Romanus the Melode ("Hymn-writer"), which, as has been proved, appeared in the early sixth century during the reign of Anastasius I, were all written in new meters and made use of acrostics and rimes.

Romanus the Melode, called the "Pindar of rhythmical poetry," was born in Syria, and it is believed that the period of his literary bloom fell during the reign of Justinian the Great. It is highly significant that Synesius and Romanus the Melode were both born in the East (Alexandria and Syria), which suggests that rime might have come to us from Arabian sources. "The marvelous work of Romanus," Professor Vasiliev continues, "in the sixth century forces the supposition that religious poetry in the fifth century must have been very highly developed; but unfortunately we have very inadequate data on this point. It is difficult to conceive the existence of this unusual poet in the sixth century without some previous development of church poetry." The latter remark applies not so much to the intellectual outlook of the poet, as to his technique,

and is especially true with regard to rime. It is difficult to imagine that such a consistent use of rime and such a great arsenal
of riming facilities as are revealed in Melode's hymns could
arise suddenly and without previous development. It is, of
course, impossible to locate the origin of rime within the spatio-
temporal boundaries of the Byzantine Empire. But it is reasonable to assume that the immense cultural authority of Constantinople during the early Middle Ages helped to establish
rime throughout Europe as a legitimate aesthetic device. It
may be of some interest to give an illustration of Melode's
achievements in the field of rimed poetry. Here is the beginning of his hymn to the Savior:

Δεύτε πάντες πιστοί προσκυνήσωμεν
    τον σωτήρα Χριστόν και φιλάνθρωπον,
τον υεόν του θεού και μακρόθυμον,
    τον δεσπότην και μόνον αθάνατον,
ον υμνούσιν αγγέλλων τα τάγματα,
ασωμάτον οι δήμον δοξάζουσιν
εκ περίνων γλωσσών ανακράζουσιν,

. . . .

In the eighth century Byzantine rime appears to have been
on the decline. This was, probably, the effect of the iconoclastic
movement. We know that by orders of the seventh Ecumenical
Council all iconoclastic literature was completely destroyed, so
that we possess but very fragmentary information as to the
literary forms practiced by the "image-breakers." But from
what we know about their tendencies from the writings of their
opponents, it is fairly clear that they were puritanically antagonistic to any form of excessive ornamentation in matters of religion, and systematically persecuted everything that savored of
mysticism or emotionalism. It is not improbable, as Bouvy
suggests, that they objected to rime on the same general principle on which they objected against excessive ornamentation in
spiritual matters. Precursors of our modern protestantism and

116

puritanism, the iconoclasts were too strongly rationalistic to be interested in the musical effect of rime. However that may be, the fact is that after the first outbreak of iconoclasm (726–780) rime falls into disrepute. John Damascene (700–760?), though an enemy of iconoclasm, nevertheless writes, not merely his great romance *Barlam and Josaphat,* but also his *Carmina* and *Hymni* without any allusion to either rime or assonance. It must have been a matter of deliberate avoidance; for John was a great stylist and knew every refinement of poetic form produced in the past. He could not possibly be ignorant of the existence of rime. If he rejected it, it must have been a matter of deliberate opposition, probably a conscious outgrowth of his general principle that *pulchritudo et elegantia futilis est.* It would be a fascinating study to trace the Miltonian opposition against rime to Byzantine sources. Here, however, we are not in position to pursue the matter any further.

Early English rimes.—It has been pointed out in support of the hymnological hypothesis that in England Latin rime preceded the appearance of rimed verse in English and that after rime had appeared rimed verse existed simultaneously with alliterative verse. We have already seen that Coelius Sedulius, a Scottish bishop, wrote rimed hymns in Latin as early as the first half of the fifth century. Almost a whole millennium elapsed between that time and the fourteenth century when rime was finally established as a regular practice. Yet even then, in the days of Gower (1325–1408) and Chaucer (1340?–1400), alliterative verse still existed in popular poems composed in the native tongue, whereas the domestic Latin was hardly affected by alliteration at all, and—what is more—made frequent recurrence to rime. *The Vision of William concerning Piers the Plowman* is written in the traditional alliterative form, whereas Gower's *Vox Clamantis,* composed practically at the same period and dealing with the same set of social problems, makes frequent use of rime, which can be seen, for instance, from the following passage:

> Hii sunt nob*is* magni sudore labor*is*
> Perquirunt virt*us*, jussit ut ipse de*us;*
> Est et eis ju*re* nostri primi patris A*de*
> Regula, quam sum*mi* cepit ab ore de*i*
> Nam deus inquit e*i*, dum corruit a Paradis*i*
> Floribus, in terr*am* cepit et ire vi*am:*
> "O transgresse, lab*or* mundi tibi sint quoque sud*or,*
> In quibus uter*is* panibus ipse tu*is.*"

Leonine rime here employed has been, as we know, practiced for centuries in the church literature, whereas English end-rime was at that time a comparatively recent innovation. It has therefore been suggested that it penetrated into English literature through the medium of Latin church poetry.

Yet in the opinion of most English scholars the ground for such conclusion appears to be quite unsafe. Courthope in his *History of English Poetry* considers it much more probable that rime is derived from Arabian sources. Guest is inclined to trace end-rime to the Old Celtic. Saintsbury, "the latest, fullest, and most important historian of English prosody," dismisses the question of origin quite promptly by saying that "rhyme appeared no one knows quite how, or why, or whence, and at the same time." As to the possible influence of Coelius Sedulius and his *Carmen Paschale*, Richardson remarks that "Sedulius was not even a significant pioneer." All we know is that rime appears to be firmly established in the fourteenth century, and that there was occasional riming before that. Let us consider a little more in detail the situation that developed in England toward the end of that troublesome century.

The causes that led to the "bolshevist" revolution of 1381, and the general fermentation, both political and intellectual, then prevailing in English society were very favorable for the development of a new, experimental poetry. The tragic memories of the Black Death and its effect upon the economic conditions of the country, the new labor legislation and the conflict of classes, the pressing injustice of the social order and the awkward steps of the government toward remedying it, the sudden realization by the laboring classes of their strength and their readiness to take advantage of the situation—all these stimulated social and political thought, at the same time promoting literature and poetry as possible means of propaganda. On the other hand, a desire to escape from the harsh realities and complexities of life into the world of imagination led to a heretofore unprecedented development of the purely aesthetic aspect of poetry. True, it was at that time that in the process of experimentation rime became firmly established. It is also true that church literature presented a source from which the art of riming, partly at least, might have been learned. And it is beyond doubt that Gower knew and utilized that source. And yet all this evidence does not yield the desired conclusion as to the Latin origin of rime. It only proves that Latin poems of that time were influenced by the forms then current in Latin poetry, and no more. Gower rimes much more consistently in French, and still more consistently in English, than in Latin. *Vox Clamantis* begins with no rime, and proceeds for some time without any assonantal construction. The first consistently riming, though brief, section occurs in the fourteenth paragraph of the first book, after which rime vanishes from the construction to appear again only in the second book, where it is employed more consistently.[11]

More or less extended riming sections are scattered all over the poem, but on the whole the poem must be regarded as written in classical hexameter without rime. On the other hand, Gower's *Mirour de l'Omme*, written in French, shows a definite and consistent assonantal arrangement similar to that which is

[11] "Multa quidem vidi, dinersaque multa notui, etc."

found in the Old French, only with a much more perfect rime scheme. Should we consider it probable that rime came to England from France? Of course not. And that despite the fact that some of the earliest English rimers, such as Robert of Brunne, were imitating the Alexandrines of the French chronicles. Robert of Gloucester, who was writing his chronicle some fifty years before Brunne and also largely in rime, used a rhythm which was seemingly an imitation of the catalectic iambic tetrameter, not borrowed from France but quite evidently derived from still more ancient domestic "Lives of Saints" and versified psalms.[12] This would again decide the dispute in favor of the ecclesiastical hypothesis.

Thus we are tossed from one source to another. It seems that antedating any document in support of one hypothesis there can be found a still older one in support of the opposite view. Both hypotheses are likely to be correct in so far as both ecclesiastical and French sources influenced the development of English rime. But whether or not the latter originated from either of those sources is an entirely different question. Rime was used in England before Chaucer and Gower, before the two Roberts, and that by poets, some of whom, at least, knew neither French nor Latin.[13] A few riming lines have been

[12] Edwin Guest, *A History of English Rhythms* (1838; new edition, 1882), pages 508–510.

[13] Staves with continuous assonantal rime, such as we have seen in the *Song of Roland*, and which we often find in Gower, are to be found, according to Guest, in all the older poems of Welsh and Irish as far as the sixth century (*A History of English Rhythms*, page 577). Among the earliest English rimers mention must be made of Richard Rolle, the hermit of Hampole, who died in 1349; Thomas Leirmouth, who lived in the time of Edward I and was known as "The Rhymour," and Kendale, both mentioned by Robert of Brunne; and Layamon, who lived in the twelfth century and whose writings (he left a large poem known under his name) are distinguished from those of his Anglo-Saxon predecessors by a great number of riming couplets (Guest, *op. cit.*, page 170).

120

found in the *Anglo-Saxon Chronicle,* and a considerable number of popular rimes have been discovered by various scholars, some of which reach as far back as the time of Henry II and still farther into the time preceding the Conquest.

Under Edward III (1327–1377) and Richard II (1377–1399) rime appears to be firmly established (not merely at the court, but also) in the popular poetry. During the period preparatory to the great revolutionary outbreak of 1381, rime assumes an important social function in coining the cutting slogans and inflaming the masses. It becomes an effective weapon of political propaganda. Well known and frequently quoted is a versicle attributed to John Ball, one of the outstanding figures in the revolt:

> When Adam dalf and Eve span,
> Who was then a gentilman?

The revolution produced a large number of popular versicles of a similar nature mostly intended to electrify the masses and to present in a brief, striking, and easily comprehensible form some evil aspects of the existing order of things. For this purpose rime was peculiarly appropriate. The form of such popular fragments points in a direction quite different from either French or ecclesiastical sources. They often produce an impression of genuinely spontaneous generation. Consider, for example, the rhythmical organization of the following fragment breathing the militant spirit of the rising "proletariat":

> But if might
> Goe before right,
> And will
> Before skill,
> There is our Mill
> Misdight.

It is written in what Amy Lowell would call "cadences"—without any regular meter, and yet decidedly in clearly perceptible rhythmical waves. Such a form, reminding one of the structure of fables, has no precedent in ecclesiastical poetry. It may have originated spontaneously or under the influence of popular forms which have not reached us, and yet the existence of which we have good reason to surmise. Describing the state of literary affairs in England after the Conquest and prior to the great peasant uprising, Sir Harris Nicolas offers the following explanation:

It may seem extraordinary, after these proofs that the art of rhyming was not unknown or unpracticed in this country in the time of Henry II, that we should be obliged to search through a space of above a hundred years without being able to meet with a single maker of English Rhymes whom we know to have written in that interval. The case I suspect to have been this: The scholars of that age . . . . affected to write only in Latin, so that we do not find that they ever composed, in verse or prose, in any other language. On the other hand, they who meant to recommend themselves by their poetry to the favor of the great, took care to write in French, the only language their patrons understood; and hence it is, that we see so many French poems, about that time, either addressed directly to the principal persons at the English court or at least written on such subjects as we may suppose to have been most likely to engage their attention. Whatever, therefore, of English poetry was produced, in this infancy of the art, being probably the work of illiterate authors and circulating among the vulgar, we need not be much surprised that no more of it has been transmitted down to posterity.[14]

In the fourteenth century such popular and anonymous rimes played a very active part in the social and political life of the country. There was, therefore, more chance for them to survive, being often registered, for instance, in the court proceedings against the unfortunate and defeated revolutionists. We know how dearly John Ball paid for his rimes. Thus in

[14] *The Poetical Works of Geoffrey Chaucer, with a Memoir by Sir Harris Nicolas*, pages 163–164.

the furnace of the revolution rime graduated to the performance of a political function. But prior to that time there was no specific reason for making any record of such "vulgar" compositions, and they perished without leaving a trace. Yet a careful search for lost poetic antiquities occasionally yields amazing funds. Among the papers pertaining to a manuscript now in the possession of Trinity College, Cambridge, there was found an amusing poem, the oldest sea-song now in existence, depicting the troubles and tribulations on board a pilgrim ship of the time of Edward III, written by a contemporary.[15] Perfect end-rime is used consistently throughout the poem from beginning to end, and a rough approximation of iambic trimeter serves as its rhythmical scheme:

> Men may leve all gamys
> That saylen to Seynt Jamys.
> For many a man hit gramys[16]
>   When they begyn to sayle.
>
> For when they have take the see,
> At Sandwyche, or at Wynchylsee,
> At Brystow, or where that hit bee,
>   Theyr herts begyn to fayle.
>
> Anone the mastyr commaundeth fast
> To hys ship-men in all the hast
> To dress hem sone about the mast,
>   Theyr takelyng to make.
>
> With "howe, hissa," then they cry,
> "What, howe, mate, thow stondyst to ny
> Thy fellow may nat hale the by":
>   Thus they begyn to crake.

   .   .   .   .   .   .

[15] The poem has been recently reprinted in Chatterton's *Ships and Ways of Other Days*.

[16] "Grieves."

Thys menewhyle the pylgryms ly,
And have theyr bowlys fast them by,
And cry aftyr hote malvesy,
  'Thow helpe for to restore!

And som wold have a saltyd tost,
For they myght ete neyther sode ne rost:
A man myght sone pay for theyr cost,
  As for oo day or twayne

Then cometh oure owner lyke a lorde,
And speketh many a royall worde,
And dresseth hym to the hygh borde
  To see all thyng be well.

Anone he calleth a carpentere
And biddyth hym bryng with hym hys gere
To make the cabans here and there,
  With many a febyll cell.

A sak of strawe were there ryght good,
For som must lyg them in theyr hood:
I had as lefe be in the wood,
  Without mete or drynk.

For when that we shall go to bedde,
The pumpe was nygh our beddes hede,
A man were as good to be dede,
  As smell thereof the stynk.

Of course, it may be pointed out, again in support of the hymnological hypothesis, that even this jolly take-off on the miseries of seasickness may very well be a product of ecclesiastical wit. There were many stray clergymen strolling around the country in those days, sharing the economic depression that made vagabonds out of many a "gentilman." Ball himself was a clergyman. The poem—we should not forget—depicts the discomfort of the pilgrims traveling to the shrine of St. James, among whom there were no doubt many monks and self-discharged ministers. Latin was certainly not an unheard language in their midst. In fact there are some popular poems of a similar nature and dating from approximately the same time, written half in English and half in Latin, such as the one published by Wright under the title "On the Rebellion of Jack Straw."[17] This absurd poetic concoction, also dating from the period of troubles, combines English and Latin in one composition, so that a verse in English is regularly followed by one in Latin. The interesting point about it is that alternating English and Latin lines rime among themselves:

> Tax has tenet us alle
> > *probat hoc mors tot validorum,*
> The kyng therof hade smalle,
> > *fuit in manibus cupidorum;*
> Hit hade harde honsalle,
> > *dans causam fine dolorum;*
> Revrawnce nede most falle,
> > *propter peccata malorum.*

And yet, a reference to such monstrosities, however numerous they may have been, does not prove that English rime was derived exclusively from Latin sources. Latin may have been one of the channels through which rime penetrated into English poetry, but it was by no means the only one. French, no doubt, was another channel. Celtic Welsh, according to Guest, constitutes still another probability. Finally, the process of spontaneous generation is not at all excluded. In any event, those who believe that the sailors' poem quoted above may have been originally produced by a monk must support their view with something more than a mere probability. The burden of proof is upon them. The rimes in that poem are too good to be regarded as an early experimental adaptation of Latin meth-

[17] Aldis Wright, *Political Poems*, 1:56.

ods to the English verse. They show that even in the popular poetry of that time rime was an established fact with a long history behind it. Sir Harris Nicolas errs rather conspicuously in believing that English rime cannot be traced beyond the time of Henry II (1154–1189). The art of riming was known in England before the Conquest.[18]

The earliest poem in English in which rime occurs regularly is, according to Guest, the so-called "Conybear's Riming Poem" first published by Conybear in his *Illustrations of Anglo-Saxon Poetry* (London, 1826). Guest determines its date as probably the late ninth century. The poem is too long to be reprinted in full; but the following extract will give the reader an idea of its rhythmical intricacy and its riming pattern:

Me lif | es onlah | : se | this leoht | onwrah |
And | thaet torh | te geteoh | : til | lice | onwrah |

Glaed | waes ic gliw | um : gleng | ed hiw | um
Blis | sa bleo | um : blost | ma hiw | um.

Secg | as mec seg | on : sym | bel ne | aleg | on
Feorh | griefe | gefeg | on : faet | wed waeg | um

Wic | ofer wong | um : wen | nan gong | um
Lis | se mid long | um : leom | a getong | um

Tha | waes waest | mum aweaht | : world | onspreht |
Un | der rod | erum | areaht | : raed | maegne of | er-theaht |

Giest | as geng | don : ger | scipe | meng | don
Lis | se leng | don : lust | um gleng | don.

Rime and grammatical parallelism.—Herder made an attempt to derive rime from the Hebrew "parallelism," i.e., the

---

[18] Edwin Guest, *A History of English Rhythm*, page 388; compare *ibid.*, pages 394–395.

126

syntactical analogy of two or more neighboring phrases. The Bible is full of such constructions, as for example:

Ye shall not make with me *gods of silver*, neither shall ye make unto you *gods of gold*.

In the highly inflectional languages such constructions naturally result in rime:

> Nec non Tarquinium ejectum Porsena jubebat
> Accipere, ingentique urbem obsidione premebat.
>
> —VIRGIL

Or:

> Aurora lucis rutilat,
> Coelum laudibus intonat,
> Mundus exultans jubilat,
> Gemens infernus ululat.
>
> —*Hymnus Paschalis*

It is evident that such rimes may arise quite unintentionally as the result of grammatical construction which repeats itself in parallel lines. It very often occurs in prose, where it attracts no attention, largely because of the different lengths of the phrases. Groups of words of various lengths do not constitute any rhythmical series, and rime remains unnoticed. But where music is added to poetry, i.e., where words are intended for song, the lines for rhythmical reason become equalized, and rime results of itself.[19]

There is hardly any doubt that parallelism played an important part in the making of rime. As long as this theory stays

---

[19] Herder; *Sämmtliche Werke*, 12:20: "Sobald Musik erfunden war, bekam die Poesie neuen Schwung, Gang und Wohllaut. Die Bilderrede hatte nur die natürlichste Dimension, ... den Parrallelismus; mit der Musik bekam sie höhere Töne, abgemessenere Kadenzen, *sebst* . . . . Reime." The theory of Semitic origin of rime has been advanced before Herder by Fauchet in his *Recueil de l'origine de la langue française*, 1581, I, pages 63 f., and by Muratori, *Antiquitates italianae medii aevi*, 1738.

within the limits of the natural history of rime it remains true, though one-sided. The confusion again begins where the natural history ends and historical guesswork begins.

We see, then, that several ingenious hypotheses have been suggested to account for the mysterious origin of our evasive muse. Cautious criticism will be slow in accepting any of them. The difficulty lies chiefly in our ignorance as to where, in every particular language or group of languages, the foreign influences end and the spontaneous generation of rime begins. It seems that if we follow the history of rime far enough, we find that alongside of foreign influences there exists in every given language a natural tendency to produce rime of its own accord. Probably any literature, if left entirely alone, would develop rimed poetry from its own sources; we have indications of this probability everywhere. But unfortunately we do not know a single literature that would afford an example of such a convenient isolation.

The question, therefore, in its general form has practically no sense. You ask about the historic origin of rime. But what kind of rime do you mean? Inner rime? assonance, alliteration? end-rime? or simply identical words at the end of certain rhythmical groups? One or another or several at once of these forms we find practically everywhere, and there is no way of telling where they originated. Dingeldein points out a large number of rimed passages in Homer and Hesiod. We even find terminal assonances in the earliest poetic fragments that have ever reached us from antiquity. In a certain ritual hymn of the Koubetes commemorating the birth of the infant Zeus, one of the oldest Greek hymns in existence, we find a number of terminal assonances which in some cases acquire almost the character of rime:

> 'Ιώ,
> ῏Ωραι δὲ βρύον κατῆτος
> καὶ βροτοὺς Δίκα κατῆχε

πάντα τ'ἄγρι' ἄμφεπε ζῶ
ἁ φίλολβος Εἰρήνα.

'Ιώ,
'Αμιν Θόρε, κε'ς σταμνέα,
καὶ Θόρ' εὔποκ' ἐς ποίμνεα

. . . .

'Ιώ,
Θόρε κε'ς πόληας ἁμῶν,
κε'ς ποντοφόρους νᾶας,
Θόρε κε'ς νεοὺς πολείέτας,
Θόρε κε'ς Θέμιν κ. . . :[20]

The terminal assonances are here more perfect than in the embryonic rimes of the *Chanson de Roland*. Is it just an accident or an effect of grammatical parallelism of construction? But suppose it is an indirect result of construction. Is not the grammatical parallelism itself an embryonic rime? The opinion has even been expressed, as we have already seen, that rime arises from grammatical parallelism. If that is true, I do not see what prevents us from regarding σταμνια and ποιμνια as an embryonic rime too, even though it was an accident. But parallelism was not an accident, certainly not in ancient poetry. Not merely identical endings, but words and whole phrases were often employed to produce musical effects, especially in hymns. In the Upanishads we often find passages like this:

Then Gargi Vacaknavi questioned him. "Yajnavalkya," said she, "since all this world is woven, warp and woof, on water, on what, pray, is the water woven, warp and woof?"

"On wind, O Gargi."

"On what then, pray, is the wind woven, warp and woof?"

"On the atmosphere-worlds, O Gargi."

"On what then, pray, are the atmosphere-worlds woven, warp and woof?"

[20] J. E. Harrison, *Themis: A Study of the Social Origin of Greek Religion.*

"On the worlds of the Gandharvas, O Gargi."

"On what then, pray, are the worlds of the Gandharvas woven, warp and woof?"

"On the world of the Sun, O Gargi."

"On what then, pray, are the worlds of the Sun woven, warp and woof?"

"On the worlds of the moon, O Gargi."

"On what then, pray, are the worlds of the moon woven, warp and woof?"

"On the worlds of the stars, O Gargi."

"On what then, pray, are the worlds of the stars woven, warp and woof?"

"On the worlds of the gods, O Gargi."

"On what then, pray, are the worlds of the gods woven, warp and woof?"

"On the worlds of Indra, O Gargi."

"On what then, pray, are the worlds of Indra woven, warp and woof?"

"On the worlds of Brahma, O Gargi."

Here we have an identical repetition of the same word at the end of each verse. Is it meant as a rime? Modern poets often apply such identical rimes to produce the effect of monotony. Grimm regards it as one of the forms of embryonic rime.

How are we to decide from which of those forms our rime has really originated? They all have contributed to its formation. If we ask, then, what is the historic origin of rime, our question has really no definite meaning. For, which kind of embryonic rime do we have in mind? And if in turn we ask about the origin of those primitive forms, we shall find ourselves in a still more precarious situation; for they are common to all languages and all peoples.[21] There is no way of saying,

---

[21] "Negro revival hymns and plantation songs, like the folk-songs of white people, abound in instances of structural repetition and in sequences of various types" (Louise Pound, *Poetic Origins and the Ballad*, page 130).

and no sense in asking, where those riming germs originally came from. For they are universal.

Rime in the making.—If, however, instead of asking about the historic origin of rime, we limit our inquiry to the study of its natural causes, we shall be able to obtain much more definite results. What does it mean to study the natural causes of rime? It means studying those linguistic factors which, within the limits of every individual language, tend to produce perfect rime. It means studying the evolution of riming forms. The historic origin of rime is obscure precisely for the same reason for which its natural cause is evident. It is everywhere. And because it is everywhere we cannot lay our hand on any particular literary document, and announce: here is the place where rime appears for the first time. For there is no first rime, as there is no first word uttered by man. Yet we can very well observe different forms of embryonic rimes. Which of those forms was really the first, and whether any one of them was first, is a question that cannot be answered. But they all contributed to the development of rime as a habit, and in this sense they all belong to its natural causes. In studying the origin of rime, therefore, we are in the same position in which the biologist finds himself in studying the origin of life. What was the first living thing on earth? Nobody knows. Yet this ignorance does not prevent us from the legitimate inquiry into the nature of various factors which contribute to the maintenance of life and which are indispensable for producing and supporting it.

There are several factors which all contribute to the making of rime. I think they all can be summarized in two fundamental laws. The first law may be stated as follows: *No matter through what influences and at what time rime appears in the poetic literature of a given country, it always proceeds from more or less imperfect forms of terminal assonance to*

131

a more accurate repetition of sound. The period of adaptation may be very brief, as it was in English poetry, or it may take centuries of development, as it did in Old French; imperfect rime may disappear completely from the poetic practice of a given language, or it may survive in certain branches of popular poetry; but traces of imperfection are found practically everywhere. *Rime develops from assonance.*

In many cases we can visualize this process by comparing early rime technique with the later developments and writing them side by side in parallel columns. Rime then appears as a variable feature. It straightens out, as it were, with time. The following forms represent the process as it runs in early English and in French poetry.

THE BOY AND THE MANTLE

EARLIER VERSION	LATER VERSION
In the third day of may	In Carleile dwelt king Arthur,
To Carleile *did come*	A prince of passing might;
A kind curteous child,	And there maintain'd his table round,
That cold much of *wisdome*.	Beset with many a knight.
He had a sute of silke	And there he kept his Christmas
About his middle *drawne;*	With mirth and princely cheare,
Without he cold of curtesye	When, lo! a strange and cunning boy
He thought itt much *shame*.	Before him did appear.
God speed there king Arthur,	A kirtle and a mantle
Sitting at thy meate:	This boy had him upon,
And the goodly queene Guenever,	With brooches, rings, and owches
I cannot her forgett.	Full daintily bedone.
I tell you, lords, in this hall;	He had a sarke of silk
I hett you all to *"heede";*	About his middle meet;
Except you be the more surer	And thus with seemly courtesy,
Is for you to *dread*.	He did king Arthur greet.

He plucked out of his potever,　　Then straitway from his bosome
And longer wold not *dwell*,　　A little wand he drew;
He pulled forth a pretty mantle,　　And with it eke a mantle
Betweene two nut-*shells*.　　Of wondrous shape and hew.

.　　.　　.　　.　　.　　.　　　　.　　.　　.　　.　　.

One while was it "gule";　　Now green, now red it seemed,
Another while was itt *greene*;　　Then all of sable hue.
Another while was itt wadded:　　"Beshrewe me," quoth king
　　　　　　　　　　　　　　　Arthur,
Ill itt did her *beseeme*.　　"I think thou beest not true."

Then spake dame Guenever　　Down she threw the mantle,
To Arthur our *king;*　　Ne longer would not stay;
She hath tane yonder mantle　　But storming like a fury,
Not with right, but with *wronge*.　　To her chamber flung away.

These verses are extracts from one and the same ballad, "The Boy and the Mantle," in two variants, of which the first, evidently the older, reveals a large number of imperfect rimes, while the second shows a well-developed riming technique, and is, according to Percy, of a later date.

Here we compare riming technique in the Old French as it progressively perfected itself from the tenth to the thirteenth century. We see that the music of words becomes more transparent. The vowels, which constitute the key in the musical sequence of words, are proficiently brought to the same characteristic frequency by repeating the subsequent consonant. Identity of other consonants adds to the rhythmical effectiveness of rime.

The second law may be expressed thus: *Rime, as the factor introducing melody into the music of vowels, appears at first in very brief musical phrases which reveal the tendency to grow until they reach the natural limit at the end of each verse line.* We have learned from the first chapter that the essential prerequisite of a pleasing musical effect in human speech is that

133

FROM *CHANSON DE ROLAND*

De fo cui calt? se fuiz s'en est Marsi*lies*
remés i est sis uncles l'algali*fes*,
qui tint Kartagene, Alferne, Garmalie,
e Ethiope, une terre mal*dite*;
la neire gent en ad en sa baillie,
granz unt les nes e lees les or*illes*,
e sunt ensemble plus de cinquante milie.
icil chevalchent fierement e a *ire*,
puis si escrient l'enseigne paien*isme*.
fo dist Rollanz 'ci recevrums martirie,
e or sai ben n'avuns guaires a *vivre*;
mais tut seit fel ki chier nes vende *prime!*
ferez, seignur, des espees fur*bies*,
si calengiez e vos morz e voz vies,
que dulce France par nus ne seit hunie!
quant en cest camp vendrat Carles mis*rie*,
de Sarrazins verrat tel discip*line*,
cuntre un des noz en truverat morz *quinze*,
ne laisserat que nus ne beneisse'. Aoi.
Quant paien virent que Franceis i out poi,
entr' els en unt e orgoill e cunfort;
dist l'uns al altre 'li emperere ad tort'.
li algalifes sist sur un ceval sor,
brochet le bien des esperuns a or;
fiert Olivier deriere en mi le *dos*,
le blanc osberc li ad desclos el *cors*,
par mi le piz sun espiet li mist fors;
e dit aprés 'un colp avez pris fort'.
Carles li magnes mar vus laissat as porz;
tort nus ad fait, nen est dreiz qu'il s'en *lot*
kar de vus sul ai bien vengiet les *noz*'.

FROM *GARIN LE LAHERAIN*

El val Galin assemblent li marchiz
ileuc avoit un fin clerc seignori,
forment se paine de damedeu *servir*,
hermites fu, et reparoit iqui:
chapele i ot, nus plus bele ne vit.
la sont venu por la paiz establir:
ileuques vint li Loherens Garins,
il et Girbers et Hernaus et Gerins,
si vavasor dont i ot plus de *mil*.
de l'autre part Fromons et Fromon-
              [dins

et li evescues de Verdun Lancelins,
li cuens Guillaumes, li sires de Mon-
              [clin,

et li lignajes a qui ja dex n'ait!
en lor compeigne de chevaliers trois
              [mil.

Garins parole, qui a cuer enterin,
'entendez moi, franc chevalier jentil.
sire Guillaume, damoisiax de Mon-
              [clin,
tu es mes homs de mon fié a te*nir*,
et mes comperes et mes riches amis.
por mes pechiés, biau sire, a la croiz
              [pris;
outre la mer irai as Sarrazins.
se nule rien a nul lor vos mesftis,
a tos vos pri por l'amor deu merci.
ci remanra l'enfes Girbers, mes fils;
s'il a mestier (jeunes est li meschins,
aidiez li, sire, si fairoiz que gentil.

FROM *LI LAIS DEL CHEVREFOIL*

Asez me plest e bien le voil
del lai que hum nume chevrefoil
que la verité vus en cunt,
pur quei il fu ja fet e dunt,
plusurs le me unt cunté e dit,
e jeo l'ai trové en escrit,
de Tristram e de la reine,
de lur amur que tant fu fine,
dunt il eurent meinte dolur
e puis mururent en un jur.
li reis Markes esteit curcié,
vers Tristram sun nevu irié,
de sa terre le cungea
pur la reine qu'il ama.
en sa cuntree en est alez:
en Suht-Wales, u il fu nez,
un an demurat tut entier
ne pot ariere repeirier;
mes puis se mist en abandun
de mort e de destructiun.
ne vus esmerveilliez neent,
kar ki eime mut lealment
mut est dolenz e trespensez
quant il nen ad ses volentez.
Tristram dolenz e trespensis
pur ceo se muet de sun païs,
en Cornuaille vait tut dreit
la u la reine maneit,
en la forest tut sul se mist,
ne voleit pas que hum le veïst.

the vowels should constitute a rime; for only in rime do we find the condition of musical melody fulfilled: only there does the musical phrase contained in the vowels receive a definite key and end with the same tone with which it begins. The reader will remember the illustration from Edgar Allan Poe:

Hear the mellow wedding bells

which contains a melody very close to the leitmotif of the *Flying Dutchman:*

Any two vowels arranged in a manner similar to the foregoing constitute a melodic fragment. For melody appears wherever the same vowel begins and ends a period, such as *e — o — e* or *o — ur — o,* etc. Such fragments are usually called inner rimes. Inner rimes may be of different length. The illustrations above are the shortest combinations that can possibly be devised of the type, *y — x — y.* They frequently occur in the oldest poetic documents. Latin is full of such inner melodies, for example:

Exegi monumentum aere peraennius

Or from Tibullus:

Ille licet Cilicum victas agat ante catervas.

In Old Germanic they often take a somewhat longer form: *y — x — y — x,* as for example in a song that is attributed to Walther von der Vogelweide:

Ich minne, sinne lange zit:
versinne Minne sich,
wie sie schône lône mîner tage.
nu lône schône: dêst mîn stât:
vil kleine meine mich,
niene meine kleine mîne klage . . . .

135

Here *"minne ... sinne,"* etc., form the so-called *Schlagreim*, which consists of two riming words in immediate proximity.[22]

The length of the musical phrase, however, may be increased either by repeating the same vowels or by inserting new ones in between. Thus originates what Grimm calls *Binnenreim*, when the riming words within a verse line are so far removed from each other that it is no more possible to speak of a *Schlagreim*. Evidently such phrases can only occur in longer verse lines, as in Wolfram von Eschenbach's song:

> Es ist nu tac, daz ich wol mac mit warheit jehen.

Here the assonance already acquires the significance of a fully developed rime, because the riming words appear in the rhythmically important places. The vowel melody is here much longer: $a - a - i - o - a$. The famous Leonine rime in Latin is of the same structure; it constitutes a comparatively long musical phrase within a single verse line.

It is possible, however, that such melodies overstep the boundaries of one line. Then they produce something that might properly be called an outer rime, in contrast to the inner rime which is always confined to the same verse line. From Grimm we obtain the following illustration:

> wolt iege*líchen*, möhte ez sîn,
> für in *líden*, möhte ez sin,
> mit ge*líchem* kumbers valle.

Professor B. O. Foster[23] gives a remarkable illustration

---

[22] For further illustration, see Wilhelm Grimm, *Zur Geschichte des Reims*, pages 185 ff. With regard to Romanic languages, *see* the material presented by Tobler, *Vom französischen Versbau alter und neuer Zeit*; Diez, *Altromanische Sprachdenkmale*; and Clarus, *Darstellung der spanischen Literatur im Mittelalter*. Mütze (*Ueber die accentuierende Rhythmik in neueren Sprachen*, page 33) remarks that assonance is *"die Mutter des Reims."*

[23] *Transactions of the American Philological Association*, Vol. XL (1910).

from Propertius, a fragment where nearly every word rimes
with some other word or words:

> quam supra nullas pendebant debita curae
> roscida desertis poma sub arboribus,
> et circum irrigus surgebant lilia prato
> candida purpureis mixta papaveribus.

Such melodies are difficult to detect. They remain largely unnoticed by the majority of readers or listeners. For the beginning and the end of the vowel melody are not rhythmically
stressed. At the present time, when we know how to arrange
our rimes in order to make prominent their acoustic effect, it is
difficult to imagine that there was a time when the poets did
not know this simple trick. Yet a great deal of experimenting
was needed in order to learn the most favorable position for an
outer rime. As we see from the illustration above, the starting-
point for the melody of vowels was sometimes placed in the
middle of a line (*"iegelichen"*); and any position in the middle
of the next line was considered good for the end of the melodic
phrase (*"liden ... gelichen"*). In the search for the most convenient and effective position of the riming words the early
poets sometimes reversed the natural order of the music of
words and made the last word of a verse line rime with the
first word of the next line:

> Der mit golde was betro*ffen*
> *offen* wandel meinte?

From the musical point of view the most natural form of riming appears to be the following arrangement:

> *ein* klôsenaere, ob erz vertrüege? ich waene, en *nein,*

where the first syllable of a line rimes with the last one of the
same line. Yet what is natural in music, is highly inconvenient
in poetry; for the relative rhythmical importance of the first

syllable is rather small. Rhythmically the most important place in a verse is its end, not the beginning. It is the last accented vowel in the verse line that is most easily retained by the ear for melodic purposes. And after centuries of experimenting, poetry finally arrived at this most satisfactory solution. The end-rime evolved from other forms of riming as, musically, the most effective scheme.

Rime and the history of music.—It may be interesting to note that the process of the gradual purification of rime stands in a definite historical relation to the development of music. I must confess that I do not have any satisfactory explanation of this remarkable relationship. But if the conspicuous events and critical turning-points in the evolution of one thing continually coincide in time with the turning-points in the development of another thing, the suggestion is obvious that the two things are somehow causally related.

The first thing that offers itself for consideration is the neglect of rime in ancient poetry and the neglect of harmony in ancient music. The modern diatonic scale into which, at least, our English vowels fit so perfectly, is best adapted for harmonic purposes. The ancient Pythagorean scales were used exclusively for melodies, and this practice continued for some time after the invention of the diatonic scale. The best medieval performers on stringed instruments still followed the Pythagorean scale when playing melody, and adopted the new scale only when they played pieces in which two or more notes were sounded simultaneously. It is therefore safe to conclude that the ancient ear was not trained for harmony and that owing to the nature of their scales the ancients were actually unable to arrange chords into any ordered sequences. They worked with individual tones and never with chords. The harmonic relation and affinity of chords remained outside of their sphere of hearing. Now, human vowels

138

are natural chords. It is, therefore, reasonable to believe that the musical affinity between various vowels escaped the attention of the ancients precisely because their ear was poorly trained for harmony. The absence of rime in ancient poetry becomes in this way reasonably intelligible. What we call "melody of vowels" is in reality the harmony of the vowel chords, for each vowel is a cluster of tones. In order to perceive and feel their musical relation, especially at a distance of several syllables, the ear must have some training for the appreciation of chords.

I am aware that this does not amount to a hypothesis; it is merely a suggested possible explanation of the chief difference between ancient and modern poetry. Those who would offhand object to the suggestion on the ground that it is utterly fantastic must first consider the further evidence in the case. Why is it that rime, if it does not exactly originate, still becomes firmly established in connection with the choral singing in the Christian churches? There is, no doubt, an intimate connection between hymns, music, and rime. The council of Toledo agreed on the definition of the term "hymn" as "a praise of God intended for singing." The clause referring to the hymns reads as follows: "*Proprie autem hymni sunt continentes laudem Dei. Si ergo sit laus, et non sit Dei, non est hymnus. Si sit . . . . Dei laus et non contatur, non est hymnus. Si ergo laudem Dei dicitur et cantatur, tunc est hymnus.*" That is: "Hymns properly contain the praise of God. If, therefore, there be praise, but not of God, this is not a hymn. If there be praise, but not intended for singing, this is not a hymn. If there be a praise of God in song, it is then a hymn." This official declaration of dependence between hymns and music is indirectly an acknowledgment of the relation between music and rime. For hymns, as we have just seen, were the first kind of poetry where rime was extensively and systematically employed.

Now hymns belong to the time when the riming tradition

139

is becoming firmly established. But even the earliest indications of rimed poetry seem to arise under the influence of music. The opinion has several times been expressed that prior to the hymnological period there existed forms of popular Latin verse in which rime and accent held the place which quantity held in classical poetry. Traces of it reached us through Roman historians. Suetonius, for instance, testifies that during the imperial triumphs soldiers used to sing satirical verses on the emperor. A fragment of a song on Caesar he preserved for us. It contains an embryonic (identical) rime:

> Gallias Caesar subegit, Nicomedes Caesarem.
> Ecce, Caesar nunc triumphat, qui subegit Gallias:
> Nicomedes non triumphat, qui subegit Caesarem.

Suetonius also preserved some popular songs which upbraided the cruelties of the emperor Tiberius. It is interesting that they contain a number of terminal assonances:

> Asper et inmitis. Breviter vis omnia dicam?
> Dispeream, si te mater amare pot*est*.
> Non es eques; quare? non sunt tibi millia centum;
> Omnia si quaeras: et Rhodos exilium *est*.

> Aurea mutasti Saturni saecula, Caesar;
> Incolumi nam te, ferrea semper *erunt*.
> Fastidit vinum quia iam sitit iste cruorem:
> Tam bibit hunc avide, quam bibit ante *merum*.

I cannot resist the temptation of mentioning another poetic fragment peculiarly interesting in view of its illustrious author. Spartianus in his *Vita Hadriani* tells us that His Majesty flattered himself with the idea of being a poet. On his deathbed he is said to have written the following lines (*et mortuus quidem hos versus fecisse dicitur*):

animula vagula blandula
hospes comesque corporis,
quae nunc abidis in loca
pallidula rigida nudula,
nec ut soles dabis jocos.

We know now that both identical rime and assonance are embryonic forms of rime. Therefore, *"Caesarem ... Caesarem,"* as well as *"potest ... est"* and, especially, *"erunt ... merum,"* may be properly regarded as embryonic rimes. They could hardly remain unnoticed. Besides we have the authority of Duffield, although he does not state his evidence, that prior to the hymns there must have existed forms of popular Latin verse in which rime and accent were used instead of quantity.

It appears, therefore, possible that the church in her hymns did not invent rime but made use, though reluctantly, of popular forms that had existed previously. It is interesting to note that from the social point of view those popular forms seem to have been of an origin very different from that of which the church could possibly approve. Being of a vulgar descent and intended for popular entertainment, they were very far in spirit from Christian piety, and we have testimony to the effect that the church originally reacted very strongly against them. But, revealing from the outset their spirit of moral adaptability and opportunism, the early clerics knew how to make use of what appealed to the majority of their uncultured congregations and arranged an application of popular forms to the church service with the same optimistic attitude with which modern Christian leaders arrange dancing parties (with a considerable application of jazz) to attract youth. For the orthodox church it was evidently a question of self-preservation, as otherwise it was unable to compete with the "heretics" who, "with a great deal of impudence"—*cum magna impudentia,* according to Tertullian—attracted large crowds to their religious assemblies by singing songs which in melody and struc-

141

ture were borrowed from the street. We know that Valentin, the leader of the Gnostics, was a gifted poet.[24] We know that he and his followers in Syria composed religious songs by which they contributed much to the dissemination of their "heresies" in the East. Whether or not these songs were really rimed we do not know. But Duffield believes that in their religious singing they used to reproduce popular forms of verse which, according to him, were based on rime and accent.[25] Thus popular rimes from the street and from banquets through the medium of heretical organizations penetrated into the practice of the official church. Therefore, even though the hymns might not have been the first rimed poetry in medieval Latin, the connection between rime and music nevertheless holds. For rime penetrated into church practice, not from the classical Latin, which neglects rime, but from the vulgar songs which, we do not know how early, began to substitute rime and accent for the antique measure. This does not mean, however, that rime originated from that source. It may have had other precedents apart from hymnology and quite independent of the late Latin street and banquet songs. The point I wish to stress is that the two spots where rime makes its appearance within the limits of Latin poetry are both directly connected with music.

This connection with music remains throughout the subsequent history of the growth of rime. Rime came into prominence in the poetry of troubadours, precisely at the time when modern European music came into existence. It is well known that the troubadours produced the first learned musicians in Europe. In the thirteenth century Adam de la Halle wrote his celebrated play, *Jeu de Robin et Marion,* which is considered the first example of pastoral play and comic opera in France,

[24] Eugène de Faye, *Gnostiques et gnosticisme (Étude critique des documents),* Paris, 1913.

[25] S. W. Duffield, *The Latin Hymn-Writers and Their Hymns,* page 93.

and is, according to Suchier, the oldest musical play in Europe.[26] At the same time it is one of the oldest dramatic experiments in which rime is extensively used. In Italy rime came into prominence with the development of the art of "canzoni," which originally were, according to Dante, poems intended for song.[27]

It has been suggested that the word "minstrel" is of English origin derived from the name of a cathedral or minster:

"Ut proprie Ministrels dicti fuerint qui in Cathedralibus Ecclesiis inserviebant choro Deum jugi cantu celebrantium. . . . . Fortasse quoque Britannis pari modo Cler dicti sunt Musici: ex quo nempe Clerici canere coeperunt in Ecclesiis."

From the record of the ninth of Edward IV, quoted by Percy, it appears that minstrels constituted a guild of professional musicians who sometimes assisted at the divine service. At the king's court they also constituted the staff of professional musicians, rather than poets; part of their duties was to sing— "to pray [exorare] which it is presumed they did by assisting in the chant, and musical accompaniment, in the king's chappel." Thus again we see, as in the case of the troubadours, that a class of rimers arises from the guild of professional musicians.

It was, however, not before the fifteenth century that rime was universally accepted throughout Northern Europe as a powerful device of literary expression. And at the same time, i.e., in the first half of the fifteenth century, John Dunsdale, an Englishman, invented counterpoint and through his musical compositions acquired an international reputation. Thus our European sense for rime appears to have been trained in the

[26] Herman Suchier and A. Birch-Hirschfeld, *Geschichte der Französischen Literatur*, page 272.

[27] Dante, *De vulgari eloquentia*, Volume 2, chapter viii: "We shall call canzoni not only the canzoni of which we are now treating, but also ballate and sonnets and all words of whatever kind written for music."

great school of music. This remarkable coincidence, it seems to me, can hardly be accidental. It is to be accounted for, rather, on the basis of the fundamental laws of hearing. Just what this connection is we are at present unable to say. But on the basis of what has been said in the preceding chapters about the musical nature of rime in the melody of vowels, it appears not improbable that a definite relation between the two phenomena will be established in the very near future. For us it is important to point out that the origin of rime is directly connected with the rise of our modern musical system. It corroborates our fundamental thesis that the same harmonic relation of tones lies at the basis of both rime and harmony.

V

HISTORY OF RIME THEORIES

$\mathbf{P}$LEASURE derived from rime long ago appeared as an object of speculation. Medieval linguists were inclined to explain the pleasurable effect of rime by reference to the difficulties associated with the art of riming: a technical difficulty successfully overcome inspires admiration—*"le beau c'est le difficile."* This principle for a long time served as a legitimate basis for explaining the artistic appeal of poetry. It is easy to see that it has nothing to do with the subsequent theories as to the aesthetic value or even the plain psychological attractiveness of rime.[1] The enjoyment derived from poetry

[1] The argument, stripped of its scholastic verbiage, appears somewhat in this form: It is pleasant to see an acrobat performing his tricks, because they are difficult. Similarly it is highly interesting and pleasant to watch a poet overcome the difficulties of finding suitable rimes, because it shows his unusual skill. Thus, the more exquisite a rime the more pleasure it gives to the ear, *"plus elle sera exquise plus de contentement elle donnera"* (J. Pelletier, *Art poétique*, 1555). This perverse theory, which considered difficulty as the

is very different from the sense of curiosity that we may occasionally display for the art of poetical acrobatism. We can sympathize with the pains of the poet; we can admire his skill; but we can hardly enjoy, as Pope suggested, the pitiful sight of "the Muses on the rack."

Disregarding the thesis of difficulty, rime theories may be classified under three heads: (A) visual, (B) acoustic, and (C) rhythmical.

A. VISUAL THEORIES

General remarks.—As far as I know no one ever attempted to explain rime exclusively on a visual basis. "Graphic principle," says Zhirmunski, "seldom appears in poetry in its extreme form demanding a rime for the eye. Such a riming principle would imply that satisfaction derived from rime is due to the symmetrical arrangement of typographical signs on paper. In this sense a visual rime is just as absurd as a paper chord."[2] And yet visual considerations played an important part in determining the rules of riming, especially in some European languages. Zhirmunski himself admits that it would not be right for scientific prosody to take an exclusively phonetic point of view on this question, as that does not cover the whole ground of facts presented for scientific analysis. The history of pronunciation in every language bears obvious traces of graphic influences; the linguistic habits of educated people are inevitably formed under the pressure of associations derived from

measure of excellence, caused a great deal of harm in the history of poetic practice. Under the effect of it the French poets for over two centuries "wasted their lives and talents upon such puerile and pernicious verbal games" as are abundantly illustrated by the *"jeux poétiques"* of the fourteenth and fifteenth centuries (L. Bellanger, *Études historiques et philologiques sur la rime française*).

[2] V. Zhirmunski, *Rime, Its History and Theory, Publications of the Russian Institute of the History of Fine Arts*, Petersburg, 1923.

146

spelling.[3] Orthography is more conservative than pronunciation. In most languages the rules of spelling are likely to be retained throughout centuries, while pronunciation changes almost from generation to generation. Words that formed a perfect acoustic rime a century ago may seem in our days merely an approximation.[4] This partly accounts for the existence of visual rimes. Yet there are other reasons why poets insist on retaining them: (1) the traditional requirement of visual symmetry (as in French); and (2) rime pauperism in certain languages (especially English).

Visual rimes in English poetry. — Nearly every Shakespearean sonnet, judging by the standards of modern pronunciation, contains at least one, often two, purely visual rimes, such as "heaven" and "even," "loving" and "moving," "ear" and "bear." That it is not entirely a matter of different pronunciation is evident from the fact that the number of visual rimes by no means decreases with time. In Byron and Shelley cases of visual rime are still more frequent. Modern English prosody, making no allowance for imperfect rimes, is willing to regard visual rimes as a legitimate means of poetic composition. This is often explained by reference to the rime-pauperism of a non-inflectional language. "The great

[3] G. P. Marsh, *Lectures on the English Language*, New York, 1887; see also F. de Saussure, *Cours de linguistique général*, page 53.

[4] Explaining the phenomenon of visual rimes historically, H. C. Wyld says: "A poet may continue to rhyme words together, after they have ceased to be true rhymes, because such rhymes are traditional, and occur again and again in the verse of his predecessors. The usage has changed; other types prevail in the current speech of living men; but certain rhymes, once perfect, now become false, may still be used because of the sanction afforded by poetical tradition. This adherence to outgrown traditional rhymes is greatly encouraged when the words to be coupled in rhyme agree in their spelling, when they constitute what are called rhymes for the eye" (*Studies in English Rhyme from Surrey to Pope*, page 11).

number of English words which are incapable of rime," says Marsh, "and the few which agree in any one of our numerous endings, reduce the poet to a very limited variety of choice, and there are many pairs of words which are found as invariably together as length and strength, or breath and death. . . . . When you see jollity at the end of a line, you do not need your eyes to tell you that frivolity cannot be far off; mountains and fountains are as indissolubly united in rime as they are in physical geography, and if a poet qualifies an object as frigid, he never fails to inform you in the next line that it is also rigid. The consequence of this perpetual repetition is a weariness of all exactness in rimes, and a tendency to great licence in the use of imperfect consonances." It is interesting to note, however, that of all imperfect consonances the visual rime, which in fact is no consonance at all, is the only form traditionally accepted by English poets. We have already seen that other forms of imperfect riming are very rare, although logically *"temper"* and *"remember"* make a much better rime than *"love"* and *"move."*

French prosody.—The visual implications of rime are especially emphasized by the French school of prosody. Many rimes which are acoustically correct are forbidden in French because they do not agree in spelling. *"Different"* and *"tyran,"* *"raison"* and *"saisons,"* *"mort"* and *"remords,"* or *"parlais"* and *"allaient"* are regarded as bad rimes because they violate the principle of visual symmetry. The origin of this rule dates from the time when the consonants before a pause, i.e., at the end of a phrase, were still pronounced (till the sixteenth century), and since rime naturally caused the reader to make a stop and to delay at the end of the line, even though it may not have been the end of a phrase, it was necessary, not merely for the sake of the eye but also for that of the ear, to consider the terminal consonants. Since that time the pronunciation has changed, but the tradition still persists in poetry.

148

Marmontel (1723–1799) is the chief exponent of the theory of visual rimes. He attempts to explain and to justify them theoretically by reference to the scholastic principle of art—difficulty (*le beau c'est le difficile*)—and confesses that he does not see any other explanation. His argument may be summarized as follows: Rime takes us by surprise. It adds some new element of vividness and grace to the expression of thought because it represents a certain difficulty which appears to have been successfully overcome by the poet.[5] The elegant gesture with which the poet performs his stunt becomes still more charming if it is intentionally made more difficult.

"La rime est la consonance des finales des vers. Cette consonance doit être sensible à l'oreille. ... Mais ce n'est point assez: on veut aussi qu'elle frappe les yeux. Pourquoi? pour la rendre plus difficile, et pour ajouter au plaisir que fait la solution de ce petit problême."[6]

Such is the reason that is supposed to justify the existence of rimes for the eyes, as given by the chief advocate of this peculiar doctrine. The argument has been already tested for its validity. Fortunately for us Marmontel knows no other reason why rimes should appeal not merely to the ear but to the eyes as well. He confesses himself that he knows no other reason (*je n'en vois pas d'autre raison*). To make rimes easier by introducing purely acoustic combinations means for him making poetry cheaper.

[5] Marmontel, *Éléments de littérature* (1819), *Œuvres*, 15:260: "La rime est enfin un plaisir pour l'esprit, par la surprise qu'elle cause: et lorsque la difficulté, heureusement vaincue, n'a fait que donner plus de saillie et de vivacité, plus de grâce, ou d'énergie à l'expression et à la pensée, soit par la singularité ingénieuse du mot que la rime a fait naître, soit par le tour adroit, et pourtant naturel, qu'elle a fait prendre à l'expression, soit par l'image nouvelle et juste qu'elle a présenté à l'esprit ... Ce plaisir est d'autant plus vif, que la rime paraît à la fois plus rare et plus heureusement trouvée."

[6] *Ibid.*, page 255.

In spite of the severe criticism to which this visual principle was frequently exposed,[7] and in spite of numerous experiments made by the symbolists and the modernists,[8] the tradition of visual rime persists in French poetry. Rimes which are based exclusively on acoustic consonance, disregarding visual symmetry, such as Verlaine's *"Nivelle"* and *"Michel,"* or *"guet"* and *"égaie,"* never attained general approval sufficient to put them on an equal footing with classical rimes. It is evident from this that psychologically the eye of an educated French-

[7] Visual complications of rime evidently irritated many a prominent French prosodist. For sometimes very passionate tirades are hurled against Marmontel's principle. Grasserie begins the paragraph on visual rimes by saying:

"C'est ici que nous devons admirer la force de la routine, la survivance des états anciens qui n'ont placé le vers vis-a-vis de la prose et fait prédominer les règles sur la loi, l'artificiel sur naturel" (*Des Principes scientifiques de la versification française*, page 121).

This attack is by no means of recent, modernist origin. More than seventy-five years ago M. Quicherat in his *Traité de versification française* pointed out that if logic presided at the establishment of the rules of riming, all consonances that the ear declares parallel, whatever their orthography, would have been pronounced acceptable for partnership. L. Bellanger, in his *Études historiques et philologiques sur la rime française*, also finds that the traditions of the classical school are not sound. In his opinion Marmontel's doctrine refutes itself by demanding rimes for the eye, while at the same time allowing it to be merely "equivalent" and not entirely identical. If symmetry for the eye is required, why then is *"instant"* allowed to rime with *"attend."* Similar objections we find in Grammont's *Le Vers français*. He writes (page 347):

Il faut rimer pour l'oreille et non pour l'oeil. ... Personne ne saurait plus aujourd'hui contester ce principe. L'idée de rimer pour les yeux, ... n'est pas moins plaisante que ne serait celle de peindre pour le nez.

[8] Symbolists allow themselves frequent violations of the visual principle. But occasionally even the classical poets violate the rules of symmetrical spelling established in French prosody. Tobler in his *Vom Französischen Versbau* (page 137), quotes a large number of visually imperfect rimes from Lafontaine. Some of these are: *"encor ... fort," "encor ... accord," "Jupiter ... desert," "fer ... sert," "artisan ... opposant."*

man takes offense at the lack of symmetry in spelling if the lines are supposed to form a rime. The mute consonants, although actually not pronounced, appear to be somehow resounding, so to speak, in his mind, and their absence, or even difference, is felt as a shock sufficient to counteract the pleasure derived from the melody of vowels.[9]

B. ACOUSTIC THEORIES OF RIME

Acoustic theories regard rime as a phenomenon analogous to the element of harmony or melody in music. For the purposes of mere analogy beyond which these theories seldom go, a more precise distinction between melody and harmony is not required. Within the limits of analogy rime may be successfully compared to either. It is of prime importance for all such theories to regard rime as merely an ornament without any substantial relation to the rhythmic composition of the verse. It is regarded as belonging to the sphere of poetic instrumentation, but not to that of rhythmic composition.

Aristotle.—An interesting and, so far as is known, the earliest mention of rime we find in Aristotle (384–322 B.C.).

---

[9] L. Becq de Fouquières argues that consonants modify the pronunciation of the preceding vowels even though they are not pronounced themselves:

"Les consonnes finales que nous ne faisons point entendre avaient précisément pour but à l'origine de modifier la prononciations de la voyelle; ainsi l'é doit être considéré comme plus bref dans les participes que dans les infinitifs, de même il sera plus bref dans 'orangé' que dans 'étranger' " (*Traité général de versification française,* page 36).

Yet, although this may be true with regard to some cases, it is by no means universally true. The principle of visual riming does not properly belong to the field of rime-psychology, but only to that of rime-philology. Visual symmetry alone has no power to produce any aesthetic emotion sufficient to modify the artistic impressions derived from the poem. We have a certain amount of satisfaction from it only because the absence of such symmetry would cause a conflict with our sense of spelling. It is pseudo-grammatical in its nature.

Aristotle considers rime as a rhetorical device. Under the name "homoeoteleuton" rime is mentioned in that section of his *Rhetorics* in which he deals with the structure and organization of "periods." It is regarded as a variety of παρομοίοσις, or "making the extreme words of both members of a period like each other" (δ'ἐὰν ὅμοια τὰ ἔσχατα ἔχῃ ἑκάτερον τὸ κῶλον). "This," Aristotle explains, "must happen either at the beginning or at the end of each member. If at the beginning, the resemblance must always be between whole words; if at the end, between final syllables or inflections of the same word or the same word repeated."[10] In this latter case paramoeosis becomes ὁμοιοτέλευτον [aequiterminal], and corresponds to what we now call end-rime. Aristotle adduces several illustrations of aequiterminal construction, one of which is in prose (presumably a humorous remark in a paternity case): οὐκ ᾠήθησαν αὐτὸν παιδίον τετοκέναι, ἀλλ' αὐτοῦ αἴτιον γεγονέναι. Rime at the beginning of a phrase is illustrated by a verse from Aristophanes:

> Ἀγρὸν γὰρ ἔλαβεν ἀργὸν παρ' αὐτοῦ.

It is interesting to note that the discussion of paromoeosis is introduced as a supplementary paragraph right after the discussion of the nature of antithesis. It is therewith suggested, though not expressly stated, that rime is a kind of antithesis. It brings, as it were, two contrasting ideas under the control of one sound. In this harmonization of the opposites lies the artistic effect and the power of rime. It helps us "to devise lively and taking sayings." "Their actual invention," Aristotle adds, "can come only through natural talent or long practice. . . . . Speech and reasoning are lively in proportion as they make us seize a new idea promptly. For this reason people are not much taken either by obvious arguments, nor by those which puzzle us when we hear them stated, but only by those which convey their

---

[10] Aristotle, *Opera; Rhetoric*, III, 9, page 1410*a*.

information to us as soon as we hear them." It is precisely for this reason that antithetical form appeals to us: it conveys information in a well-ordered, easy, and, as it were, "taking" manner. If rime is a variety of antithesis—which seems to be directly implied by the Aristotelian discussion of the matter—then its poetic effect can be explained only by its power to convey contrast in an easily accessible and obviously striking form. Rime, then, facilitates grasping and retaining ideas by our mind, a function which has ever since been attributed to all riming expressions as fundamental.

These ideas of Aristotle became fundamental for the development of our views on rime. Many even today regard rime as a rhetorical device, used largely in poetry, to assist memory and to economize the expenditure of intellectual energy (Herbert Spencer). Aristotle was the first to discover and to formulate this specific power of acoustically identical endings (or beginnings) to stimulate thōught. Yet he offered no explanation for it. His remarks on rime, like a large number of his ideas, are of a purely descriptive nature. He states the fact, and assigns its logical place in the natural system of other facts. He shows us the connections, and—a difficult task to do in the beginning of any theoretical discussion—he defines the fundamental category (in our case, antithesis) to which the fact in question belongs and of which it appears to be a manifestation. But he has no theory to offer.

Cicero and Quintilian. — Prior to Aristotle, according to Dingeldein, rime was theoretically known to Plato and was evidently practiced by Gorgias. For in the passage from *Symposium* where Agathon's speech—which is supposed to represent Gorgias' school of eloquence—reaches its climax (197*D*), it changes into a consistently rimed prose. Similarly Quintilian (35–100) and Cicero (106–43 B.C.) were familiar with the phenomenon of rime. The latter writes (*Oratio*, 12, 38):

153

datur etiam venia concinnitati sententiarum et argutiis, certique et circumscripti verborum ambitus conceduntur; de industriaque non ex insidiis, sed aperte ac palam elaboratur, ut verba verbis quasi dimensa et paria respondeant, aut crebro conferantur pugnantia comparenturque contraria, aut pariter extrema terminentur eundemque referant in calendo sonum.

Rime is defined by Quintilian as *"similis duarum sententiarum vel plurium finis"* (*Institutiones Oratoriae*, IX, 3, 77), and it is pointed out that there are different kinds of rime of which ὁμοιοτέλευτον, as a resemblance in grammatical endings, is merely a special case (IX, 3, 78).

Dante.—In Dante (1265–1321) we have, in all probability, the earliest exponent of what may be regarded as a theory of rime. It is interesting to note that he attached great musical significance to vowels and was inclined to regard the word "poet," in a mystical fashion, as being derived from the five principal vowels of human speech. This interesting passage —the first vague presentiment of the idea of the "music of words" — is worthy of being quoted in full. He writes in the *Convivio,*

Be it known that "authority" is nought else than the act of an author. This word may spring from two roots; the one is that of a verb, dropped very much out of use in Latin, which signifies "binding words together,"—*aueio*. And whoso regards it well, in its first form, will clearly perceive that it shows its own meaning; for it is made of nought save the bonds of words, that is to say, of the five vowels alone, which are the soul and juncture of every word. And it is composed of them in such a manner as to form the figure of a tie. For, beginning with *a*, it turns to *u*, and then goes straight by *i* to *e*, whence it goes back and returns to *o*, so that truly it images forth the figure of a tie. And in so far as "author" is derived and descends from this verb, it is understood only of poets, who have bound their words with the art of music.

154

Such fantastic philology suddenly acquires a profound significance if viewed in the light of what we now know about the physical structure of vowels. Dante may have erred as regards the philological derivation of the word *aueio*. But he is almost prophetic, in anticipating the modern views regarding the musical value of the five vowels and their significance for poetry. Prose deals with the meaning of our ideas; it can therefore be easily translated into other languages. Poetry, on the other hand, is concerned not merely with the meaning but also with the music of words. It is therefore untransferable from one language to another. It seems that Dante was the first who really grasped the significance of this fact. "And therefore," he writes, "let everyone know that nothing which has the harmony of musical connection can be transferred from its own tongue into another without shattering all its sweetness and harmony."

Rimed verse is especially inaccessible for translation, because rime is a special case of harmony. Dante defines it as "that harmony which it is customary to make in the last syllable." At the same time he is conscious of the rhythmical significance of this beautiful invention of modern ages. He insists that rime is not merely acoustically pleasant but also rhythmically constructive; that it is an effective device for organizing verse-lines into stanzas, thereby rhythmically dividing larger poems into a number of elementary thought-units. His theory of rime is not purely acoustic. It combines both rhythmic and acoustic factors into the supreme unity of a great artistic effect. "Men," he says, "call that thing beautiful the parts of which duly correspond, because from their harmony pleasure results." And he chisels his tercets like atoms of a huge statue. Within each atom there is infinite life, strict "correspondence" and organization. And the organizing principle of each atom is rime. He says that rime "links the lines together"; by a system of "echoes" it helps to arrange the words into the larger units of stanzas. It creates the primordial rhythmic tides of the poem.

At this early stage the rime theory does not yet clearly discriminate between purely melodic and purely rhythmic elements of poetry. In fact, Dante's views appear to be embryonically undifferentiated with regard to the question whether the end assonance is of a purely acoustic or of a rhythmic nature. After Dante those two elements were differently stressed by all the different authors who ever wrote on the subject. But it is difficult to find any author who considered only one of the two elements to the complete exclusion of the other. None who ever emphasized the acoustic or melodic value of rime denied its rhythmic significance; and those who laid stress on its rhythmical character could not possibly deny that it was the rhythm of sound that they were analyzing. Our classification—like most classifications, in fact—is merely an approximate one. By presenting the two types of rime theories I do not mean to contend that they actually exclude each other. The classification implies merely that, as a rule, one of the elements predominates. Thus the English school, for example, from the outset laid stress on the rhythmic factor, while the Germans, on the contrary, were always inclined to emphasize the musical or acoustic element. Yet neither school was ever totally blind to the other factor. The early English prosodists, for instance, had more interest than their successors in the musical side of the problem.

George Puttenham.—We shall see later that Dante's views were widely known in England in the sixteenth century, when modern English prosody was in the process of formation. Indirectly they gave rise to an ingenious rime theory, one constructed on a purely musical basis, developed by George Puttenham (d. 1590) in his *The Art of English Poesie,* published in 1589. The author maintains that poetry has its basis in the "musical proportion" of syllables and accents. "There is,"

156

he explains, "an accomptable number which we call 'arithmet-ical' (arithmos) as one, two, three. There is also a musical num-ber, fashioned by stirring of tunes and their sundry times in the utterance of our wordes, as when the voice goeth high or low, or sharp or flat, or swift or slow; and this is called rithmos or 'numerositie' . . . . such as the toung easily utters, and the ear with pleasure receiveth." In the ancient languages, he adds, this effect was produced by quantitative scansion, "by the smooth and delicate running of their feete, which we have not in our vulgare." To effect the same rhythmical smoothness we, therefore, are obliged to apply an artificial device of "con-cords," or "tunable consentes in the latter end of our verses," which is called rime. "For this purpose serve the 'monosillabes' of our English Saxon excellently well, because they do natur-ally and indifferently receive any accent, and in them if they finish the verse, resteth the shrill accent of necessitie."[11]

Rime, therefore, being of a musical nature, helps to pro-duce rhythmical units, or waves, which Puttenham, quite in accordance with modern poets, calls "cadences." "This ca-dence," he says, "is a fall of a verse in every last word with a certain tunable sound which being matched with another of like sound do make a concord."[12] It "maketh your meter symphonicall." It is precisely for this reason that "rhymes are fit to excite our emotions," and that, varying the rime scheme, the poet is able to modify his emotional effects. This is what Puttenham calls producing "proportion by situation," i.e., cre-ating artistic effects by variously arranging rimes into stanzas —Dante's motive. "This proportion consisteth in placing every verse in a staffe or ditty by such reasonable distances, as may best serve the case for delight, and also shew the poet's art and

[11] Puttenham, *The Art of English Poesie* (1589), Arber Edition, page 90.

[12] *Ibid.*, page 93.

variety of musick." Differences in "situation" alter the nature of poetic composition, making it "either lighter or graver, or more merry, or mournful, and many wayes passionate to the ear and heart of the hearer, seeming for this point that our maker by his measures and concords of sundry proportions doth counterfeit the harmonical tunes of the vocal and instrumental Musickes."[13] As every particular arrangement of rimes defines, so to speak, an emotional "situation," so the presence of rime results in a certain peculiarity of style which might seem "pleasing to one or vulgar to another." "Since the actions of men with their circumstances be infinite, and the world likewise replenished with many judgments, it may be a question who shall have the determination of such controversie as may arise, whether this or that action or speech be decent or indecent." Thus in the matter of the rime-controversy Puttenhem defers to the "discretion" of every individual poet.[14]

Sir Philip Sidney.—Similar views are maintained by Sir Philip Sidney (1554–1586). He observes that "ryme striketh a certain musicke to the ear." It is precisely for this reason that he acclaims the poet the monarch of all sciences. "Of all the sciences," he says, ". . . . our Poet is the Monarch. For . . . . he beginneth not with obscure definitions, which must blurre the margent with interpretations, and load the memorie with doubtfulnesse: but hee commeth to you with words set in delightful proportion, either accompanied with, or prepared for the well enchanting skill of Musicke."[15]

This musical appeal of rime, according to Sir Philip Sidney, recompenses the modern poetry for the loss of the antique quantity, a statement that was afterward so many times re-

[13] Puttenham, *The Art of English Poesie*, page 98.
[14] *Ibid.*, page 270.
[15] Sir Philip Sidney, *The Defence of Poesie*, 1595.

peated in the literature on rime. "Of versifying," he points out, "there are two sorts, the one ancient, the other moderne." The ancient is based on quantity, the modern on the equal number of syllables in the verse, and on rime. "The moderne," he continues, "observing onely number, with some regard of the accent; the chiefe life of it, standeth in that like sounding of the words, which we call Rime." Both ways of versification, in his opinion, have equal right to exist, for both are equally delightful, each in its own fashion. The modern poet, he says, "likewise with his rime striketh a certain musicke to the ear: and in fine, since it doeth delight, though by another way, it obtaineth the same purpose, there being in either sweetnesse, and wanting in neither, majestic."

There is another idea concerning the nature of rime of which Sir Philip Sidney, that "verray parfit gentil Knight," scholar, soldier, and statesman, appears to be the originator. It is the connection between rime and memory. "Verse," he points out, "far exceedeth Prose in the knotting up of the memorie." The reason for this is manifest: "the words being so set as one cannot be lost, but the whole woorke fails: which accusing it selfe, calleth the remembrance back to it selfe, and so most strongly confirmeth it. Besides one word, so as it were begetting an other, as be it in rime or measured verse, by the former a man shall have a nearer guesse to the follower." In other words, rime supports memory because it binds words in such a way that they seem to belong naturally together, and the omission or change of one affects the whole structure by ruining the "musicke" of the phrase. This idea often recurs later on in various theories of rime (Herder, Schlegel).

James Beattie.—It is interesting to note that James Beattie (1735–1803) in his *Theory of Language* (1783) comes very near to the modern interpretation of speech sound. Though lacking the experimental basis furnished by modern physical re-

159

search, he nevertheless seems to be on the right track when he writes: "Let it be observed that in speech the voice .... does not ascend or descend by those musical intervals which are called notes, but rises and falls by degrees incomparably more minute, and which our musical language has no terms nor symbols to express. A musician, sounding the string of a violin by drawing his bow across and at the same time making his fingers slide up and down the string without fitting it would produce a sort of sound somewhat similar .... to those varieties of accent which take place in language." This passage, so far as I know, is the first attempt to describe the peculiar character of the "music of words," without any reference to mystical terms, by a well-fitting analogy.

H. Blair. — Following in Puttenham's steps, H. Blair (1718–1800) regards rime as an ornamental device recompensing modern poetry for the loss of the antique quantitative meter. Modern nations, he says, "who did not make the quantities of their syllables be so distinctly perceived in pronouncing them, rested the melody of their verse upon the number of syllables it contained, upon the proper disposition of accents, ... and frequently upon that return of corresponding sounds, which we call rhyme."[16] He points out that there is something in such returns "which is grateful to the ears of most part of mankind." He does not suspect that this mysterious "something" is the real music of the overtones vaguely perceived through the tone quality of the vowels as they are uttered; but he is aware of the fact that the presence of rime greatly contributes to the "sweetness of sound" and to the musical power of language: "If anyone," Blair writes, "after reading Mr. Pope's *Rape of the Lock,* or *Eloisa to Abelard,* shall not admit our rime with all its varieties of pauses to carry both elegance

[16] H. Blair, *Lectures on Rhetoric and Belles Lettres,* 1801.

and sweetness of sound, his ear must be pronounced to be of a very peculiar kind."[17]

Blair seems to believe that the charm of rimed endings lies exclusively in its melodic or purely acoustic effect. The powerful by-rhythm that results from this music he regards as a disadvantage. In attempting to determine his practical position with regard to the controversy, which was still raging at that time in England, concerning the value and advisability of rime, Blair says: "The principal defect of rime is the close which it forces upon the ear, at the end of every couplet." In other words, it seems to him that rime makes verse rhythmic to the point of monotony—too rhythmic. Therefore an epic poem, or tragedy, he maintains, which requires a larger freedom of rhythm, would be fettered and degraded by the application of rime; while in compositions of a "temperate strain," where no particular vehemence is required in the sentiments, such as pastorals, elegies, epistles, satires, etc., rime is constructively beautiful.

J. S. Schütze.—A year after the publication of Blair's *Rhetoric* in England appeared in Germany J. S. Schütze's *"Essay on Rime"*[18] (1802) in which, for the first time, the aesthetic connection between rime and meaning was established. Like Blair, Schütze regards rime as an acoustic phenomenon, as

[17] This musical effectiveness of rime serves him as the salient point of his attack against Milton's criticism of it. Though he agrees with those moderate opponents of rimed verse who believe that rime has no application for the "higher regions of poetry," yet he does not feel that he can join in opinion with those for whom rime appears to be "a mere barbarous jingling of sounds, fit only for children, and owing to nothing but the corruption of taste in the monkish ages." Latin and Greek quantitative poetry was good enough without rime. But this is not to say that it is objectionable in English.

[18] *Versuch einer Theorie des Reimes nach Inhalt und Form,"* 1802.

a "similar sound of two syllables at the end of two verses."[19] But he has the advantage of working upon the intellectual background of Kantian aesthetics, and displays a great deal of philosophical training, which Blair lacked. Thus the formal definition of rime by reference to the acoustic similarity of endings does not satisfy him. He proposes to investigate, not the empty form, but the real nature of rime, trying to find out "why" the similar sounds at the ends of two verses produce an aesthetically enjoyable effect. "Since rime secures pleasure," he argues, "there must be something in the nature of the human mind which causes such a pleasure, or rather something that makes us capable of it." The cause of pleasure lies, according to him, in the artistic ability of our mind to bring two different ideas under the control of one sound. Schütze maintains with Aristotle and Kant that it is generally characteristic of our mind that it likes to see the diverse elements of experience intuitively united by means of a given sensation or, possibly, emotion. In support of his views he refers to the common aesthetic sentiment and common experience. "Do we not contemplate with pleasure paintings which contain—as we call it—a great deal of expression, i.e., where we find several emotions shining through, and united by means of one single gesture? What makes a face interesting? Is it not the co-ordination of a number of apparently contradicting tendencies, which are united in what we call one's spiritual expression? Wherever the human mind has nothing to divine, nothing to survey and to compare, where it sees no unity to be disclosed in the variety of details and, vice versa, no details to be gathered into a unity; in a word, where there are no parts to be contemplated within an ideal whole, there is no stimulus for any inspiration or intellectual activity, and consequently no artistic enjoyment. On the contrary, such

[19] The acoustic character of rime is axiomatically admitted by the author: "Der Reim eigentlich ist nur für's Gehör bestimmt."

a flat and uniform object would bore us and leave us aesthetically indifferent." By a large number of illustrations taken from various branches of art the author tries to convince the reader that the "soul" derives a great deal of satisfaction and pleasure from pressing two different ideas or images into one sense-object. In this lies the enchanting game of artistic intuition.

Rime, in this sense, is a special case of artistic intuition. It fulfils the function of placing two or more different ideas under the control of one sound (*idem in sono, in significatione aliud,* as Augustin had previously put it). Therefore, reference to ideas seems to belong to the very essence of rime, and must be retained in its definition. The formal definition of rime as a case of similarity of sound at the end of two verse lines does not adequately describe the essence of riming. For one does not see why a mere similarity of sound should please us at all. It is rather to be expected that the artistic effect of such similarity would be painful in its monotony, and therefore unpleasant. "Suppose we knew nothing of rime and somebody came and said: I have invented a new kind of ornamentation for poetical language which consists of placing words in rows and making every row end with the same sound. Should not we find such an idea strange, and point out to the inventor that such a poem would sound too monotonous? Should we ever believe that such a method could please any reader?" And yet all Western nations know from experience that rime is aesthetically enjoyable. In fact all peoples have in various degrees accepted and practiced the art of riming, and many of us would not consider an unrimed poem really a poem. This universal appeal of rime can never be accounted for by reference to the superficial "similarity of sound." It must have a deeper ground in the nature of human mind.

This deeper ground is seen by the author in the relation of sound to meaning. Rime produces an artistic effect, not because it invents an empty verbal echo to be mechanically produced between the two rows of words, but because it confronts and conveys different ideas through the harmony of identical sounds. To obtain, therefore, an adequate insight into the essence of rime we are obliged to consider not merely the physical consonance of words as uttered but also the content of thought which takes the form of consonance. These factors, the sound and the thought, are not, as it is commonly believed, independent of each other. To produce an artistic effect both rime and meaning (form and content) must grow organically together, and build a unity. Rime that depends merely on sound and leaves meaning out of consideration is poor. Every child can produce rimes. For "it is easy to find a rime," declares Tennyson. Every translator can find riming words to make his work appear as poetry. It does not make him a poet, though. To "build the lofty rime" one has to consult logic. In order to be artistically effective a rime must be filled with meaning; it must originate in connection with the context, and must be felt as a necessity, not merely as an ornament.

Just what is that unity? What does it mean? In answering this question it is very difficult to avoid what may be termed linguistic mysticism. After Schütze the question was debated many times, especially among the romanticists and the early symbolists. We shall see in the next paragraph what amusing views were sometimes offered for its solution. But very seldom did anybody rise above the vague assertion of some mysterious connection between the meaning and the sound of words. Schütze himself is far from clear on this difficult point. But, however vague, he seems to be beyond the reproach of mysticism—and in our present set of problems that is a great advantage.

Schütze tries to attack the problem from the point of view of the psychology of creative genius. Just what is riming from the point of view of creative poetical work? Is is a game of

164

finding suitable consonance to a given word? No, the process is much more complicated. The right rime does not come so easily and so mechanically. It emerges gradually from what the poet wishes to express. And often that which he wishes to express is not quite clear to him until he finds the rime. What he means to say depends largely on how he says it, and is not at all clear before he actually succeeds in saying it. In this process meaning and rime mutually aid and hinder each other. Suppose a poet wishes to express, what he but vaguely feels, that each day brings its own troubles and tragedies. The idea, perhaps, is not quite distinctly visualized but is just vaguely present in his mind as a presentiment of something that is bound to happen during the day. It occurs to him that the troubles of the day may be compared and perhaps even attributed to the conspiracy of evil forces. Conspiracy is an act that suggests beginning. Suddenly the word *"Morgen"* appears on the periphery of his consciousness. It is in the morning that all coming troubles commence. What is the word for troubles? —do not forget that our poet thinks in German—*"Kummer," "Leiden."* .... Suddenly the word *"Sorgen"* comes to his mind, and the phrase results of itself:

> Der frühe Morgen weckt mich zu Sorgen.

Here the idea, however vague, appears to have preceded the rime.

But it often happens that rime precedes and produces the idea. In the struggle for expression the poet often feels, to use Pope's phrase, blessed in advance "with sure returns of still expected rimes." The returns come to the poet in the form of sudden flashes of unexpected thought. Schütze seems to believe that it is logically possible to connect any given ideas into a phrase that would not be entirely senseless. Even words which are but distantly related may be successfully put together into a phrase provided a sufficient number of mediating words are given to connect them. Occasionally such artificial unions may result in unexpected sayings and even in great discoveries. The realm of wisdom is infinite. The number of words at the disposal of wisdom is limited. There are millions of potential expressions in which any given pair of words may occur with meaning and more or less profound significance. Consonance in this respect is highly suggestive. Combination of ideas that would probably never occur to us may be easily suggested by a given rime. In arranging his rimes the poet may hit upon new and original ideas. In this sense rimes are creative of new meanings. "Rime," so Schütze formulates the idea, "often convinces us of the natural affinity of two entirely different ideas." In other words, there are many, so to speak, underground passages leading from one word to another. The poet often roams in darkness until an ingenious rime helps him out into the light. In such moments he suddenly finds his own vision.

In view of all this, Schütze defines rime as "coincidence of two different ideas within two phonetically congruous words" (*das Zusammentreffen zwei verschiedener Vorstellungen in zwei gleich-klingenden Wörter*). This definition includes expressly in its phrasing a reference to ideas. Moreover it lays stress upon the unity of rime and meaning; it says that rime is not merely a coincidence of sounds, but a way of binding ideas. Practical consequences of such definition are very important. The definition may be applied to test the quality of verse. Reading Goethe, for instance, one can never tell which of the riming lines was first in the poet's mind. It seems that the poet does not seek his rimes, but that they come naturally to him, without any effort. The last word of the second line does not appear to be made to order, but seems to arise from the meaning of the context as a logical necessity. Such is true and genuine riming.

However, this part of Schütze's argument, from the point

of view of the world's literature on the subject, presents no novelty. The union between rime and sense was for a long time a school requirement. It was mentioned by Dante. In English prosody it was, I believe, first theoretically proclaimed by William Webbe, who in his set of rules for successful riming recommends "to wrest no word from his natural propriety," nor to make violence to grammatical order for the sake of rime.[20]

The Romantic school.—The unity of rime and meaning proclaimed by J. S. Schütze received a further development and somewhat mystical turn at the hands of Romanticists. The Romantic school with its cult of emotions was inclined to emphasize the musical aspect of language. It is not the logic but the music of words that speaks to our soul in poetry and reveals to us the greatest secrets of artistic intuition. In his *Lehrlingen zu Sais* Novalis (1772–1801) tells his dream of an ideal language that has the magic power of song to penetrate into the inner depths of nature, and decompose its every entity. Its words are keys to the souls of things, its vibrations the echoes of the world's mysteries. The sound itself apart from its conventional meaning appears now as a sign. Not merely words but separate syllables and individual letters acquire now a symbolic value. A. W. Schlegel (1767–1845) invents a whole scale of colors corresponding to human vowels, and he attributes a special significance to every particular conjunction of the vowel-color. *A* represents the light, clear red (*das rote licht-helle A*), and signifies Youth, Friendship, and Radiance. *I* stands for celestial blue, symbolizing Love and Sincerity. *O* is purple; *U* stands for violet, and *OO* is adorned in navy blue. This subjective vowel-symbolic was at the time very popular among the Romanticists and the Symbolists. Much eloquence was wasted on

---

[20] W. Webbe, *A Discourse of English Poetrie*, 1586.

the question whether *A* is really red or yellow. Gaspar Poggel at a latter date resumes the argument, and even the scholarly Grimm lends it a certain amount of favorable consideration. However arbitrary and subjective, this vowel-mysticism is an important element in the Romantic theory of rime and poetry.

Friedrich Schlegel (1772–1829), brother of A. W. Schlegel, goes so far as to attribute sense and mystical significance to the inarticulate sounds of animals and birds. As a single howl or chirp brings to expression some flitting need or temporary discomfort, so repetition of the same sound always indicates a lasting and persistent peculiarity. Thus many animals constantly repeat the same tone of noise, "as if wishing to proclaim to the world the identity of their species. They rime." Such animal rimes, he believes, are the intoned characteristics or musical portraits of some specific organizations.[21]

Such fantastic views[22] did not prevent German Romanticists

[21] Fr. Schlegel would probably find very much to his liking the observations of Beckstein concerning the language of birds (*Naturgesichte der Stubenvogel*). Beckstein made an attempt to represent the singing of a nightingale in the form of human vowels, whereby it was revealed (Brehm admits it too) that nightingales sing in strophes. Here are some of the strophes quoted after Gross (*The Play of Animals*):

Quio, didl li lulyli
Ha gurr, gurr, quipio
Qui, qui, qui, qui, qi, qi, qi, yi, ji, ji, ji, ji

Gollgollgollgoll gia hadadoi
Quigi horr ha diadiadia si
Hezezezezeze .... quarr hoze hoi
Quia, quia, quia .... ti

It is remarkable that on a close observation the lines rime.

[22] Jespersen in his *Language, Its Nature, Development, and Origin* (page 396) informs us that Greek and Latin grammarians often indulged in similarly fantastic speculations concerning the symbolic correspondence between sound and meaning in words. He mentions grammatical views of a certain Nigidius Figulus who said "that in pronouncing *Vos* one puts forward one's lips and sends out breath in the direction of the other person, while this is not the case with *Nos*." With these early writers, Jespersen continues, "to make guesses at sound symbolism was the only way to etymologize. .... But this does not justify us in rejecting any idea of sound symbolism '*abusus non tollit usum*.' " The origin and formation of language is not entirely arbi-

from contributing many valuable ideas to the problem of rime. The musical factor in rime and poetry was never analyzed with more profound consideration, the intellectual interest for it never elsewhere attained such intensity and earnestness, as among the representatives of the Romantic movement. A. W. Schlegel, following the path of the Elizabethan prosodists, proclaims that "poetry is music for the inner ear." With this statement he makes himself, on the question of rime, a disciple of Sir Philip Sidney, and joins the camp of those who consider the acoustic element the principal component of rime. Repetition of sound, according to him, attracts our attention and makes our mind compare words as such. Those words which display a similar musical formation are easily noticed, even if they stand far apart. They reach and, as it were, touch each other across the lines (*pedum amiticia*). Thus sound has the power of establishing connections between words which would never be established either logically or rhythmically. Rime as a complete assonance, the effect of which is intensified by its position as a terminal chord, serves the same purpose. It is one of the most effective means of establishing underground passages leading from one word to another independent of their grammatical or logical connections. Without the intricate apparatus of physical analysis, by sheer intuition and keen artistic sense, Schlegel observed that "rime creates expectations even within a single verse." This "expectation"—analogous to Helmholtzian "tension" in the structure of melody—compels pleasure if resolved in the correct way. Pleasure, then, attracts attention to the pleasing words, makes them more prominent than others, and chains them to our memory. Thus through musical pleasure rime assists memory.

trary, and is governed by laws the significance of which is seldom clear. Selection of certain sounds to represent certain meanings is, therefore, not entirely a matter of accident. Within reasonable limits Jespersen himself supports the idea of sound-symbolism.

It is to be regretted that these ideas were never expounded by Schlegel in systematic form. Although in his correspondence with his brother he several times refers to his intention to make the question of rime a topic for a special inquiry, he never did so. His views on rime are scattered through his numerous review and critical articles and are difficult to study. Some very valuable suggestions are contained in his lecture notes, which give us at least the skeleton of his theory of rime.[23]

Similarly, Tieck (1773–1853) in his *Critical Studies* writes: "It was anything but lust for artificialities and difficulties that first caused the introduction of rime into poetry; it was rather the love of tone and harmony, the feeling that similarly intoned words must be somehow mysteriously related to each other." Here again the acoustic nature of rime serves the aesthetic task of connecting and binding words together. In his introduction to the old Germanic minnesongs Tieck further maintains that a rimed poem is a "tightly bound whole in which the riming words are better discriminated and brought closer together, as if being wedded in love or reaching to each other longingly from a distance."[24]

[23] In his lectures, as is evident from his notes, he discussed the following questions concerning rime: "Wirkung des Reimes überhaupt . . . . Verknüpfung, Paarung, Vergleichung . . . . Erregte Erwartung schon im einzelnen Verse und Befriedigung . . . . Errinerung und Ahnung, statt dass die alte Rhythmik immer in der Gegenwart fest hält, and allen Theilen gleiche Dignität gibt . . . . Daher liegt im Reime das romantische Prinzip . . . ."

[24] The affinity of sound, in the opinion of some Romanticists, is in a very large number of cases closely associated with and probably causally related to the affinity of meaning. The leader of Romantic philology of the early nineteenth century and the founder of what Schlegel aptly called "grammatical mysticism," R. Moritz, in his *Essay on Germanic Prosody*, proclaimed that partially similar sounds in a language always have a partially similar meaning. This proposition was for a long time regarded as an axiom of Romantic philology. A. F. Bernhardi, for example, in his *Sprachlehre* asks after the fashion of Moritz: "Who does not recognize by intuition the sim-

Hegel.—It is to be regretted that Hegel's views on rime (as, in fact, on many other problems connected with literary art) largely remained inaccessible to the philologists owing to the peculiarly difficult form in which this profound thinker was accustomed to clothe his ideas. It is highly unfortunate that his views reached and influenced the science of language indirectly through the hands of his less gifted and more fantastically endowed followers such as Caspar Poggel, who in his book on rime expounds Hegelian ideas which he only shallowly understood and strongly flavored with his own mystical idiosyncrasies. And yet even such authorities as J. Minor, in his chapter on rime, acknowledges his debt to Poggel without even mentioning Hegel's name. Such a regrettable occurrence is due solely to our modern prejudice against anything that claims its origin from abhorred metaphysics; whereas, on closer inspection, those dreadful metaphysical treatises of the past often contain a great deal more of sane and plain physical wisdom than many a book of our modern positivists. Stripped of its peculiarly difficult form, Hegel's theory of rime (as developed in his *Aesthetik,* 1823–1827) may well be stated here.

ilarity between '*Luft*' and '*Duft*,' '*Muth*' and '*Blut*,' '*Jugend*' and '*Tugend*,' or '*alt*' and '*kalt*'? Who would consider it a mere accident that '*Liebe*' rimes with '*Triebe*' and '*Sonne*' with '*Wonne*'?" Even the sober English mind of Shelley partially supports this view. "Sounds as well as thoughts," Shelley writes in his *Defense of Poetry,* "have relation both between each other and toward that which they represent, and a perception of the order of those relations has always been found connected with a perception of the order of the relations of thought. Hence the language of poets has ever effected a sort of uniform and harmonious recurrence of sound, without which it were not poetry, and which is scarcely less indispensable to the communication of its influence than the words themselves without reference to that peculiar order." There is no doubt an element of truth in the idea of that "peculiar order" of sound independent of and yet correlated with the logical order of thought. As we saw in the foregoing chapters, the musical order of words really has meaning and significance apart from their sense.

An interesting fact of international co-operation of thought is worthy of being mentioned at the outset. What English thought contributed to the theory of rime appears to be the starting-point of Hegelian speculations. The ideas of Puttenham, Ascham, and Blair were well known on the Continent in Hegel's time, and he was familiar with them most probably through the medium of Herder. He agrees with the English school in believing that the decay of the ancient quantitative principle of versification made it necessary for modern languages to lay stress upon the musical aspect of verse. But he goes beyond the English school in his ingenious interpretation of this historical fact. With the loss of quantity, he explains, there remained nothing in the nature of speech by which it could maintain its "physical" reality except the sound. In ordinary speech, in prose, we entirely *forget* about the physical existence of words as signs or sounds. Meaning, ideas, is what we *get for* it. With their physical reality forgotten, and forsaken, the words become transparent; they become completely "mentalized" (*vergeistlicht*), i.e., fully resolved into what they mean. Poetry is called upon to save the physical element of words and bring it to our attention in the name of art. For art and beauty require visible or audible forms through which the ideas may shine. Thus sound, the music of words, acquires an independent artistic value which is largely indifferent to the meaning or sense of it. Therefore Hegel writes: "If the quantitative principle is renounced, and yet despite of it, but in accordance with the necessary demand of art, the sensuous medium is permitted to retain a certain force of resistance as against the exclusive assertion of ideal content, ... there remains no other means left at our disposal save the express and artificially modulated sound of articulate speech as such. And this leads us to our second main type of versification, in other words, rime." For rime is a means of increasing the sensual intensity of words in contrast to their logical meaning.

172

An articulate sound, if it is to command an independent attention, must be of a far more insistent kind than the mere succession of vowels and consonants, such as was sufficient for ancient verse; and its assertion must be of a far more overwhelming character than the stress of syllables can lay claim to in ordinary speech. Through the emphasis of repetition sound acquires, so to speak, an independent existence for itself, and "wins for itself a relatively secure stability." It attracts our attention as a purely empirical entity. But its empirical, physical beauty stimulates an emotional response in our soul. It speaks to our temperament, to the depths of the subjective. We find in rime, therefore, a physical reverberation of our own soul. It evokes emotions, and—since emotion is one of the forms under which the soul perceives itself—it reveals the nature of our ego. Rime is a product of the Romantic age.

It is, therefore, for Hegel by no means a matter of accident that rime makes its first appearance in Europe with the advent of Christianity. For when with the general shift of values caused by the appearance of Christianity the "inner self" of man was rigorously asserting itself against the brutalities of the physical and social world, it became psychologically necessary that language, especially that of poetry, should become more intimate and soulful. "It was after the barbarian invasion, and after the assertion of that uniquely personal note of emotion for which Christianity was responsible, that the rhythmical system of versification passed into that of rime." Although at present we cannot so readily accept the hypothesis of the hymnological origin of rime, yet we must agree with Hegel that the Latin hymn was one of the sources through which rime penetrated Europe. This appears to Hegel to be fully in accord with the general tendency of the time when the rising Christianity was laying stress upon the element of inner subjectivity and "feeling." In this sense rime appears to him as a historical force that moulds and shapes our languages.

Under the pressure of this force new languages arise, such as Italian and French (Romance languages), whose poetical wealth and youthful vigor move largely in the direction of musical, not rhythmical, exploitation of speech.

Goethe.—In the second part of Faust, in that scene where Helen of Troy arrives in Arcadia and is received by Faust in his new, romantic palace, Goethe (1749–1832) introduces an interesting discussion on rime which is fundamentally in harmony with Hegel's views. The whole scene is strangely fantastic and obscure. Faust enters the reception hall of the palace accompanied by Lynceus in chains, whom he intends to punish for not having announced the arrival of Helen. Lynceus, the mythological lynx, who is supposed to have supernaturally keen eyes which can see everything on or beneath the earth, and which have enabled him to collect all sorts of treasures from the tombs of past civilizations, is blinded by the beauty of Helen, and (for no apparent reason) offers her all those treasures in very beautiful rimed tetrameters. It speaks highly for the observation power of the distinguished Greek lady that she immediately perceives the unusually melodious form in which Lynceus' speech is delivered. Greek language knows no such form. We are led to believe that Lynceus obtained it from those remote northern tombs, most assuredly Gothic, from which he obtained all other treasures—a poetic allusion to the Gothic origin of rime. Helen describes her impression of the rimed speech by calling it "strange and friendly." The riming words seem to "caress" each other:

> Vielfache Wunder seh' ich, hör' ich an;
> Erstaunen trifft mich, fragen möchte ich viel.
> Doch wünsch' ich Unterricht, warum die Rede
> Des Mannes mir seltsam klang, seltsam und freundlich.
> Ein Ton scheint sich dem anderen zu bequemen,

174

Und hat ein Wort zum Ohre sich gesellt,
Ein anderes kommt, dem ersten liebzukosen.

It is evident that Helen is impressed by the intimate, soulful, romantic aspect of rime. Faust is proud and happy that his "queen" seems to be so fascinated by "his peoples' " tongue. He explains that it is easy to speak in this manner; one must only speak "from one's heart":

Es ist gar leicht, es muss von Herzen gehen.

This is the same romantic doctrine that rime is a matter of "heart," of "soul." According to an Oriental legend it originated in a love romance between a slave girl and her master "dadurch, dass die geliebte Sklavin die Worte ihres geliebten Herrn mit gleichgemessenen und gleichtönenden Worten wiederholt habe." Goethe mentions this legend in the *Wahrheit und Dichtung*, and gives his rendering of it in his Oriental sketches, *Suleika*:

Behramgur, sagt man, hat den Reim erfunden,
Er sprach entzückt aus reiner Seele Drang;
Dilaram schnell, die Freundin seiner Stunden,
Erwiderte mit gleichem Wort und Klang.

Und so, Geliebte, warst du mir beschieden,
Des Reims zu finden holden Lustgebrauch,
Dass auch Behramgur ich, den Sassaniden,
Nicht mehr beneiden darf: mir ward es auch.

Thus, in Goethe's conception, rime is an expression of "soul," especially of a loving soul:

Ist's nicht der Liebe hochverklärtes All?

Schiller.—It is this element of subjective expressiveness that, according to Schiller, saves rime from the hostile attacks upon its "unpoetic and common origin." In a letter to Goethe (18 June, 1796) Schiller writes:

Herder's unversöhnliche Feindschaft gegen den Reim ist mir auch viel zu weit getrieben, und was er dagegen aufbringt, halte ich bei weitem nicht für bedeutend genug. Der Ursprung des Reims mag noch so gemein und unpoetisch sein, man muss sich an den Eindruck halten, den er macht.

Caspar Poggel.—In Poggel's work on rime one finds Hegelian ideas going to seed. Following Hegel, he maintains that the word-sound is an expression of "feeling."[25] And in so far as rime emphasizes the musical element of poetic speech, it helps the poet to find the unity of feeling (*die Einheit des Gefühls*) which is the ultimate cause of its artistic excellence. But "feeling" and "meaning" must be co-ordinated. Therefore the sound of words is expected to correspond to what the poet wishes to say. In the process of his creative work the poet looks not merely for suitable words to express his ideas but also for the right sounds to express his emotions. When he finds one he is anxious to retain it, to make it more prominent and emphatic. Hence he rimes, i.e., repeats the sound which he considers properly expressive.[26]

With all this, Poggel brings very little novelty into the theory of rime. His theory is a combination of Schütze's ideas with a strong dose of romantic Hegelianism. This latter element manifests itself in Poggel's work not merely in the legitimate co-ordination of "feeling" with the "music of speech," but also in the pseudo-dialectical tendency to deduce facts from pure and largely fantastic assumptions. In explaining the origin of rime, for example, he suggests that it lies in the na-

[25] C. Poggel, *Grundzüge einer Theorie des Reimes und Gleichklänge*, 1836.

[26] C. Poggel, *Über das Verhältniss von Form und Bedeutung*, 1836.

176

ture of rime to be produced by Northern people. That, for him, sufficiently explains the absence of rime in Greek and Latin poetry. "South corresponds to light," he meditates, "light corresponds to the eye, the eye to imagination, and therefore to plasticity and rhythm. North, on the other hand, corresponds to darkness, darkness to motion, and this to sound and ear; the latter corresponds to feeling, feeling to music, and music to rime."

Thus with the false profundity of an unscientific mind he believes himself to have dialectically deduced rime from the nature and essence of "North."

Since Poggel the musical or acoustic theory of rime has been on the decline. It was precisely the element of mysticism invariably associated with such theories that caused the reaction.[27]

---

[27] Among modern scholars there are but few who advocate the acoustic theory in its pure form. Among those who late in the nineteenth century persisted in regarding rime as a purely acoustic, i.e., musical phenomenon, mention must be made of Alexander Ehrenfeld, who in his *Studien zur Theorie des Reims* regards rime as a "limit for different forms of assonance." Dr. Ehrenfeld proposed to analyze rime from the point of view of modern experimental psychology, but unfortunately, as far as I know, never carried out his intention beyond the outline of a program. It is therefore difficult to discuss him historically, for most of his own ideas are presented in the form of suggestions, or even questions. On the whole, he seems to follow Schütze's views, often simply translating his Romantic dialect into the language of modern psychology, without, however, mentioning Schütze's name even in the historical part of his work.

The nearest approach to our own views appears to be made in J. P. Dabney's explanation of rime as an element of verse composition analogous to musical tonic. This author is inclined to regard rime as an indispensable element of melodious poetical language. Although it is formally possible, she admits, to attain melody in verse with subtler devices, and to dispense with rime, "this has seldom been, in English, a successful experiment, and instances are few in which unrhymed verse can truly be called poetry." Rime is just as indispensable in versification as the keynote or tonic in a musical melody.

177

Sidney Lanier.—We cannot omit mentioning Sidney Lanier's work, *Music and Poetry*, although it does not directly belong within the scope of our problem. Lanier's opposition to the popular belief that "music is a species of language," and his emphasis on the converse idea that "language is a species of music," make him near and dear to the author of the present essay. Although my own work on rime has originated wholly independently of Lanier's suggestions and I came to know his contributions to the problem of the music of language only after my own ideas had been completely formed, yet with all this I feel happy that the present study falls within the range of a great American tradition.

It is quite plain to all those who read *Music and Poetry* that its author was on the right track with regard to the nature

If a melody does not end in its keynote there is no sensation of repose or completion produced upon the ear. The reason for this, Miss Dabney believes, is "that in the tonic chord, or triad, ... we have the only perfect cadence producible in music." The chord of the dominant is called half-cadence because it leads directly into the chord of the tonic, or full cadence. "In the tonic chord alone the ear makes no demand for farther progression because, for that theme, it is the end—is complete in itself . . . . In exactly the same way, in any rhymed stanza, the first word of the rime prepares or introduces a tone which the last rhyme is required to complete." On the basis of this musical analogy Miss Dabney defines rime as "the cadence correspondence of verse." "But of course," she adds, "such comparisons are elementary and cannot be pushed far." It is indeed unfortunate that Miss Dabney in her analysis of the musical nature of rime does not actually go beyond comparison. In 1901, when *The Musical Basis of Verse* was published, the physical analysis of vowels had already made considerable progress. The author appears to be acquainted with the results of this analysis through the work of Professor Max Müller, *Science of Language*, which she quotes. But she does not seem to be aware of the actual presence of a melodic motion in the lines of a poem, nor does she associate her theory of rime with the theory of vowels. Instead of testing her hypothesis by the evidence obtained by the physical acoustics, she ends in the same Romantic "soul-center," "the spiritual keynote," the great "C Major of this life."

178

of the relation between musical sounds and human words; and had he known the modern work on vowels, he would probably have come to the conclusions which are expounded in this book. Even those of his conclusions which are obviously erroneous, such as his conviction that English verse has for its basis not accent but a strict musical quantity, point practically in the same direction. For in the absence of the characteristic vowel-tones he had no other means of distinguishing them musically than that of their musical quantity. The latter implies, and to a certain extent determines, the qualitative differences of various syllables, whereas accent is nothing but an expression of the brutal force of sound.

Lanier (1842–1881) is interested in the relation between the words of a poem and their possible musical interpretation. "What common ground," he asks, "exists to conventionally significant words and the unconventionally significant tones of the modern orchestra?"[28] For him the question means: what elements of a poem may be properly utilized for musical composition? What is there in poetry that is capable of being translated into music? It seems to be his conviction that ideas cannot be translated. Only the mood is accessible for music. Therefore, the vaguer the intellectual content of a poem, the more musical it appears to be.

An attentive consideration of this principle will go far toward a complete reversal of the generally received opinion that a poem for musical representation ought to be perfectly clear, smooth, and natural. . . . . The illuminating power of music (if one may so express it) is, when compared with that of the non-musical inflections of the human voice in pronouncing words, about as moonlight when compared with sunlight. Now fancy that a capricious sovereign should order his court-painter to execute a picture which was to be looked at only by moonlight; what would be the artist's procedure? In the first place he would choose

[28] Sidney Lanier, *Music and Poetry* (New York, 1898; second edition, 1924), page 81.

a mystical subject. . . . . He would next select gigantic figures, for the same reason; and while these figures would have to be even harshly outlined in order to make them distinct, the painter would permit himself indefinite liberty as to the background and as to the space between separate figures, in order to fill these as far as possible with the same vague and dreamy subtleties appropriate to moonlight.[29]

A poet, therefore, who is called to write a text for music, or a composer who is trying to interpret a poem by song, is precisely in the position of a painter called on to paint a picture for moonlight. They have to extract from poetry its "musical" elements. And these consist of non-intellectual ingredients.[30]

C. RHYTHMICAL THEORIES OF RIME

The inherent vagueness of the acoustic theories and their association with the elements of linguistic mysticism made modern scholars reject the "musical" explanation of rime and adopt a more exact basis for attacking the problem. · This they found in the phenomenon of rhythm. Rime, according to this view, appears to be artistically effective because it gives a powerful assistance to rhythm. It is not merely ornamental but has an important compositional value as it helps to organize the poetic material into larger rhythmical units. It is not merely musical or vaguely sentimental; it is fundamentally creative, being instrumental for keeping the verse in proper "balance" and artistic "equilibrium."

We have seen in the beginning of this chapter that Dante regards rime as not merely acoustically pleasant but also a rhythmically constructive factor. It is very significant that the chapter dealing with the question of rime in *De Vulgari Eloquentia* bears the subtitle: "Rime in Relation to the Arrangement of the Parts of the Stanza." It indicates at once Dante's

[29] Sidney Lanier, *Music and Poetry*, page 87.

[30] *Ibid.*, pages 4 ff.

180

fundamental point of view: rime has a structural value, it "links the verse lines together" into stanzas, thereby producing larger rhythmical tides within the poem. It is only on the basis of rime that the *Divine Comedy* may be presented as a continuous stream of "tercets." Blank verse excludes any such division.

This aspect of Dante's conception of rime was an embryo from which most modern theories on the subject have grown.

William Webbe.—Among the early English prosodists mention must be made of William Webbe, whose *Discourse of English Poetrie* (1586) played a prominent part in the controversy between the advocates and the antagonists of rime. Webbe sides with the classical prosodists and condemns rime as a "rude kinde of verse" borrowed from the barbarians. Anything approaching a constructive rime theory is therefore hardly to be expected of the pugnacious "graduate," as he chooses to style himself. Yet his *Discourse* formulates certain assumptions and definitions which entered as part and parcel into nearly all later discussions on rime. In the first place, rime becomes properly and formally defined as "the falling out of verses together in one like sound." Rime's essence, therefore, following Aristotelian tradition, was definitely placed in sound, and not in the visual image of written or printed words. Secondly, Webbe assumes, contrary to Puttenham's point of view, that rime is primarily of rhythmical nature, a crude derivative of number. Rime, he explains, is taken from the Greek word ῥυθμός, and "is properly the just proportion of a clause or sentence, whether it be in prose or meeter, aptly comprised together." Thus, next to the definition of rime as an acoustic phenomenon, we find in Webbe's *Discourse* a description of its nature as a "just proportion," i.e., as the right measure or reading unit in the organization of verse. This latter idea became fundamental for all subsequent rime theories based on rhythm.

181

Milton and Dryden. — Milton (1608–1674) evidently takes it axiomatically for granted that rime belongs to the category of rhythmical effects. It is well known that he objected to this barbarous device on the basis that it introduced "wretched matter and lame meter." It appears to him to be beyond any dispute that rime does assist the poet in keeping his rhythm; he objects to it only because it seems to him to be a "barbarous" way of keeping rhythm. It imposes additional and altogether unnecessary fetters on the poet.

Those who defended rime against this Miltonian "sophistry" pointed out that it was precisely these additional fetters that made rime valuable. Above all, Dryden (1631–1700) takes this position. He tries to justify the use of rime by referring to its power to control our fancy; it restrains the imagination, and brings "bounds" into the poet's often too luxurious flow of ideas; it keeps his verse in balance with the wealth of his thought; in a word, it controls his spiritual rhythm, for bounds and balance are rhythmical categories. In the Dedication to *The Rival Ladies*, the first of the famous prolegomena in which he expressed his views on poets and poetry, Dryden says:

The advantages which rhyme has over blank verse are so many, that it were lost time to name them. . . . . But that benefit that I consider most in it, because I have not seldom found it, is, that it bounds and circumscribes the fancy. For imagination in a poet is a faculty so wild and lawless, that, like a high-ranging spaniel, it must have clogs tied to it lest it outrun the judgment. The great easiness of blank verse renders the poet too luxuriant; he is tempted to say many things which might better be omitted, or at least shut up in fewer words; but when the difficulty of artful rhyming is interposed, where the poet commonly confines his sense to his couplet, and must contrive that sense into such words that the rhyme shall naturally follow them, not they the rhyme; the fancy then gives leisure to the judgment to come in, which, seeing so heavy a tax imposed, is ready to cut off all unnecessary expenses. This

182

last consideration has already answered an objection which some have
made that rhyme is only an embroidery of sense, to make that, which
is ordinary in itself, pass for excellent with less examination. But certainly, that which most regulates the fancy, and gives the judgment its
busiest employment, is like to bring forth the richest and clearest
thoughts.[31]

Rime therefore means discipline for thought. Rimed verse
"circumscribes a quick and luxuriant fancy, which would extend
itself too far on every subject, did not the labor which is required to well-turned and polished rhyme, set bounds to it."[32]
"Bounds" is a word vaguely expressing the relation between
rime and rhythm. The task of the subsequently developed
theories was to clear it up.

Herder (1744 – 1803). — Logically, "balance" and
"rhythm" are kindred notions. But they stand far apart, although in the same series, in the same category of ideas. They
are but distantly related. The idea of symmetry makes the
relation clearer. For symmetry, no doubt, is a perfect balance.
And at the same time it is the beginning of rhythm. If a line,
a phrase, or a sound is repeated twice, it constitutes a symmetry.
If it is repeated three times, there is already rhythm. Thus
reducing rime to symmetry, one merely defines more precisely
what is meant by saying that rime is "balance." This was done
by Herder.

Herder derives rime from oriental parallelism, i.e., from
the artistic method of expressing nature in the form of balanced
dualities: heaven and earth, love and hate, good and evil, etc.
Rime he defines as "progressive parallelism," i.e., as a symmetrical correspondence of lines. Its beauty is similar to that
of the human body with its corresponding right and left. There

[31] John Dryden, *The Rival Ladies*, Dedication.
[32] John Dryden, *An Essay of Dramatic Poesy.*

183

is a natural tendency toward rime in all languages, for there is a natural tendency toward symmetry of expression. By means of symmetrical arrangement the verse lines appear to be united, tied together, and therefore easy to remember. This mnemonic power of rime points back to Sir Philip Sidney, who long before Herder emphasized the connection between rime and memory.[33]

Wackernagel, W. Grimm, and Pott.—Wilhelm Wackernagel in his *Geschichte des deutschen Hexameters und Pentameters* (1831), Wilhelm Grimm (1789–1859) in his well-known *Zur Geschichte des Reims,* and the rather fantastic Pott in his essay on *Doppelung* have followed Herder in believing that rime originates from grammatical parallelism. A syntactic construction, if repeated, results in the identity of endings. Therefore, thought-parallelism in poetry often results in involuntary rimes. All these authors, especially Grimm, contributed a great deal to our knowledge of the history of rime but accomplished little toward clarifying its theory. Therefore they do not properly belong to the range of our present inquiry, and little more than a mere mention of their names may suffice to acquaint the reader with their contribution to our problem.

L. Becq de Fouquières.—It would be inexpedient to discuss all those who in the last fifty or sixty years have written about rime. Nearly every textbook of prosody or essay on poetry contains a chapter on rime. Those which I have been able to inspect contain very little that is new on the question of the rela-

---

[33] Ehrenfeld in his *Studien zur Theorie des Reims* (Zurich, 1897–1904), page 8, erroneously ascribed the first statement of the mnemonic function of rime to Herder. Long before Herder this idea was discussed in English treatises on rime.

184

tion between rime and rhythm. It is, however, impossible to omit the views of such prominent prosodists as L. Becq de Fouquières, R. de la Grasserie, Guest, and a few others.

L. Becq de Fouquières (1879) gives an extraordinarily clear, rhythmical explanation of rime. He contends that the most fundamental rule that is imposed upon the poet is the requirement of establishing and maintaining a certain relation between the word of the poet and the ear of his audience. It is essential to the success of a poem that the audience should be able to perceive the rhythm that regulates its recitation. The ear—be it merely in the imagination of the reader—must hear the periodic returns of the same units. For obtaining such an effect it is necessary that the end of each verse should receive a vibratory stress similar to that of a tympan. For otherwise how should we recognize the end of a line? How could we perceive a verse as a rhythmical unit? The ancients possessed an adequate measure in the length of their syllables; each line evidently corresponded to the conditions of breathing. The lines were of equal duration. But our verses are of different length as far as time is concerned. How should we know the beginning of a new rhythmical unit? Who shall announce it to us?

Rime assumes this auxiliary function. It gives us a signal. It defines, not theoretically but audibly, the end of each verse. Assonance may be, of course, used for the same purpose. But its musical effect is negligible. A vowel alone gives a very feeble signal. Yet it was frequently used for that purpose in the old poetry. The feebleness of the signal was then redeemed by the persistence with which it repeated itself. It was customary in the old French poetry to repeat the same vowel at the end of each verse line for ten, fifteen, and more lines in succession.

That system, however, proved unsatisfactory. The later poets realized the necessity of a more efficient signalization. This task was achieved by adding alliteration to the assonance.

185

Thus perfect end-rime was formed. It represented a transition to an entirely different system of versification. Owing to rime, the ancient rhythm, which was based on respiration (necessary to pronounce a line), was transformed into our modern acoustic rhythm of accentuation. Rime helps us to count the accented syllables; and since our verse is based on the number and not the length of the syllables, it announces to the ear the very substance of our verse.[34]

R. de la Grasserie.—Similar views are expressed by Grasserie. He also believes that the chief aesthetic effect of rime lies in its function as a "signal" of the verse end.[35] But he attempts to explain this marking effect by reference to a more general and basic phenomenon. To accomplish this he first studies the nature of assonance, of which he establishes three kinds: (1) mechanical assonance (*assonance amorphe ou mécanique*), (2) assonantal parallelism (*assonance de parallelisme*), (3) rhythmical assonance (*assonance rythmique*). The first consists of producing like sounds within the verse without any constructive aim, for the sole purpose of creating agreeable sounds. The second has the psychological function of uniting ideas into harmonious wholes by returning to the same word, or the same thought, or, more rarely, to the same grammatical phrase (*rime grammaticale*). The third kind of assonance is assonance that assists rhythm. The latter leads us to the

[34] L. Becq de Fouquières, *Traité général de versification française* (Paris, 1879), says (page 29): "La rime est caractéristique de l'unité de mesure; c'est elle qui clôt, par un effet d'acoustique, le temps expiratoire. L'oreille, qui compte les chocs qu'elle reçoit et qui groupe ses sensations acoustiques est ainsi avertie que les douze sons du vers sont écoulés et que la période mélodique est terminée."

[35] R. de la Grasserie, *Des Principes scientifiques de la versification française* (1900): "Sans doute, l'emploi le plus essentiel de la rime est celui qu'on a souvent signalé, de marquer puissamment la fin du vers. ... "

186

phenomenon of rime, which has "a rhythmical function in helping to construct the unity of the verse."[36]

The general principle on which rime rests, according to Grasserie, is that of repetition. Our ear derives a peculiar satisfaction from repeating the same sound after certain intervals of time. This "law," the author of *Des Principes* points out, holds true with regard to our aesthetic activity in general, especially in music, where it forms the basis for all composition. It is also true with regard to our linguistic expressions, and our thinking in general. "For some mysterious reason our mind delights in returning to the same idea after certain more or less prolonged détour."[37] Such is, for example, the origin of the refrain in poetry. The same tendency lies at the basis of rime.[38]

[36] *Ibid.*, page 98: "Si la musique recherche dans l'ensemble d'un poème musical le leit-motiv et à la fin de diverses périodes, des sons concordants, le sentiment humain ne recherche pas moins le retour des mêmes impressions, et l'intelligence humaine dans la mémoire, le rappel des mêmes idées. D'où à côté de la rime phonétique, la rime psychologique. Cette dernière consiste soit dans le retour du même mot: rime d'idée, soit dans le retour de la même phrase: rime de pensée; elle consiste aussi, mais plus rarement, dans le retour du même dessin grammatique, rime grammaticale." Psychological or grammatical rime is often applied in proverbs: "Il s'agit d'unir deux incises ou deux mots, soit synonymes, soit antithétiques, au moyen d'une assonance, en général, terminal de même que nous verrons qu'on peut les unir par une allitération initial. C'est ce qui a lieu dans de nombreux proverbes français" (*ibid.*, page 145).

[37] R. de la Grasserie, *op. cit.*, page 93.

[38] *Ibid.*, page 95: Telles sont les deux fonctions principales de la rime: (1) une consciente et cherchée qui consiste à marquer fortement la fin du vers pour le distinguer du suivant; (2) une inconsciente et mécanique qui est celle de retour, d'écho, de ressouvenir du même son ou de la même idée." And further (page 104): "Une des fonctions importantes de la rime ... c'est de former le lieu de l'unité rhythmique." See also page 94: "Telle est la double impression causée par la rime, il en resulte le plaisir esthétique que nous trouvons au souvenir ou retour, celui musical résultant d'un accord, celui tout psychique, du sentiment répété."

Thus rime is understood as a special case of a general psychological law that operates quite extensively in many other manifestations of our mind. Its function is far from being only ornamental.[39] Its function is to create within the verse a system of rhythmical echoes which help us to distinguish the end of one verse from the beginning of another.[40]

Edwin Guest.—Guest (1800–1880) defines rime in a traditionally formal way as "the correspondence which exists between syllables containing sounds similarly modified." But this definition, in Guest's opinion, does not describe rime's function and significance. What does this formal correspondence accomplish within the verse? What happens when the terminal syllables are "similarly modified" in sound? When the same modification of sound recurs at definite intervals, the coincidence very readily strikes the ear; and when it is found in accented syllables, the latter fix the attention more strongly than if they merely received the accent. This calling of attention makes rime significant and artistically effective. "It is not, as is sometimes asserted, a mere ornament; it marks and defines the accent, and thereby strengthens and supports the rhythm. . . . . It separates each verse from the other by a strongly marked boundary, and has ever a tendency to make the sense accommodate itself to these artificial pauses." Therefore, Guest points out, it has been long called a "time-beater."

[39] R. de la Grasserie, *op. cit.*, page 91: "Mais, la rime une fois trouvée, on ne peut méconnaître son profond effet; l'oreille la cherche, l'attend, l'absorbe avec un plaisir acoustique qui double le plaisir esthétique; elle donne au vers le timbre qui lui manque. Elle n'est donc poin artificielle."

[40] *Ibid.*, page 90: "Mais, lorsqu'au systéme de la quantité s'est trouvé substitué, à la suite de la conversion de l'accent d'élévation, un accent d'intensité, le rythme accentuel dont les divisions étaient moins régulières, le besoin se fit sentir de marquer la fin du vers par la rime."

G. Saintsbury.—Saintsbury, objecting to Guest's theory on some minor points, accepted his fundamental point of view:

The circumstances pointed at in these queries, the unbiassed examination of the documents of the period before us, and the whole course of the present inquiry, will be found . . . . to support a theory somewhat different from Guest's, even in first appearance (though it agrees cordially with his in acknowledging the importance and time-marking effect of rhyme), and leading up to another theory of the whole of Middle and Modern English versification, which is directly opposed to his. The theory may be thus stated: Rhyme, when accepted by any language, gradually but necessarily breaks up prosody by versicles or sections merely, and substitutes prosody by feet, that is to say, by minor internal divisions which are batched and brought to metrical correspondence by the rhyme itself.

This explanation supports that of Guest in the one respect that is important for our inquiry: it corroborates the view according to which rime and rhythm are not only related but actually depend upon each other's support; this co-operation is so intimate that the historical appearance of rime within the boundaries of a given language breaks up traditional rhythms and introduces different systems of versification.

Russian school.—Russian literary criticism of the nineteenth century was almost exclusively under the influence of the sociological school, which regarded every literary composition in the aspect of its social significance. A reaction became imminent after the appearance of symbolism. Symbolists were the first to arouse interest for purely formal problems of structural analysis. In direct contrast to the realistic school, they emphasized excellence of form and methods of workmanship. They rediscovered the value of sound in poetry and stimulated interest in the study of poetic technique. Andrei Baily and Valerij Brusov, prominent poets as they were, contributed much to the advancement of scientific research in "poetics." Under the influence of their ideas and methods originated the so-called formal school of literary criticism, which favored purely technical, often statistical, studies of words and word-coloring, of poetic ornamentation and causes of emotional appeal. This interest is still growing. Its scope becomes larger every year. Revolution seems to have contributed much to the popularity of such purely formal studies; for form appears to be a way of escape from the oppressive inconsistencies and contradictions of "content." A number of valuable contributions have been recently made to the discussion of rime, rhythm, and poetic technique in general.

Among those contributions we find one especially interesting for our present purposes. It is V. Zhirmunski's *Rime, Its History and Theory* (Petersburg, 1923), which was preceded by a number of preliminary special studies: *Compositions of Lyric Verse* (1921) and *Poetry of Alexander Block* (1922) by the same author. Zhirmunski attempts to coin such a definition of rime as would include reference to rhythm as a part of the definition itself. Traditional definitions he considers insufficient precisely for the reason that they omit that factor in the nature of rime which is most indispensable for its successful functioning. Therefore, taking rhythm as his basis of departure, Zhirmunski defines rime as an "acoustic repetition that carries an organizing function in the metrical composition of the verse." Compared with this definition the traditional school formulas which define rime as a verbal echo appear to him adequate; he misses in them the reference to what he considers the most substantial attribute of rime, its rhythmically compositional function.

Thus in his definition of rime Zhirmunski lays stress upon the organizing function or compositional value of rime. This function is twofold. First, it describes the limits of a rhythmical series, i.e., defines the limits of verse lines; and, secondly, it binds certain rhythmical groups together into larger units of

190

inter-strophic composition: it creates the super-rhythm of the stanzas. Rime not merely introduces variability into the form of stanzas but in many cases it presents the only possible basis for distinguishing one stanza from another. In poems with alternating masculine and feminine endings the limits of each stanza are well-defined simply by the endings. But in such poems as employ exclusively feminine endings—in Polish, for example, no other endings are possible—neither stanzas nor periods would be clearly divided from each other if it were not for the rime. In such poems as Byron's *All for Love:*

> O talk not to me of a name great in story;
> The days of our youth are the days of our glory;
> And the myrtle and ivy of sweet two-and-twenty
> Are worth all your laurels, though ever so plenty.

the lines could not be arranged into stanzas without the assistance of rime. For it would be impossible to know of which type the stanza is to be formed. Suppose "story" does not rime with "glory," nor "twenty" with "plenty"; how should one know whether the poem is arranged in couplets or in *abab*-form, or perhaps even in tercets? Without rime it becomes undetermined with regard to the stanza form, and rhythmic organization of the thought units, therefore, is handicapped.

This binding function is not necessarily confined to the end-rimes. It may be very successfully accomplished by alliteration or inner rimes. Inner rime is often used for the purpose of rhythmical composition especially to attract attention to some particular word which appears logically important. If the sound of the word which the poet wishes to emphasize coincides with the preceding rime, our ear involuntarily catches this word and brings it to our attention. For instance:

> Chilled in the slave, and burning in the *free*
> Like the *sealed* cavern by the sparkling *sea*.
> —HOLMES

191

The characteristic epithet "sealed" that modifies "cavern" is the point of originality in this couplet, and the poet naturally wishes to impress it upon the reader's mind. This is artistically accomplished by the assonance of "sea." And yet neither alliteration nor assonance possesses the rhythmical power of end-rimes.

Opinions of modern aestheticians. — Modern aesthetic theories are inclined to emphasize the rhythmical element in the nature of rime. Among the means of poetical language that "are utilized to assist rhythm," R. Müller-Freienfels mentions the old Germanic *Stabreim* (alliteration and assonance near together) and also end-rime. Similar ideas with regard to the nature of rime we find among such modern thinkers as Th. Lipps and G. Santayana. Lipps maintains that rime belongs to the class of rhythmical phenomena; its function lies in dividing and connecting the elements of verse.[41] Similarly, Santayana sees the principal justification for rime in its power to give "an artificial relationship to the phrases between which it obtains, which, but for it, would run away from another in a rapid and irrevocable flux."[42] It is understood, of course, that the relationship that thus obtains between the phrases is not of an intellectual character. It is the rhythm of sound, not that of meaning, that binds them together. Thus we again approach the Hegelian conception which regards rime as a vehicle to save the acoustic element in human speech in view of its threatening annihilation by the force of meaning.

In this connection it is necessary to mention an interesting analysis of rime by Professor DeWitt H. Parker. "In ordinary

[41] Th. Lipps, *Aesthetik*, pages 400–401: "Zum Versrhythmus tritt der Reim, als ein verwandtes und doch auch wiederum dazu gegensätzliches Element. .... Der Endreim scheidet und verbindet verse. Er schliesst unmittelbar aufeinanderfolgende Verse zu einem Ganzen zusammen."

[42] G. Santayana, *The Sense of Beauty*, page 173.

192

speech," Mr. Parker writes, "the sound and articulation of a word, although indispensable to utterance, and therefore a necessary part of it, are of little or no value in themselves. . . . . But in poetry, which is speech made beautiful, the mere sound of the words has value. In hearing poetry, we not only understand, but listen; we appreciate not only the ideas and emotions conveyed, but the word-sounds and their rhythms as well. Even in silent reading, poetry is a voice which we delight to hear." Repetition of the same sound (rime) intensifies the relative pressure of the acoustic factor in speech: "there is a joy truly surprising in the mere repetition of vowels and consonants."[43] The aesthetic value of this repetition is explained by the author on a purely rhythmical basis. He appreciates rime just as a repetition (rhythmically), without any reference to other vowels, i.e., not as a reference point in the melody of verse but solely as a reflected sound. And he explains the pleasure of it psychologically:

If the repetition of the same color or line in painting, the same tone in music, can delight us, why not the repetition of the same word-sound? In all cases a like feeling of harmony is produced. And the same general principle applies to explain it. All word-sounds as we utter or hear them leave memory traces in mind, which are not pure images, but also motor sets, tendencies, or impulses to the remaking of the sounds. The doing of any deed—a word is also a deed—creates a will to its doing again; hence the satisfaction when that will is fulfilled in the repeated sound, when the image melts with the fact. And the same law that rules in music and design holds here also: there must not be too much of consonance, of repetition, else the will becomes satiated and fatigued; there must be difference as well as identity—the novelty and surprise which accompany the arousal of a still fresh and unappeased impulse. This is well provided for in alternate rimes, where the will to one kind of sound is suspended by the emergence of a different sound with its will,

---

[43] DeWitt H. Parker, *The Principles of Aesthetics* (1920), page 192.

and where the fulfillment of the one balances the fulfillment of the other.[44]

Volkelt regards rime as one of the means to emphasize the acoustic element in human speech, and to bring about what he calls "freedom from reality":

> Insofern die Dichtung sich in gebundener Rede, in Rhythmus und Reim, bewegt, liegen rein-spielende Wortverknüpfungs-Gebilde vor. Nach ihrer geistigen Seite hin freilich haben Verszeilen, Strophen, Reimgefüge dingliche Bedeutung; insofern sie aber Wortverknüpfungsformen sind, ist ihre dingliche Bedeutung gleich Null. Die gebundene Dichtung ist nach ihrer Wortseite freies, wirklichkeitsentrücktes Spiel. Den Rhythmen und Reimen als solchen entsprechen nur stoffliche und technische Bedeutungsvorstellungen.[45]

The latter are not so much intellectual ideas as emotional tendencies—what Mr. Parker calls the will to some particular kind of sound and Volkelt designates as *"stimmungsartige Strebung."*[46]

Jonas Cohn takes a purely rhythmical view of rime, believing it to be a vehicle of rhythmical unity:

> Der wiederkehrende Klang des Reimes und noch mehr des Refrains wirken vereinheitlichend. Das Sonett verdankt seinen starken Einheitscharacter wesentlich der Reimverschlingung.[47]

M. Carriere follows Hegelian argument in Poggel's version. He also points out that in poetry the sound of words acquires an independent value:

> Das Wort kommt hier seinem Klang, seinem Accent, seiner Zeitdauer nach in Betracht, der Laut als solcher kommt zur Geltung neben

[44] DeWitt H. Parker, *op. cit.*, pages 196–197.

[45] J. Volkelt, *System der Aesthetik*, 1 : 120.

[46] *Ibid.*, page 207.

[47] Jonas Cohn, *Allgemeine Aesthetik*, page 87.

194

dem Gehalt des Gedankens, der in ihm vernehmlich wird. Gruppen von Silben sind in den Worten zu Lautgebilden verbunden und werden zu rhythmischen Reihen aneinandergefügt, mannichfaltig wie die melodischen Tonfolgen in der Musik.[48]

Yet, under the influence of Poggel, Carriere gives a rather fantastic explanation of this acoustic fact. He believes that the ear tends to give a similar sound to similar ideas and that from this tendency rime arises:

Und so entspringt der Reim dem Bestreben bei dem Denken ähnlicher Vorstellungen auch dem Ohr einen ähnlichen Klang zu bieten, oder die innere Beziehung zweier Sätze oder der Glieder eines Satzes auch äusserlich laut werden zu lassen, und so durch die Harmonie des Sinnlichen und Geistigen das Gemüth zu erfreuen.[49]

All these theories seem to agree on one point: that rime has the power to stimulate our emotions independently of the intellectual content of the verse. It achieves this object by introducing a new variety of rhythm; that is, its power to stimulate our emotions depends directly on its rhythmical power.

It is precisely this power that constitutes the crucial point of the rime problem. We have seen that, according to many authorities, rime plays an organizing function in the rhythmical composition of poetry. The question now arises, what makes it fit to perform such functions? What is there in rime that attracts our attention? For it must first attract our attention in order to be able to serve us rhythmically. Is it merely the identity of the sound that gives rime this power to control rhythm? Why is it then that the identity of consonants (alliteration) proves to be much less efficient in this respect? And after all, why should the identity of sound attract our attention at all? What is there in the identity of sound that makes it

---

[48] M. Carriere, *Aesthetik*, 2:518.
[49] *Ibid.*, page 532.

emphatic and pleasing for the ear? Certainly it is not rhythm, for rhythm is just the result of that stress which our attention conveys to the riming syllables. Rhythm itself needs explanation.

Moreover, there are other means for metrical and symmetrical organization of verse quite different from rime.[50] The Old Germanic verse, for instance, is based on alliteration, which, according to Liddell, fulfills in the metrical composition of the Old Germanic and Anglo-Saxon poetry a function very similar to that of end-rime: it serves the purpose of metrical punctuation. In modern poetry, too, alliteration is often used to emphasize and to organize the units of thought. Comparing, for instance, the master character of Lincoln with the complacent pettiness of the "sneering and jeering crowd," Robinson coins the expression:

'Twas ours to soar and his to see.

The s-alliteration of "soar" and "see" attracts our attention to those words and thereby divides the line into two symmetrical parts. Similarly here:

The perfect word that is the poet's wand.

The w-alliteration of "ward" and "wand" brings forth prominently the two successive waves of the same thought unit, and makes the sound co-operate with the sense. The words, as if by music, direct and control the rhythm of expression. In Old English poetry alliteration serves decidedly as an organizing principle of metrical composition.

And yet very early in the history of English poetry end-rime appears as an additional, although not at all obligatory, device. And now it may be asked, why is it that this new device, with which Beowulf plays but occasionally and rather timidly,

[50] Compare R. de la Grasserie, *Des Principes scientifiques de la versification française* (1900), pages 164 ff.

grows up so rapidly that at the beginning of the second millenium it has already acquired general recognition, and toward the middle of the thirteenth century gains a complete victory over the old verse based on alliteration? What is there in rime that makes it more suitable for the purposes of versification than the old form of alliterative verse? For a number of centuries—approximately from 700 till 1000—alliteration was quite successfully performing the function of rhythmical composition. Why was it that it had to retire before its historical rival, rime? If the identity of sound is the thing that attracts our attention, why is it that alliteration is less successful than rime? It is certainly not because consonants are less noticeable than vowels, for in the history of languages consonants reveal considerably more constancy than vowels; they form the solid skeleton of words which identically persists throughout the ages of evolution, while the vowels change from generation to generation, from one dialect to another. There must be something else in rime that makes it more suitable for purposes of versification than the old device of alliteration. What is it?[51]

The advocates of the "rhythmical" theory maintain that it

[51] The solution is foreshadowed by R. de la Grasserie. He writes: "Sans doute, ce besoin de retour peut être satisfait d'autre manière, par exemple, par la symétrie finale des diverses périodes d'un dessein rythmique, soit quantitatif, soit accentuel. En plaçant régulièrement à la fin des vers, soit un dactycle, soit un spondée, ... non seulement on en marque ainsi la fin, mais on cause un leit-motiv mécanique et phonétique. Cependant, ce dessin rythmique est moins puissant que le retour du même son. C'est ce dernier qui est vraiment musical, qui frappe directement l'ouïe et en même temps l'esprit, ou plutôt le sentiment. On sait combien un son musical, ou une chanson entière, ou son refrain, lorsque les circonstances les ont liés à une émotion concrète, ont la faculté de ressusiter ensuite cette émotion qu'elles conservent. Où un vers frappant se termine par une sonorité marquée, cette sonorité se répétant à distance rappellera l'idée suggérée, et ainsi le lien d'unité, d'acoustique qu'il était, deviendra psychologique" (*Des Principes scientifiques de la versification française*, page 94).

197

is rhythm that creates rime. This explanation, however, fails to account for the peculiar power of rime to assist rhythm. Why is it that rime is rhythmically more effective than blank verse? Why is it effective at all? Granted that rime does assist the rhythm of the verse, what makes it fit to do so? The rhythmical function of rime thus becomes, not a vehicle, but an object of explanation. The musical nature of rime comes here to the rescue. Rime is fit to perform a rhythmical function because it appeals to us musically. Thus acoustic theory becomes an indispensable part of the general theory of rime. Moreover, it is the most important part of it, as it furnishes us with a pivot, using which we can hope to reduce the phenomenon to something more fundamentally familiar to us. This cannot be accomplished by reference to rhythm; for rhythm is not something that produces rime, but, on the contrary, something that is produced by rime. In order to be rhythmically effective, rime must be already accepted as a musically effective phenomenon.

The existing acoustic theories of rime, however, fail to reduce the phenomenon to something more familiar. Instead, as a rule, they reduce it to something with which we are less familiar: to the mysterious "musicke" that it "striketh in our ear," to the acoustic symbolism of individual vowels, or even to a mystical soul-center, to the "great C major of life" (as Dabney did). Therefore, in accepting any one of the foregoing theories we risk laying ourselves open to the fallacy of *"obscurus per obscuriorem."* A successful reduction to something more familiar can only be expected from the physical analysis of vowels. On the basis of this analysis we come to the conclusion that identical sounds at the end of the verse lines attract our attention, not because they are identical nor because they are rhythmically important, but solely because they satisfy our musical sense of melody. And only because they do that, they appear rhythmically important and are able to perform an additional function of assisting rhythm.

198

Physical analysis shows the presence of musical motion in a series of uttered words. It further shows that only rime, i.e., a return to the original tone, makes the motion actually melodic by furnishing it with a definite center of reference. We know, besides, that melody is always associated with a definite artistic reaction of a more or less pleasurable kind. This pleasure, then, associated with the riming words makes them more emphatic, i.e., makes it possible to use them as a basis for rhythmical composition. Let us investigate now what is the relation between the music and the rhythm of words?

VI

RIME AND RHYTHM

Quodcirca omne metrum rhythmus,
non omnis rhythmus etiam metrum est.
—St. Augustin, *De Musica*

Scholastic minds insist on definitions. And yet there is logically nothing more difficult, and more dangerous, than a formal definition. In defining a term, such as rhythm for instance, we are at least expected to make an exact statement as to what the term means for us. Such a formal "statement of meaning" is, indeed, a prerequisite to intelligent discussion. But whether or not such statements can ever be "exact" is an entirely different question. Even in mathematics the exact meaning of a definition can only be obtained from the process of its application. In philosophy every statement relevant to the matter in question modifies its meaning. The more elementary a thing seems to be, the more difficult it is to grasp and to formulate its exact meaning. What

200

is "line"? What is "differential"? What is "number"? In the
process of study the meaning of these terms grows more and
more complicated, although their formal definitions are but
slightly changed.

It is one of the most embarrassing paradoxes of our knowledge that the more we study the less we know. However
this proposition may be doubted with respect to the extent
of our knowledge, it is certainly true with respect to its basic
elements — definitions. With growing knowledge, definitions become more wavering and less dependable. It therefore
often happens that after a long period of experimental definitions of a certain evasive term the scholars finally resign the
task and presumptuously announce that the thing is undefinable. Fortunately in prosody we have not reached yet this
stage of academic sophistication and thus cannot consider ourselves free from the painful obligation to define rhythm.

What is rhythm? "The fact is," remarks J. H. Scott, "that
we are too familiar with rhythm to recognize it; *we know it
only in its absence.*" "Meter," he adds, "an adulterant of
language, is notoriously easy to talk about. The very first step
to an understanding of rhythm, however, is the coming to a
realization that it is in no wise metrical."[1] And yet this step is
logically insufficient, as it is purely negative. Affirmatively the
nature of rhythm has never been satisfactorily determined, nor
does the present work make a claim to any such determination.
The best we can do is to give some current historical definitions
of rhythm and see if they sufficiently agree among themselves
to yield a working basis for what we wish here to show.
Rhythm is most frequently defined with respect to time as an
order or measure of temporal intervals (τάξις χρόνων). According to Roman rhetoricians (Quintilianus), rhythm is a "system

[1] J. H. Scott, *Rhythmic Prose* (University of Iowa Studies, 1925), page
118.

of time intervals arranged according to a given order" (ῥυθμός ἐστι σύστημα ἐκ χρόνων κατά τινα τάξιν συγκειμένων). This phrase has served as a theme for innumerable variations.[2] Its weakness lies in the fact that there are rhythms which are in no wise associated with time. Therefore, at a very early age it seemed desirable to eliminate time from the definition of rhythm. Plato was the first to give a formula which in itself contains no reference to time. He says (in *Phaedros*) that rhythm is a disposition of elements measured with respect to each other (ῥυθμός ἐστιν συλλαβῶν κειμένων πως πρὸς ἀλλήλας ἔμμετρος θέσις). This was a source of more cautious definitions. Thus, in our time Volkelt defines rhythm as a repetition of the same, or a very similar, sensory element or group of elements.[3] Repetition only subjectively, not objectively, requires time.

In full view of the inherent difficulties in defining rhythm, modern psychologists and aestheticians concentrate their attention "on what rhythm does, rather than on what it is."[4] It is easy to see that a single point in space, or an item in time, are aesthetically indifferent. But a complex of such points, or a series of items, regularly repeated, possesses certain artistic weight or dignity.[5] It is a well-known psychological observation that a repetition of impressions stirs our emotions (*anima numeros agit, et numeris agitur*). Impressions which in an isolated condition possess no emotional value become emotionally

---

[2] Compare, for example, a definition given by E. A. Sonnenschein in his *What Is Rhythm?* (1925): "Rhythm is that property of a sequence of events in time which produces on the mind of the observer the impression of proportion between the durations of the several events or groups of events of which the sequence is composed." D. W. Prall, in his recently published *Aesthetic Judgment*, 1929, also defines rhythm as a specifically temporal structure. See *Aesthetic Judgment*, pages 138 ff.

[3] J. Volkelt, *System der Aesthetik*, 1:566.

[4] E. A. Sonnenschein, *What Is Rhythm?*, page 5.

[5] S. Witasek, *Algemeine Aesthetik*.

pleasing if repeated at certain regular intervals.[6] If I make a sign like this: ∟ it hardly has any artistic value whatsoever. If only I add another horizontal line to it which makes the figure symmetrical, I thereby produce a figure which has a certain elementary artistic appeal ⅂. It has a rhythm, the horizontal line being repeated twice, and it is artistically no more indifferent. It has an aesthetic sense, and may be utilized as a sign (our letter z). If the configuration be repeated in a horizontal position combining, as it were, two z's in one pattern, a design is produced that has a strong artistic appeal and is often employed as an element of ornamentation —the so-called "swastika" 卍 a rhythmical arrangement of geometrical lines, a decorative design known to man from gray antiquity. Its artistic appeal lies precisely in the rhythmical repetition of the lines.

From this illustration it follows that rhythm is not the same as beating time.[7] There is rhythm of lines and colors, as well as that of sounds and accents. The popular conception that identifies rhythm with the regular succession of time intervals causes a great deal of confusion and aesthetic blindness. Under the effect of this error we do not see and do not appreciate rhythm where it is obviously present: in painting, in sculpture,

[6] Bücher, *Arbeit und Rhythmus.*

[7] See H. R. Marshall, *The Beautiful*, page 94. Compare Verrier, *Essai sur les principes de la métrique anglaise*, 2:3: "Le rythme ... est constituée par une division perceptible du temps ou de l'espace en intervalles sensiblement égaux. On peut dir aussi que le rythme est constitué par le retour, à intervalles égaux, d'un phénomène déterminé."

203

etc.; on the contrary, we are inclined to misinterpret certain a-temporal rhythms, such as rhythm of accents, as wholly dependent on a mere succession of time intervals. There are simultaneous rhythms, such as those of lines and curves; and there are other rhythms which, although possible only in time, yet are not properly rhythms of time intervals, such for instance as a series of accented and unaccented syllables in poetry. Modern painting makes an extensive use of simultaneous rhythms. The art of design is all based on the rhythm of lines and curves. We find in many modern paintings that a certain line or curve, introduced first as an element of landscape, is then repeated in the position of human bodies, in their gestures, in the configuration of clouds, the motion of waves, etc. One of Anisfeld's paintings introduces a system of curves in a caravan of camels and then rhythmically repeats this system by the configuration of the hills rising in the background. Roerich paints ocean waves by rhythmically repeating the same elementary design. Gauguin constantly makes one part of the human body rhythmically repeated by other parts.

Thus rhythm is not necessarily dependent on time. Any repetition of identical, or even similar, sensory elements is rhythm. Illustrations of rhythm, therefore, may be seen in a row of columns, in the arrangement of vaults in a church, in simple undulatory line of a cornice, or in positions of folds in a woman's dress.

Rhythm in poetry.—Two different kinds of rhythm run through the history of poetry: one being based on time, that is, length of syllables; the other on accent, that is, relative loudness of syllables (*"l'accroissement d'intensité"*).[8] Different languages display different preferences for one type or the other. But, I believe, there is no language that is based entirely on one

[8] Provided that one agrees to regard accent as a matter of relative loudness.

type to the complete exclusion of the other. Theoretically there are systems of poetry that are believed to be built exclusively on the basis of quantity or exclusively on the basis of accent. But practically every language combines both types in an individual proportion. Ancient Latin and Greek were theoretically based on quantity, and yet accent could not have been altogether abandoned in reading. The Russian language allows only tonic versification; but naturally different syllables are pronounced with slight differences in length. Modern English seems to present a case of a successfully achieved balance between the two kinds of rhythm. It is just for this reason that English rhythm appears to be exceptionally rich and complicated.

The length of vowels still plays an important part in English speech. Although there are no rules of prosody to determine the sequence and distribution of the long and short vowels, yet there is some evidence that such distribution is not entirely lawless. It is, however, left wholly to the poetic instinct and has never been canonized. Analysis of photographic records hardly shows any regularity of time intervals between individual syllables. If there is a temporal rhythm in English poetry, it evidently reveals itself in the organization of larger rhythmical units, "wave-lengths," or, as Amy Lowell prefers to call them, "curves," which correspond to the periods of breathing (*les groupes de souffle*).

For our present purposes the length of individual vowels comes into consideration only in so far as it determines certain qualitative variations of the vowel sounds. The so-called long vowels sound different from the short ones. But so far as the actual (physical) time is concerned, the short syllables often cover just as much time as the long ones, and even more. Therefore, we may simplify our task by concentrating our attention exclusively upon the rhythm of accents. This, no doubt, is an artificial isolation of a certain aspect of the living rhythm, and an abstraction. But then, science always proceeds by abstractions. We admit that the picture of rhythm thereby produced is incomplete. But it is not therefore incorrect.[9]

Considering accents, we observe that the structure of verse reveals a certain rhythmical regularity that makes it different from ordinary prose. Verse consists of a succession of accented and unaccented syllables arranged in a certain regular order. This arrangement, as every one knows, is supposed to follow certain rigid forms or rules, which are called meter. But it seldom does. Meter, the illegitimate child of rhythm, is merely an artificial abstraction, a convenient scale for measuring verse. But it is not the actual law of versification. The latter is much more complex. Conventional scanning done according to some rigid metrical scheme often kills the poetry. "Nothing," writes Dr. Patterson, "is more astonishing than to find the evidence for some remarkable rhythm adduced in the form of bare conventional scanning."[10]

There is nothing new in the distinction between rhythm and meter. In our day it has become almost a second convention to attack "conventional scanning." Let us see what is wrong with meter.

---

[9] We are not in position here to dwell exhaustively on the problem of rhythm. The literature on the question is immense. It goes beyond the scope of this work even to give a bibliography in the field. We are here interested in rhythm in so far as it touches upon the question of rime. One who wishes to acquaint one's self with the problem of rhythm in its most general form from the linguistic point of view may profitably read Paul Verrier's *Essai sur les principes de la métrique anglaise*, the second volume of which is devoted to the general theory of rhythm, and on which the present discussion is largely based. Apart from the fundamental works by Neumann, Minor, Sievers, Guest, Saintsbury, and Bücher, one may with a great profit and real pleasure read the recent works of J. H. Scott, published in *University of Iowa Studies, Rhythmic Prose* (1925), and *Rhythmic Verse*. A thorough analysis of rhythm from the point of view of the experimental psychology may be found in Dr. Patterson's *The Rhythm of Prose*.

[10] W. M. Patterson, *The Rhythm of Prose*, page 96.

Rhythm and meter.[11]—"Perhaps," writes Edwin Guest, "no man ever paid the same attention to the quality of his rhythm as Milton. What other poets effect, as it were, by chance, Milton achieved by the aid of science and of art; he studied the aptness of his numbers, and diligently tutored an ear which nature had gifted with the most delicate sensibility. In the flow of his rhythm, in the quality of his letter-sounds, in the disposition of his pauses, his verse almost ever fits the subject; and so insensibly does poetry blend with this—the last beauty of exquisite versification, that the reader may sometimes doubt whether it be the thought itself, or merely the happiness of its expression which is the source of a gratification so deeply felt."[12] Even a foreigner who begins to read *Paradise Lost* in the original feels the tremendous effect of its rhythmic power. It

---

[11] The author of this essay is heartily in agreement with Professor J. H. Scott in regarding meter, and its attendant time, as "but subordinate factors in determining rhythm" (*Rhythmic Verse*, page 48). Feeling against the tyranny of meter has been ripening in our critical literature for the last sixty or seventy years. Sidney Lanier writes: "I am strongly inclined to believe that English poetry might be a great gainer if it would at once frankly recognize this rhythmic but unmetrical verse as a strictly rhythmized prose, and print it as such without the deceptive line division" (*The Science of English Verse*, page 235). Ed. Sievers maintains "dass jedes als metrisch anzuerkennende Stück neben seinem äusserlichen metrischen Schema einen deutlich und leicht erfassbaren Rhythmus . . . . habe" (*Metrische Studien*, page 18). This principle serves him as a valuable method for research. P. Verrier in his *Essai sur les principes de la métrique anglaise* makes the following remark: "C'est pourtant sur ce fondement imaginaire, qu'on édifice à priori la plupart des métriques anglaise. On commence bien quelquefois par dire que les vers se compassent de pieds; puis, sans même définir ce mot, on énumère les differents pieds dont peut se compose un vers. Mais ces pieds, comment les obtient-on? Est-ce par l'analyse des vers? Non. On les reçoit tout simplement de la tradition, ou bien on les retrouve en combinant de toutes les manières possibles des syllabes classées a priori."

[12] Edwin Guest, *A History of English Rhythms* (new edition edited by Rev. Walter W. Skeat, 1882), page 530.

207

is a veritable ocean of primordial rhythmic waves, indomitable and yet, one feels, strangely logical. It is plain that this logic is not that of metrical forms. To measure Milton with an iambic foot is as impossible as to exhaust the ocean with a bucket. Let us study, therefore, not the rules but deviation from rules in Milton's prosody. Let us analyze his verse, not in so far as it follows a certain metrical scheme but rather in so far as it violates that scheme.

From the metrical point of view the first line of the *Paradise Lost* is an iambic pentameter:

> Of Man's first disobedience and the fruit . . . .

In accordance with the metrical scheme it should be represented by five unaccented and five accented syllables. We should, therefore, expect the energy curve to be as shown by the dotted line in the figure below. In fact, however, the accents of the second foot "first dis-" are reversed, for "first" is, no doubt, accented while "dis-" is left with only a secondary accent. The fourth foot, "and the" has no accent at all, for the conjunction "and" is unaccented in normal speech. The actual distribution of accents in this line, therefore, is quite different from the expected theoretical form. Photographic analysis corroborates this difference. The actual fluctuation of energy in this verse line is shown by the following curve:

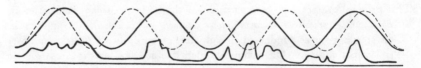

This curve is obtained by taking a contour line from the photographic record shown in the frontispiece. The lower part of the record is here used for the drawing. The curve, therefore, reads from left to right. It is rather irregular, and shows only four maxima of energy. This record is fairly representative. I have several records of this verse, and they all display the same peculiarity: a number of unaccented syllables are gathered around the four accented ones like small mountains around the four massives of greater height.

These two curves visualize the difference between meter and rhythm. Moreover, they represent with fair accuracy the fluctuation of energy of sound in the process of utterance. It is an objective record of the events in the air, and is independent of possible auditory or rhythmical illusions. It represents the physical situation when the first line of *Paradise Lost* is uttered. The value of such records is very great. They give us an objective picture of what happens in the surrounding air when we speak, and afford easy measurement of the length of individual syllables as well as a fairly accurate comparison of the amplitudes associated with different elements of speech.

In the author's opinion the controversy between objective and subjective rhythmologists is a matter of sheer misunderstanding. The subjectivists regard rhythm as merely a subjective reaction, as something that is felt in reading or music but does not objectively exist. They often believe that objective analysis falsifies the matter by substituting mere numbers for something that can only be intimately felt. What is there physica'ly is not rhythm, but a dead repetition of aesthetically irrelevant elements. Rhythm is purely psychological. Objectivists, on the other hand, are inclined to attach too much importance to their experimental results and forget that what they are studying is a mere skeleton of the living rhythm. They regard rhythm as merely an objective situation, while in reality rhythm cannot be anything else but a subjective reaction to an objective situation. It has both physical and psychological aspects.

When the results of the author's statistical studies on rhythm were communicated to an objective rhythmologist his comment was, Why did not the author do the job physically?

The rhythmologist could not trust the results because in his opinion there was nothing to trust. There was no objective material, nothing even to criticize. But when at the annual meeting of the Modern Language Association of America in 1928 the author presented a paper in which a reference was made to some physical experiments in connection with the study of rhythm, one of the objections raised in the process of discussion was that the author made the matter unnecessarily complex and difficult to follow. Every lover of poetry, it was pointed out, knows very well what is rhythmical and what is not. The objector refused to see that any problem was involved. The author was particularly criticized for considering English rhythm as exceptionally complex. In the speaker's opinion English rhythm was very beautiful and very simple.

Thus we see that it is hopeless to try to please both sides at once. And yet we feel that it is impossible to give preference to merely one aspect totally excluding the other. We cannot help imposing upon the subjective rhythmologist some physical considerations even though they are "difficult to follow." We can only promise to reduce the physical material to a minimum, and in order not to interrupt the continuity of the argument we refer to Appendix I those readers who may be interested to know how our material was obtained. In Appendix II the reader will find some additional photographic records illustrating the most important rhythmical figures mentioned in the text. For the consolation of the subjectivists we may, however, be allowed to remark that all the physical material here adduced serves the sole purpose of merely confirming the correctness of our subjective impressions concerning the rhythmical structure of certain verse lines. It is to be borne in mind that our photographic records are not intended to impose any kind of scanning upon any of the lines used. They show only that by experienced dramatic readers and learned phoneticians certain lines have been read in a certain fashion. By comparing their interpretations of various lines with the records obtained from the oscillograph we are able to formulate certain types of rhythm (not meter), or rhythmical figures which often repeat themselves, and are—we believe—associated with the same emotional response.

To avoid possible misunderstanding it is important to note that neither our photographic records nor the statistical tables given below are intended to *explain* rhythm as a physical phenomenon, but only to *describe* it. The question for us is, not *why* a certain rhythm produces a certain impression on our mind, but *what* constitutes this "certain rhythm." Our task is purely descriptive, and not explanatory. We here propose a certain technique for rhythm registration, just as our musical notation provides a technique for registering melodies and harmonies. In the case of a melody the question concerning its structure is answered in a perfectly definite form by its score. The musician reads what melody is from the score. The reader of poetry is in a less advantageous position. He can only read words. Rhythm is supposed to go along with those words. It is not customary to indicate rhythm in poetry. And when it is indicated, it is usually indicated in a wrong way by means of the underlying metrical scheme. In most cases the reader is unaware of what constitutes the rhythmical motion. The question of "what" is therefore of prime importance.

Let us call any deviation from regular meter an interruption. Thus the quoted line contains two interruptions: one in the second foot, "first dis-," having a trochee instead of an iambus; the other in the fourth foot, "and the," showing in normal, non-rhetorical, reading a very slight accent or no accent at all. Such interruptions are by no means exceptional. They exist in all languages. Poetry would be unbearably monotonous if we were obliged to follow strictly any prescribed metrical scheme. The emotional character, the reading quality, of each line depends largely on the distribution of interruptions.

211

There are, of course, several different ways to read each verse. And, perhaps, several of those ways are equally good. Professor Scott reminds us that a certain group of words was found susceptible of being marked for stress, pitch, duration, and weight, in several hundred ways. "The number of choices is tremendous," he writes, "and enough to destroy utterly the possibility of depending on any scanning for the rhythm of a passage." We do not deny all this; although we suspect, with Professor Scott, that "several hundred" is probably an exaggeration and that a good many of the possible variations are so small as to be entirely negligible. Yet there are many different ways of reading a line. Many a high-school student would read the first verse of *Paradise Lost* with a regular accent on each foot:

Of Mán's first disobédience ánd the frúit . . . .

Many a college student does the same thing, even though you tell him that "first" was, in all probability, designed to be accented. Moreover, the amount of accent placed on "dis-" differs very considerably in the interpretation of different readers.

And yet all these considerations only support our argument. Our contention is that the reading quality of the verse depends on whether or not an accent is placed on "first," and whether or not "dis-" and "and" are regularly accented. Photographic records have shown that good dramatic readers do accentuate "first" and leave "dis-" and "and" without any appreciable accent. But the amount of accent placed on "dis-" varies even among good and experienced dramatic readers. This suggests that a certain amount of uncertainty may be associated with any poetic line. But on the whole it cannot be denied that there are lines which move with solemn dignity, and others that read with a peculiar ease and playful elegance; there are whole passages that move with an almost alarming gravity

212

and others which run along like drops of molten silver. The question is what constitutes the difference. Of course, there are many causes for each effect. We claim that we have found only one of them. Distribution of interruptions is responsible for numerous variations in the reading quality of the verse. An iambic pentameter with a spondee in the first foot, such as:

Sing, Heavenly Muse, that on the secret top . . . .

is quite different in its rhythmic character from one which has a spondee in the second or third foot, such as:

Nor the deep tract of Hell—say first what cause . . . .

A line that has no accent in the second foot reads differently from that which has a similar interruption in the fourth foot. Absence of accent in the second foot in English pentameter produces an elegant and effective swing that reads lightly and with an ease:

Of Oreb or of Sinai . . . .

while a missing accent on the fourth produces a quite different impression, difficult to describe yet easy to grasp with what Sievers calls "das rhythmisch-melodische Empfinden des Lesers." *Paradise Lost* again provides us with a classical illustration of this rhythm:

Of their great Sultan waving to direct

Our emotional response to a verse line as a whole depends substantially on two factors: the distribution of vowels (musical response), and distribution of interruptions (rhythmical response). In the latter case our emotional reaction depends not so much on the mere presence of interruptions but largely on where those interruptions take place. *Our emotional response is a function of accelerations and retardations variously distributed within different lines.*

213

Graphic representation of various rhythms.—In order to be able to study the effect of interruptions it is highly important to register them graphically. This can easily be done by representing each foot in a verse line by a small quadrangle and indicating interruptions by some specific signs.[13] Thus a line in iambic pentameter must be divided into five spaces: ▭▭▭▭▭. If it has no rhythmic interruptions, that is to say, if it reads regularly, having metrical accent on each foot, all those spaces must be left vacant. Thus the diagram above may be taken as representing an, in English, rather exceptional line, such as:

As fár remóved from Gód and líght of Héaven.

If an accent is missing, its absence is marked by a point placed in the corresponding cell. For instance, the verse:

Restóre us, and regáin the blíssful séat . . . .

which has an interruption in the second foot (missing accent), will be graphically represented as follows: ▭▪▭▭▭ . The point in the second quadrangle corresponds to "and," which has no accent (or, in normal reading, but a very slight accent).

The inventor of this method, Andrei Baily, limited his observations exclusively to the field of Russian iambic tetrameter. Having arrived at certain important conclusions with regard to the rhythmical structure of Russian four-foot iambi he stopped his investigations and as far as I know he never developed them any further. If one wishes to apply his method to the study of other languages, one has to modify his system by introducing a number of other signs corresponding to different kinds of rhythmical interruptions. For Russian interruptions consist almost exclusively of "missing accents";

[13] This method was originally devised by a Russian poet, Andrei Baily, in his work on *Symbolism.*

214

no other marks but "points" are, therefore, needed to represent Russian rhythm. English rhythm is much more complex. It not merely tolerates but makes an extensive use of trochees within iambic verse and vice versa. Occasionally there are spondees, especially within the lines of high specific gravity. The anapestic foot is another very common form of rhythmical interruption frequently employed in English poetry. The application of all those forms at the same time makes the matter much more complicated. And yet this complexity is by no means an objection against the application of the graphic method to the study of English poetry. One only needs to introduce a special sign for every particular class of interruptions.

Following Baily's method, I have adopted a black point (.) to represent a missing accent. A circle (o) is used for a trochee; a cross (×) stands for a spondee; and an added syllable (anapestic foot) is marked by a triangle (△). Those four signs are sufficient to represent graphically even such complicated rhythms as English.[14] Such a verse as:

Dove-like sat'st brooding on the vast Abyss . . . .

shows three different types of interruptions in one line. "Dove" is no doubt accented, while "like" will be in all probability left without any appreciable accent (or at least with less accent than "dove") by most dramatic readers. Therefore the first foot must be regarded as a trochee. The second foot is a spondee, for both "sat'st" and "brooding" are fairly equally accented. "On" evidently has no accent. The whole line may therefore be graphically represented as follows:

Advantages of the graphic method.—The advantages of the graphic method in studying the problems of rhythm are

[14] There are in English some other minor deviations from the regular metrical scheme, but they occur but rarely and are of small importance.

obvious. In the first place, it makes certain peculiarities of rhythm actually visible. We not merely hear the rhythm; we actually see the distribution of accents within a line. This gives to the fleeting and evanescent phenomenon of rhythm a stabilized existence for the eye. In other words, it helps us to transform certain auditory series into visual series, with the understanding that at any time the visual symbols can be again retransformed into their original pattern.

By making rhythm accessible to the eye this method helps us to compare different rhythmical effects and to describe them briefly and precisely. An exhaustive analysis of such effects may be of great practical assistance to poets. Especially, it may be discovered which effects are rhythmically inconsistent and therefore to be avoided in poetic composition. Thus the graphic method may possibly lead to the discovery of a negative canon, the study of which may prove just as profitable for the purposes of rhythmical composition as that of the fallacies is profitable for correct logical composition. At least in the Russian language such studies have actually affected the practical work of poets.

The graphic method also greatly facilitates the statistical study of rhythm. By visualizing rhythmical processes we are in position to compare not merely the peculiarities of rhythm in different languages, but also the idiosyncrasies of individual poets. We may occasionally find that certain rhythmical figures appear more frequently in certain authors and constitute what we but vaguely feel as their peculiar "manner."

It is to be understood that the graphic method does not protect us against the influence of subjective interpretation of rhythm. We must here warn the reader against a possible misconception. The explanations given may be construed as implying that the graphic representation gives us a true and objective picture of rhythm as it really is. It must be pointed out, however, that rhythm never is, or exists, unless it is read by someone. Therefore, an allowance must be made for the subjective interpretation of the reader. The graphic method does not register an objective rhythm as it exists in itself—for there is no such thing as an independently existing rhythm—but only my own reading of it. It is true that verse lines are ordinarily scanned by most readers in an identical manner. Yet there might be, and in fact always are, minor disagreements, especially on the question of spondees.

In the subsequent analyses I have seldom used my own scanning as the basis for graphic representation. For different languages I decided to obtain the assistance of different persons thoroughly familiar with the particular language subjected to test as well as with the graphic method to be applied. A considerable portion of the work presented in this chapter was done by the members of my language class. Their scanning may not always coincide with that of a dramatic reader or a learned philologist; but on the whole, I believe, we succeeded in registering a fairly intelligent scanning, on the principle that a verse line should be read naturally and without poetic affectation.

Comparative study of English, German, and Russian rhythms.—The advantages of the graphic method can be easily demonstrated by comparing rhythms of different languages. On page 218, thirty-two lines each from Milton's *Paradise Lost*, Goethe's *Faust*, and Pushkin's *Boris Godunov* are thus shown.

The first column represents the first thirty-two verses from *Paradise Lost*. One observes at a glance the unusual complexity of the English rhythm, as compared with those in the other two languages. The first column is full of all sorts of "interruptions." On closer inspection, we see that it contains a large number of trochees (reversed accent) and spondees; there are 18 interruptions of this kind. We also notice that, for the most part, they fall on the first foot. The question arises: is it a typically Miltonian characteristic, or a peculiarity of English pentameter in general?

The second column represents thirty-two lines taken from Goethe's *Faust*, the section beginning with:

Ich grüsse dich, du einzige Phiole!
Die ich mit Andacht nun herunterhole,
In dir verehr' ich Menschenwitz und Kunst.
Du Inbegriff der holden Schlummersäfte ....

Paradise Lost, 1–32	Faust, 690–721	Boris Godunov, 1–32

O – trochee
● – accent missing
× – spondee
△ – anapest

The trochees here are considerably fewer. The rhythm is formed rather by omitting than by adding accents. Very few lines in the English column contain less than five accents; the English rhythm displays a tendency toward increasing the number of accents in the line. The German language, on the contrary, appears to be fond of omitting accents. The first line in the quotation from *Faust* contains only three, instead of five, accents. There is but a very slight accent on *"dich,"* and no accent on *"-ge."*

The third column represents a part of the fountain scene from *Boris Godunov*, which in English transliteration reads as follows:

> Tenj Grosnovo menya oosynovila,
> Dimitri'em iz groba narekla,
> Vokroog menya narodi vozmootila
> I v zhertvoo mne Borisa otdala.

Trochees are here entirely absent. There are neither spondees nor anapests. The rhythm consists exclusively of interruptions of one kind, missing accents, which appear in Russian much more frequently than in English.

A glance at the diagram reveals another interesting fact. From the Russian and German column we can see that the interruptions fall largely on the second and fourth feet. This is by no means accidental. For such an arrangement of interruptions makes a verse line symmetrical. It is, no doubt, for this reason that such lines afford the greatest rhythmical satisfaction; for symmetry in any form appears to be aesthetically effective. Considering the structure of the lines of this type we observe that they have only three accents:

> Ich grüsse dich, du einzige Phiole!

or,

> Und froh ist wenn er Regenwürmer findet.

These accents are symmetrically arranged: two at the ends and one in the middle. Graphically represented, it is: ☐•☐•☐ the vacant quadrangles representing the accented feet, and the points standing for the missing accents. Such symmetrical arrangement is perceived, in the process of reading, as a highly pleasing effect. It creates a rhythmical swing of unusual poetic power and may properly be called the "ideal figure."

History of symmetrical lines.—Analyzing the iambic tetrameter in Russian, Andrei Baily made the interesting discovery that symmetrical lines of the form ⬚▪⬚▪⬚ do not appear in Russian poetry before the nineteenth century. They were introduced by Pushkin.

There was at once a great deal of argument about Pushkin's rôle in the history of Russian versification. Even the earliest critics felt, of course, that Pushkin actually revolutionized Russian verse. For the expression of this feeling many stereotyped phrases were coined. There was much talk about the "peculiar charm" and "magic beauty" of Pushkin's verse, about the peculiar "ease" and "crystalline clearness" of his composition. But what was the technical cause of this charm and this ease remained a mystery until Andrei Baily pointed out that Pushkin was the first to shift missing accents from the second to the first foot. It is sufficient to read a page or two from Derjavin to convince one's self that pre-Pushkinian versification (as far as iambic tetrameter was concerned) was based on the rhythmic formula, ⬚⬚▪⬚⬚. This form, in Russian, produces the impression of a heavy, emphatic rhythm, with a certain touch of pseudo-classical dignity. It does not mean, of course, that the form should be altogether discarded, nor that it does not occur in Pushkin or in modern poetry. Only, the predominance of this form in a long run is annoying. And in pre-Pushkinian poetry this form predominates. Pushkin's reform consisted of introducing rhythms of different formation. He first shifted the missing accent, as has already been pointed out, from the second to the first foot. By doing that he created the possibility of producing symmetrical lines of the form, ▪⬚⬚▪⬚. Such lines, in Russian, are unusually easy to read, very elegant and graceful.

220

A similar situation we find in the history of German poetry. The graphic analysis of iambic pentameter in German revealed an interesting fact: verse lines with symmetrical structure such as described in the preceding paragraph are exceedingly rare in German poetry before Goethe. The analysis of two hundred lines from Kleist revealed only ten verses which were unmistakably of this type. Two hundred lines from Lessing were found to contain only eight lines of this kind, all of which were doubtful. The only perfect line of this kind in Lessing's *Nathan der Weise* seems to be:

Da Kommen die Kamele meines Vaters

where *"die"* is obviously unaccented and *"meines"* receives but a very slight secondary stress. The claims of other lines for being counted as examples of the same form may be disputed. In some cases the rhythm of the verse, which otherwise would be of a symmetrical nature, is broken up by the interference of another person speaking. For instance, the verse:

Gebaut, und ein bequemeres. Schon wahr!

actually contains only three accents symmetrically distributed about the unaccented *"ein"* and *"-res."* In reality, however, the line is broken into two rhythmically independent fragments, which makes the perception and appreciation of symmetry very difficult and almost impossible, for its parts are distributed between two voices:

NATHAN

Dann, Daja, hatten wir ein neues uns

Gebaut, und ein bequemeres.

DAJA

Schon wahr!

The same situation we find in the following fragment:

221

DAJA

Verschwúnden!

NATHAN

Nicht auf ímmer, will ich hóffen.

In the remaining five cases of symmetry the value of the secondary accent may be disputed. Thus the number of symmetrical lines in the analyzed fragment from *Nathan der Weise* is practically negligible.

Herder seldom writes in iambic pentameter. In *Die Gräfin Linda,* which contains one hundred and forty verses, we were able to count five and in *Not und Hoffnung* only one line with symmetrical distribution of accents; while Goethe's pentameter is full of symmetrical lines. In thirty lines from *Faust,* as can be seen from the diagram, there are six undoubtedly symmetrical verses.

In order to allow a symmetrical distribution of accents, a verse must have a peculiar and difficult structure. In order to avoid accent on the second foot the poet has a choice of two possibilities: either he may make use of a longer word for the first foot or he may fill up the second foot with logically insignificant parts of speech, such as pronouns, prepositions, or auxiliary verbs. The same applies to the fourth foot. This is rather difficult to do in German, for iambic pentameter quite naturally leads to various combinations of monosyllabic and disyllabic words. Here is an illustration of pre-Goethean pentameter (Herder):

Der Érde Sáat ist unser kúre Múh',

Sie sínket léicht, und frísch erstéhet sie.

Wie júnges Grün soll unser Hóffnung grünen,

Báld ist es Frúcht, wo Blüten nur erschíenen.

222

Reading these lines one almost feels that it is impossible to avoid accent on the second foot. *"Der Erde Saat," "Sie sinket leicht," "Wie junges Grün,"* etc.—all these expressions seem to result naturally from the metrical scheme. This initial rythmic figure became so standardized that it needed Goethe's genius to break through its rigid form. At first sight doing so may seem almost impossible. Goethe has shown that it can be easily accomplished if the methods indicated are used.

> Ich grüsse dich, du einzige Phiole!
>
> . . . .
>
> Du Inbegriff der holden Schlummersäfte
>
> . . . .
>
> Ich sehe dich, es wird der Schmerz gelindert,
> Ich fasse dich, das Streben wird gemindert.
>
> . . . .
>
> Nicht fratzenhaft bewegt, wohltätig milde

The accent on the second foot is here successfully avoided either by using insignificant words, such as *"dich," "es," "der,"* etc., or by introducing long words with secondary accents, such as *"Inbegriff," "fratzenhaft,"* etc., where the accent falls largely on the first syllable, leaving the end of the word (*"-griff," "-haft"*) but slightly accented. It is a thing that is not so easily done in German. And indeed, before Goethe it was never done extensively. *"Ich grüsse dich, du einzige Phiole,"* is a supremely Goethean verse, the peculiar beauty of which depends largely on the symmetrical distribution of accents. The line sounds as an artistically organized motion consisting of three ascending waves each followed by a deep descent. The rhythm is simple, and its organization is transparent.

223

Double interruptions.—The rhythmical figure that we have just been discussing represents the simplest case of double interruptions. There are verse lines with only one accent missing, such as:

Restore us, and regain the blissful seat,

where "and" in the second foot is not stressed. The verse, therefore, has one interruption on the second foot. It is of the form, ☐☐☐•☐ . There are, on the other hand, verses with two accents missing out of the total number of five accents. Goethe's symmetrical line is a very good illustration of such rhythms. The position of missing accents, however, is by no means confined to the second and fourth feet. A glance at the second column of our comparative table of rhythms reveals the interesting fact that Goethe's verse is very rich in double interruptions of various forms. Open at random any section of Faust that is written in iambic pentameter, and you will find plenty of illustrations. For instance:

Ich schaffe, was ihr wollt, und schaffe mehr;

Zwar ist es leicht, doch ist das leichte schwer;

Es liegt schon da, doch um es zu erlangen,

Das ist die Kunst, wer weiss es anzufangen?

The first line has but one interruption on "*was.*" In the second verse the first phrase: "*zwaristesleicht,*" has but one accent on "*-leicht*"; the second rhythmical phrase (after the caesura), "*dochistdasleichte schwér,*" lacks the accent on "*-ist.*" The third verse allows no accent on either "*um*" or "*zu,*" thereby producing a very peculiar rhythmical effect of two successive interruptions with an inverse accent on "*doch*": ☐☐•☐•☐ . The last line has again but a single interruption. The whole fragment may be graphically represented as follows:

It is interesting to compare Goethe's verse and that of his predecessors with regard to the application of double interruptions. I have attempted to compare Kleist, Herder, and Goethe. And although the statistical results of such comparisons do not belong within the scope of this essay, I cannot resist the temptation to illustrate by an extract from my tables. The picture may speak more plainly than numbers. In the drawing below the right-hand column represents thirty-two lines from Kleist's *An Wilhelminen*, beginning:

Jetzt wärmt der Lenz die flocken-
        freie Luft;
Der Himmel kann im Bach sich wie-
        derspiegeln.
Den Schafer labt der jungen Blumen
        Duft;
Sein Wollenvieh hüpft auf begrassten
        Hügeln.

The whole fragment contains only two lines with double interruptions. The whole column is strikingly pale if compared with the first column, which represents the same familiar lines from *Faust*. The latter shows fifteen double interruptions, and a much larger number of other forms of violated meter. Such unusual variety and richness of rhythm accounts (partly, at least) for the supreme beauty of Goethean verse. The comparison is representative. The density of interruptions in Goethe's poems is sometimes even

225

greater than the one which is here depicted; and other sections from Kleist appear even paler than this one. It seems that the richer the rhythm, the more expressive and effective it is.

Emotional value of interruptions.—All these subtle distinctions of rhythm that have just been discussed are of far greater significance than might appear at the first glance. They determine the reading value, the so-called swing of a given verse line. Our emotional response to the different forms of interruptions is different. A verse line that contains no deviations from regular meter is not merely formally but emotionally different from a line that shows the presence of interruptions. It is sufficient to compare two verse lines of which one has all regular accents and the other contains a missing accent on the first foot in order to feel the difference at once. If the interruption falls not on the first but on one of the subsequent feet, the impression is again different. For instance:

> Thou taintest all thou lookst upon! The stars
> Which on thy cradle beamed so brightly sweet,
> Were gods to the distempered playfulness
> Of thy untutored infancy; the trees . . . .

In this fragment each line reveals a different rhythmical physiognomy. The first line has no interruptions; every second syllable is noticeably accented. It sounds "rigorously formal," may be described, perhaps, as "conventionally poetical." If all lines were of the same type, the poem would be unbearably monotonous. The second line has an interruption on the first foot, for "on" receives no accent. As a contrast to the first line, which is rigorously correct, it reads with a sudden "playful elegance," perhaps due to the fact that in reading we lightly pass over the first three syllables as if but playfully touching them with our voice (acceleration on the first foot). The third line has a missing accent on the second foot, for "the" receives

226

no stress. It makes on me an impression of "emphatic serious-ness," or of "sudden pensiveness after a playful smile." I may be mistaken, but it seems to me that such a rhythmical figure is highly appropriate for expressing serious thought, or for a phrase that has logical weight. The fourth line has an inter-ruption in the third foot. Our emotional response to it, it seems to me, is similar to that of the second line; it reads with ease and a certain undefinable poetic elegance.

Now my interpretation of our emotional response to each of those lines may be wrong. It is impossible, in such questions, to avoid what is called the subjective factor. Yet the crucial point of the argument is thereby not invalidated. The emo-tions associated with different types of rhythm may be differ-ently described by different persons, but it must be admitted that in each case they are different. The second line of the fragment given above sounds rhythmically different from the first line. Just what this difference is subjectively cannot be scientifically described, but it is immediately "felt." Yet all those differences can be very precisely described objectively. The graphic method makes it possible for us to register ac-curately every single deviation from the regular metrical scheme; and, knowing that every such deviation releases a specific emotional response, we are thereby placed in the po-sition of preparing convenient maps of our subjective reactions to any given poem.[15]

Rhythmical idiosyncrasies of individual poets.—Individual authors display definite preferences for certain rhythmical pe-

---

[15] Poetic accelerations and retardations, to be sure, are not mathematically determinable factors. Grammont says: "Ces différences de vitesse n'ont la rigueur mathématique que nous leur avons, attribuée qu'en théorie" (*Le Vers français*, page 105). Yet there is something in them that can be studied mathematically (statistically or otherwise). And it is precisely this element that interests us here. It by no means uncovers the whole "mystery" of poetry; yet it enables us to understand at least some elements of that mystery.

culiarities. The graphic method furnishes a convenient way of determining and discovering such peculiarities. To illustrate this point, which is of considerable importance for the whole of our argument concerning the relation between rhythm and rime, I am obliged to refer to certain statistical data.

Analyzing Pope, for instance, one arrives at the conclusions that (1) his rhythm is comparatively poor in interruptions, and (2) he systematically avoids missing accents in the second foot. Whether it is a matter of deliberate effort or of instinctive preference is of course impossible to say. The graph below represents two hundred lines from "The Temple of Fame."

The poverty of interruptions here immediately strikes the eye; if it were not for the trochees, a large number of lines would be metrically correct, i.e., would retain all the five accents in the right places. More than 25 per cent of the entire number of lines have no interruptions of any kind, not even trochees. The whole diagram looks very pale, the density of interruptions being comparatively low. There is a remarkable scarcity of missing accents in the second foot; in two hundred verses there are only seven interruptions of this kind. The verse regularly retaining accents on the second foot acquires the character of solemn dignity and classical decorum. This effect is intensified by an overwhelming abundance of trochees in the first foot. Pope almost deliberately avoids accelerations; there are comparatively few accents missing; there are one hundred sixteen lines with all the five accents distinctly present. Instead, his verse displays a noticeable tendency for *retardando*. Hence the unusual number of trochaic and spondaic feet. For spondees, accumulating accents, make the motion of the verse slower. The trochees have practically the same effect, because by reversing the accent we interfere with the normal rhythm of the verse, breaking up the habitual motion and thereby causing an involuntary delay. All this contributes to the slow dignity of classical verse. Similar peculiarities we find in the rhythmical

228

structure of Dryden's verse. The same overabundance of trochees on the first foot, the same scarcity of missing accents.

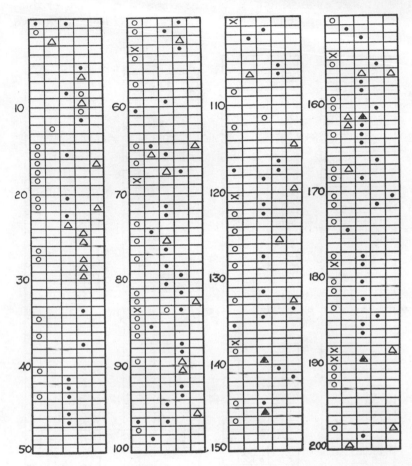

These rhythmical peculiarities are evidently responsible for the solemn character of pseudo-classical poetry. In remarkable contrast to the stiffness and rhythmic monotony of pseudo-classics the romantic poetry of the early nineteenth century displays notable abundance and variety of rhythmical forms.

229

To see the contrast it may suffice to throw even a superficial glance at the graphs representing Shelley's "Spirit of Solitude." The number of missing accents is here considerably larger than in the preceding diagrams. There are many lines with two missing accents.

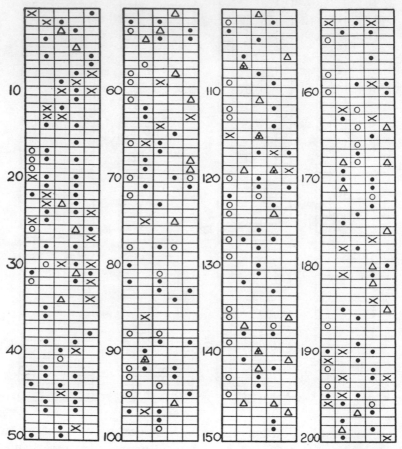

Double interruptions in English poetry.—In four hundred verse lines from Dryden and Pope combined we have found only one verse where two accents were missing:

230

The Jéwish rábbins, though their énemies.

And even this line is doubtful, for the last syllable in "enemies" receives a strong secondary accent on "*-ies*," which is intensified by the rime. As a contrast to this, in two hundred lines from Shelley we were able to identify thirty lines with double interruptions of this kind, as can be seen from the graph.

Two missing accents in a verse produce varied and peculiar effects. If the missing accents mark the second and fourth feet, the verse line, as we have seen, becomes symmetrical. It closely resembles what Professor Stewart, in his *The Technique of English Verse,* calls the "dipodic verse." One finds a sufficient number of perfect lines of this type in Shelley. For example:

Enóugh from incommúnicable dréam

. . . .

Suspénded in the sólitary dóme

. . . .

And mótions of the fórests and the séa

. . . .

The páuses of her músic and her bréath

Such lines read with a remarkable ease and graceful swing in all languages.[16] We have discussed them at length in connection with Goethe. In English such lines are often accompanied by spondees in the last foot, such as:

[16] This seems to contradict the "quadral theory" recently advanced by Mr. Scott. Yet the contradiction is merely apparent. The symmetry involved in the illustrations above can be easily reconstructed according to Mr. Scott's method into a "dual" form. See, for example, the last phrase in the list of illustrations on page 18 of his *Rhythmic Verse,* and his rhythmic model for it.

231

In charnels and on coffins where black death

· · · · · · · · · ·

Thy shadow and the darkness of thy steps

· · · · · · · · · ·

Made paler the pale moon, to her cold home

· · · · · · · · · · ·

In terror at the glare of those wild eyes

· · · · · · · · · · ·

That wasted him, would call him with false names

· · · · · · · · · · ·

It rose as he approached, and with strong wings

One feels at once that our emotional reaction to such lines is quite different from that of the preceding group. Psychologically they require more attention, because the last two words are stressed. In reading them we cannot avoid a considerable *retardando* at the end of the rhythmic period. They read more heavily. I have selected the lines at random without considering their meaning at all. But it is interesting and highly significant that in meaning, too, they present a marked contrast to the preceding group. They all are "serious," "weighty," even "tragic," which can be seen from the words they contain: "black death," "cold home," "wild eyes," "false names," "strong wings." In contrast to those grave words the preceding group speaks of dreams, forests, and seas. The rational content of the words is evidently reflected in the rhythmic structure of the verse. It is an objective proof of the greatness of the poet that his rhythmic form and rational content constitute a union.

From these illustrations we also see that rhythm is a very sensitive thing. An additional accent at the end of a rhythmic phrase produces an effect which radically changes our emotional response. The rhythmic phrase of the form: ☐☐•☐•☐ is changed almost into its opposite by adding an extra accent. Comparing the rhythmical impression of the two verse lines:

And motions of the forests and the sea

and

In charnels and on coffins where black death . . . .

we immediately feel that the latter line is not merely different from the first, but that it is almost opposite in its effect. The elegant ease of a symmetrical rhythm is gone. The line shows a high specific gravity. There is nothing changed in it rythmically except the last foot, and yet the line appears with an entirely different physiognomy.

The effects that Shelley achieves with his double and triple interruptions, combining missing accents with trochees and spondees, are practically innumerable. It would lead us far beyond the scope of the present work to describe even those combinations which occur quite regularly. It may serve as a theme of a special inquiry. Here we are interested in it only in so far as it illustrates the principle of rhythmic interruptions and shows their association with emotional responses. Generalizing the results so far obtained, we feel justified in saying that every particular distribution of interruptions releases a specific emotional response. Just for the sake of curiosity a few exceptional and exquisite lines may be demonstrated. If, for instance, the accents are missing on the third and fifth feet together, the result is very peculiar and striking. For example:

Of fire and poison inaccessible

. . . .

The red volcano overcanopies . . . .

No one can miss the peculiar effect of such a rhythmical figure. It sounds totally different from that of other lines, to the extent of falling almost out of time. It is evident that the strange effect is reached neither by the meaning of the words (for there is nothing especially unusual in the meaning of these lines), nor by the music of the vowels (which contains no exceptional effects), but exclusively by the peculiar distribution of interruptions: ▭▭•▭▭•▭. Moreover, we see that of all possible kinds of interruptions only "missing accents" are here employed. And yet the effect is unique, and noticeable even to the most inexperienced ear.

Another rhythmic phrase that is markedly different from others is: •▭○▭▭•▭ . For instance:

And my heart ever gazes on the depth

which combines two missing accents with a trochee in the second foot. The effect of such a phrase is especially noticeable when it appears in contrast with other lines of more regular formation.

There often occurs in Shelley a charming phrase:•▭▭•▭▭ which combines two missing accents, one in the first and another in the third foot, such as:

There is a voice, not understood by all

. . . .

For in the air do I behold indeed

. . . .

As in despair, and with his sinewy neck

. . . .

It is interesting to note that the number of missing accents in Shelley's poetry is comparatively large, 146 accents missing in two hundred lines, as against 83 missing accents in the two hundred lines from Pope. It seems to me that missing accents contribute much to the emotional grace, spondees and trochees to the intellectual weight, of poetry.

234

Rhythm and rime.—From the preceding paragraphs we see that a metrical scheme is never strictly followed in the practical composition of poetry. Only trisyllabic meters show a constant, uninterrupted regularity. But such rhythms deviate considerably from the nature of our normal speech and approach rather the nature of a song. In iambic and trochaic poetry the meter is continually interrupted by missing accents, spondees, anapests, dactyls, etc.

Now, *rime restores the rhythm distorted by interruptions.* No matter where the interruptions are produced—they may occasionally fall upon any syllable of the verse—rime, like the beats of a drum, brings back the distorted meter. Owing to the musical value of the rimed endings, our attention is directed toward them. And although they may not be actually stressed—in fact, the photographic records show that the beginning of a line is more stressed than the end, probably owing to the nature of breathing—yet the musical pleasure derived from the riming vowels is sufficient to attract our attention, and thereby to produce the impression that they are stressed. Rime, therefore, creates a regular super-meter which is seldom interrupted. This super-meter is so strong that it is necessary to exercise some effort to conceal it. Everybody knows that one of the difficulties of good dramatic reading—the most elementary difficulty, in fact—lies in the avoidance of accents at the end of each line.

Thus rime has an organizing function in the metrical composition of the verse. It helps us to recognize the end of a metrical period *by beating its melodious drum.* As we saw, verse fails to repeat the prescribed accent on every second syllable; rime repeats it regularly after a certain fixed number of syllables. It, therefore, *counts* our steps in reading. In ordinary poetry it is essential to count steps. For a definite number of syllables belongs to its form. It might be objected that such an artificial procedure does not constitute the nature of poetry, that a poet may write verses without any definite number of syllables in a line and without any regular meter. This is true; and yet ordinarily in metrical poetry the number of syllables in a verse is supposed to be constant. Their number, therefore, belongs to its intention, its form. The poets who wrote in iambic pentameter evidently wished us to appreciate the regularity of their artificial scheme. They counted their syllables very painfully, and they evidently expected us to keep this definite number in mind. Of course, we are not supposed to be conscious of the number as such; they do not expect us to count one, two, three, and so forth, but only to have an impression of equality among the lines. The application of arithmetic would spoil the aesthetic enjoyment. Therefore the required equality should be conveyed in a more effective and direct manner. *Rime is this manner.* It comes without counting.

Psychologically we are able to retain a certain mental image of a small number of beats without actually counting them. Three, four, even five beats have their own peculiar physiognomy. But beyond five our subconscious counting does not go. The image becomes vague and obscure. It is therefore possible without actual counting to retain the image of a verse written in four or even five iambic or trochaic feet, if the meter be regular. But as we saw, our meter is constantly interrupted by missing accents, added syllables, etcetera. That makes the subconscious counting of syllables practically impossible. We cannot depend on the number of feet (three, four, five, etcetera), for the feet do not appear regularly. And yet the poets by virtue of tradition insist upon the importance of a given number of steps. They are therefore obliged to provide us with an auxiliary means that will assist us in following their scheme. They give us rime for help.

But rime would not be able to do the job, if it had not been in position to attract our attention. Poets select rime for rhythmical purposes, because it sounds fit to do the work. But

236

it must have certain qualifications before applying for the job. It must be something apart from rhythm in order to be able to assist us rhythmically. This something is already known to us from the previous chapters. It is the musical value of rime as the key in the melody of vowels. Only because it affects us melodically can it be further utilized to assist us rhythmically. The general error of the majority of the rhythmical theories of rime lies in neglecting this preliminary aspect of the inquiry. The advocates of these theories often compare rime with a drum. But they forget that what is obvious in the drum is not at all obvious in rime. If the drum had no sound, it would not be fit to perform its function. Does rime possess an extra portion of sound energy? Of course rime is an acoustic phenomenon. It therefore has a sound. But is this sound any stronger than that of other syllables? Does it possess an extra energy? It does not seem plausible that just because a word or a syllable sounds similar to another word or syllable it acquires a stronger accent. In fact it does not. Rime strikes our ear not because it is rhythmically prominent, but because it is pleasing melodically. It attracts our attention first on the musical ground; and only because of this extra amount of attention that we pay to the riming syllable are we in position to utilize it for rhythmical purposes.

Why end-rime?—We have defined rime as the key in the melody of vowels. We have seen that of two riming words the first introduces a musical phrase and the second closes it up. Rime, therefore, appears in the beginning and at the end of the phrase. The length of the phrase cannot be determined by rules. Musical phrases constituted by the vowel sounds may have any length within certain limits determined only by the ability of our mind to perceive the effect. In ordinary cases of inner rime the phrases are very brief, usually not reaching beyond the limits of two neighboring feet:

237

Thrilled me—filled me with fantastic terrors *never felt* before

But an assonantal phrase can be easily perceived at a distance of several feet:

. . . . *rapping* at my *chamber* door

. . . .

And the silken, sad, *uncertain* rustling of each *purple curtain*

. . . .

Open here I *flung the shutter* . . . .

In some exceptional cases assonance may reach from the beginning of one line to the end of the next one. Zhirmunski gives an illustration from Walter von der Vogelweide:

. . . . *wâ* hat freude sich verborgen?
die ensinden ich hie noch *dâ.*

. . . .

. . . . *waz* bedarf ich saelden mêre?
wie kan mir gelingen *baz.*

In Russian poetry assonance is more easily perceived than in English. We therefore often find assonances reaching far beyond a single verse line, especially in modern poetry (Brusov, Balmont). For instance:

O volny mors*kiya,* rodnaya sti*hiya* moya;
Vsegda wy bezhite svobodno v i*niye* kraya.
Vsegda odinoki v holodnom dvizhen'ye svoyom,
A my bezuteshno tos*kooyem*—odni i vdvoyom.

Zachem ne mo*goo ya* di*shatj* i be*zhatj,* kak volna,
Ya v mire odin i doo *sha* oo menya holodna . . . .

— BALMONT

Connection with rhythm is evident in all these examples. Assonance falls exclusively on the accented syllables. This is

238

partly because only the accented vowels retain their full characteristic quality, and partly because it evidently belongs to the intention of the poet to emphasize the rhythm by making it more prominent with assonance. Effective assonance on an unaccented syllable is difficult for the poet to handle, even in languages which, like Russian, are highly sensitive to assonantal effects. And even if it is handled skilfully, the effect usually escapes the attention of the average reader. A good example of such unaccented assonance we find in Igor Severyanin's:

Ya povses*ér*dno ootv*ér*zhdyón.

Thus a musical phrase within a verse may begin and end anywhere. It may be completed at a distance of three or four feet; it may start at the beginning of a line and terminate only at the end of the next one, as in the example given from Walter von der Vogelweide; it may begin somewhere in the middle of a line and end also somewhere in the middle of the next one. But if a musical phrase begins and ends at the rhythmically important places, it may be easily detected even though it is fairly long. That is the reason why at the end of a verse line the assonance becomes especially effective. Here rhythm and assonance mutually help each other; melody becomes rhythmical, and rhythm melodious.

Hemistichs and distichs.—That part of the verse on which assonance, alliteration, or rime falls receives an additional stress. It is therefore convenient to utilize those devices for the rhythmical organization of verse. Rime, as a combination of both assonance and alliteration, is the most effective means for regulating rhythm. And indeed it is used not only at the end of the verse lines to straighten out the rhythm distorted by interruptions but also in the middle of the verse in order to divide it rhythmically into two distinctly perceivable halves—

239

hemistiches. This is especially profitable when the lines are comparatively long. Edgar Allan Poe's "The Raven" may again serve as a classical illustration of this method:

"Surely," said I, "surely *that is* something at my window *lattice;*
Let me see, then, what *thereat is,* and this mystery explore—

Through Poe this method penetrated into Russian poetry and found a wide application and further development in Balmont's work. Balmont translated "The Raven," retaining the riming scheme and rhythmic structure of the original. Those who are interested in knowing how "The Raven" sounds in Russian will find the beginning of it here:

Kak to v polnoch, v chas oogrumoi, polnyi tyagostno'you doomoi
Nad starinnimi tomami ya sklonilsya v polusne.
Gryosam strannim otdavalsya; vdroog, neyasnyi zvook razdalsya,
Boodto kto to postoochalsya, postoochalsya v dverj ko mhe.
"Eto verno," prosheptal ya, "guostj v polnochnoi tishine,
Guostj stoochitsya v dverj ko mne."

This scheme Balmont reproduces in numerous variations. True, it was known and used before. Pushkin applied it in some of his ballads. Lermontov and Fet occasionally experimented with it. But no one before Balmont made so extensive a use of this method. It was Poe who stimulated the development of this form in Russian.

In French, the "foot" is considered by many as an artificial and purely theoretical unit. "Trochee and iambus have little relativity to the French line; indeed these terms, though used by the older French prosodists in the classical period, are generally ignored by modern authorities, as having small significance."[17] It is, therefore, impossible in French verse to keep time and consider measure except by numbering syllables or by rime, which, to use Mitford's expression, is "the powerful and

[17] C. F. Richardson, *A Study of English Rhyme,* page 56.

almost only indicant of measure in French verse." In fact, rime is considered in French prosody an indispensable device, without which verse turns into prose. "Profoundly as French poetry has been influenced by the classical spirit, the forms of classical verse become mere shadows when imitated in French. Indeed, the syllable itself is sometimes called the foot. In the all-prevalent Alexandrine one has to think of the twelve syllables rather than of any six stresses, with a strong caesura, as in English. Rime of some sort is therefore an essential of French poetry, in which blank verse can hardly be made distinguishable from good prose." We have seen that Fouquières considers rime the characteristic feature of the verse on which rests the unity of the measure; it is rime, according to him, that marks the time of respiration as well as the places where the "melodic periods" are terminated. Similarly R. de la Grasserie emphasizes the necessity of marking the ends of the verse lines in French by means of either effective assonance or rime; otherwise rhythmical confusion would prevail. Perhaps we can find the best acknowledgement of rime's service to French poetry in Sainte-Beuve's address to rime, quoted by Richardson:

> Rime, qui donnes leurs sons
> Aux chansons,
> Rime, l'unique harmonie
> Du vers, qui, sans tes accents
> Frémissants,
> Serait muet au génie.

As rime appears in French as almost an exclusive device for keeping measure within the poem, it becomes often desirable, and even necessary, to break up longer verses into halves, which can be easily accomplished by inner rimes. Regular hemistiches appear, therefore, in French poetry more frequently than in English.

The division of the verse into hemistiches serves the purpose of abbreviating the musical phrases within a line. But with the assistance of rhythm musical phrases can be easily extended far beyond the limits of one line. The mechanism of it is not difficult to explain. Suppose that a verse line ends with the long *o*. This vowel appearing in such a rhythmically important place introduces into the motion of the vowels a definite keynote, which in this case happens to be B♭. If the next line fails to satisfy our sense of tonality by returning to the original B♭, the feeling of musical suspense is increased, the tension becomes greater, and the satisfaction more complete when the following verse finally strikes the long-expected note. Thus the satisfaction derived from alternating rimes appears even greater than that which arises from riming couplets. The real rhythmic unit, then, becomes larger than a verse line. The unit of repetition in such cases, corresponding to the length of the musical phrase, is not a verse, but a distich or period.

Stanza.—Thus rime comes to fulfill another important function in the rhythmical organization of the poem. It binds the verse lines together, organizing them into larger rhythmic units. The simplest form of such organization is the couplet, where the rhythmic unit represents a simple and uninterrupted musical phrase and serves at the same time as the foundation for the thought-unit. A good illustration of it is the English heroic couplet:

> A little learning is a dangerous thing;
> Drink deep, or taste not the Pierian spring.

The heroic couplet is defined as a distich with a "decided sense-pause at the end."[18] The "sense-pause" is essential; for the

[18] G. P. Shannon, "The Heroic Couplet in the Sixteenth and Early Seventeenth Centuries," 1926 (an unpublished dissertation, Stanford University).

242

couplet is supposed to be logically "closed," i.e., to present a thought completed within the two verses. The distich just quoted from Pope affords a good illustration of this: "it is a sense-unit and is grammatically independent." At the same time it is musically complete; it presents the simplest case of an interlinear vowel phrase. The key of G is introduced at the end of the first line and the phrase is musically completed at the end of the next line, which leads us back to the same tone in "spring," *i* having the characteristic frequency of 2,950 vibrations per second, which lies near G of the sixth octave.

The key, once introduced, has a tendency to be retained. On the basis of our theory we should expect, therefore, that the next line should similarly end in *i*. And in fact, it may be regarded as the best indirect proof of the correctness of our analysis that in the infancy of rime there was a tendency to construct stanzas of indefinite length based on one particular vowel. We have already seen that in early French poetry, based on assonance, the same vowel appears at the end of each line, causing all musical vowel phrases to return to the same fundamental tone:

> Dis e set anz, n'en fut nient a dire,
> penat son cors el damne deu servise:
> por amistet ne d'ami ne d'amie,
> ne por honors qui lui fussent tramise,
> n'en volt torner tant com il ad a vivre.

In this passage taken from the *Vie de Saint Alexis* of the eleventh century the *i*-key constitutes the musical reference point, or the unity of the strophe. In *Gormund et Isembard*, also of the eleventh century, we find groups of forty and even more monorimes.[19] Such an arrangement occurs continuously until the beginning of the thirteenth century, when rime finally

---

[19] *Le Tezaurs* of P. de Cordiac contains a passage with 110 lines ending in -*ens* (Bartsch).

evolves from assonance. This shows conclusively that the ear of the poet and his audience at that early time found a peculiar satisfaction in returning to the same vowel at the end of each line, retaining thereby the same key for all musical phrases constituted by the vowel sounds. The resulting monotony was amply compensated for by the simplicity of structure. It evidently seemed to those early rimers that no other way of arranging their stanzas was satisfactory or even possible. For a sudden appearance of a line ending with a different vowel seemed to be nothing else but a discord. It was a great structural discovery to utilize such discords as starting-points of new melodic developments.

If we omit the vowel melodies of individual lines, and indicate by musical signs the characteristic frequencies of only the last accented vowels, such as five times repeated *i* in the illustration from *La Vie de Saint Alexis,* we obtain the series:

which[20] represents the succession of identical keys (*i*'s) within the stanza. In a long run such a series produces a very monotonous impression. To break this monotony the poets very early began to couple their lines, giving to each couple a different key. In England it became customary to give one complete thought within the limits of such melodic units. Thus originated the practice of the so-called heroic couplet. Illustration may be taken from Dryden's translation of Ovid's *Metamorphoses:*

[20] This is a very rough approximation to reality, because the French pronunciation of *i* is different from that in English.

Of bodies changed to various forms I sing: —
Ye Gods, from whom these miracles did spring,

Inspire my numbers with celestial heat,
Till I my long laborious work complete;

And add perpetual tenor to my rhymes,
Deduced from nature's birth to Caesar's times.

Again omitting the melodies contained in the verse lines, and
registering only the keys, we obtain:

This series shows no definite structure. It can be indefinitely
prolonged without revealing any arrangement of keys. Therefore, strictly speaking, we cannot regard a couplet as a stanza
(*un distique ne fait pas une strophe.*) It is not even an embryonic stanza. For the latter represents a definite arrangement
of keys; whereas the couplet represents a solitary key, not supported by any others.

What is it that the couplet lacks if compared with a fully
developed stanza? Certainly it is not the unity that we miss in
a distich. For it appears to be a prototype of melodic unity in
poetry. What we miss is variety. To introduce this variety, the
poets very early began to make various arrangements of two
different keys. The simplest, and possibly the earliest form of
such an arrangement is that of alternating rimes (*le quatrain
croise*). If the authority of Ph. Martinon is to be trusted,
Marot was the man in France who, in the beginning of the
sixteenth century, inaugurated this form. The monotony of
continuous monorimes, distichs, and tercets of the form *aab*
was broken once for all. The experiment proved to be extraor-

245

dinarily successful, and served as the foundation for the "crossed quatrain" both in classical and in modern French. Thus Marot's psalm *"Tes jugements"* must be regarded as the oldest poem with alternating rimes in French (at least in the form of a quatrain):

> Tes jugements, Dieu véritable,
>   Baille au Roi pour régner,
> Veuille ta justice équitable
>   Au fils du Roi donner.
>
> Il tiendra ton peuple en justice,
>   Chassant iniquité.
> À tes pauvres sera propice,
>   Leur gardant équité.
>
> Les peuples verront aux montagnes
>   La paix croître et mourir,
> Et par coteaux et par campagnes
>   La justice fleurir.

In England this form was introduced at a much earlier date. Robert Manning, or Robert of Brunne, who in his miscellany of *Handlinge Sinne* speaking of

>   That tyme
>   That I began thys English Rhyme.

mentions[21] four different ways of arranging verse-lines into stanzas:

> I made it not for to be praysed,
> Bot at the lewed menn were aysed.
> If it were made in ryme couwee,
> Or in strangere or interlace,
> That rede Inglis it ere inowe

---

[21] In his English translation of the French chronicle of Peter of Langtoft.

246

That couthe not haf coppled a kowe,
That outhere in couwee or in baston
Som suld haf ben fordon,
So that fele men that it herde
Suld not witte howe that it ferde.

The "ryme couwee" that he mentions in this passage evidently is an English equivalent of the French *"strophes couées,"* which are tercets of *aab* form consisting of lines of different lengths. The meaning of "strangere" and "baston" is uncertain. But "interlaced" evidently means alternate rimes. Thus, although we have no reason to believe the boastful statement of the author of *Handlinge Sinne* that he really "began thys English rhyme,"[22] yet we cannot possibly mistrust his testimony with regard to the existence of the "interlaced" rimes. In view of the fact that Robert of Brunne wrote between 1290 and 1340, we must assume that the practice of "interlacing" rimes must have been introduced some time before the beginning of the fourteenth century.

Whoever might have been the first in England to use this form, it was a great discovery. For it marks a revolution in the melody of verse. It not merely introduces variety in the riming scheme; it completely changes the principle of the melodic relationship among the vowels of the verse. By using alternate rime the poet introduces a principle which has never been used in music until very recent times: the method of simultaneous application of two different keys. This has been done recently in some ultra-modern compositions, but evidently without much success. In poetry it constitutes the basis of all modern arrangement of vowels.

[22] We know that rime was introduced in England at a considerably earlier date. Although it is impossible to say when it actually began, yet it is quite possible to see when it was already practised. We know, for instance, that the so-called "Canute Song," which probably dates from the early twelfth century, exhibits (comparatively) very good rimes.

What does alternating rime mean from the musical point of view? At the end of the preceding paragraph I have already outlined the answer. Let us explain it by some well-known illustration. Take the first stanza of Gray's *Elegy:*

> The curfew tolls the knell of parting day,
> The lowing herd wind slowly o'er the lea,
> The ploughman homeward plods his weary way,
> And leaves the world to darkness, and to me.

The last word, "day," of the first line introduces the key: E♭ (the high characteristic frequency of the long *a*). Psychologically it corresponds to releasing a tendency (we call it "desire") to return to the same tone. If the next line were to end in "way," this tendency would be satisfied, the melody would be completed. But the next line does not rime. It ends with the word "lea." This word fails to satisfy our sense of tonality. For, instead of taking us back to the original E♭, it strikes another rhythmically prominent tone, G of the sixth octave (the high characteristic frequency of the long *e*). Thus at the end of the second verse line the anticipated solution is not reached. The tension becomes greater, and the melody of the next line more effective. Finally, the third line takes us back to the long-expected E♭ in "way," and the melody originally introduced in the key of E♭ is closed. But the preceding "lea" is too strong a discord[23] to be dismissed without causing considerable uneasiness. As a discord it cannot be easily forgotten. The musical image of it evidently persists in our mind; for when the next line leads us back to the same tone in "me" we perceive it with satisfaction as the legitimate end of an independent musical phrase.

Thus in this passage we have an actual interlacing of two musical phrases, of which the second begins before the first is

[23] See Hytier's theory of discords in chapter iii, above.

finished. The end of the second line is not merely perceived as a discord, but owing to its rhythmical prominence it sets another key which may or may not have a solution. If it is not resolved, i.e., if the last line does not rime, the impression from the discord persists, and the stanza lacks melodic unity; it does not end melodically. The melody of the vowels flows over without achieving an end at the end of the stanza. Therefore the stanza does not appear to be ended at all. The quatrain does not obtain. In fact, such a grouping of lines into a quatrain is very seldom, if ever, employed in English: *abax; x* always represents a discord. In this particular case the group ends with a discord which makes it appear unmusical. Moreover, from the rhythmic point of view the group is asymmetrical, and its harmony has no definite shape. Suppose we have two stanzas with *oaou* and *ieia* as their respective end-vowels. If we represent them in musical signs we obtain a highly asymmetrical form:

Our musical theory of rime affords a reasonable explanation of why such arrangements are generally avoided. Under this scheme, *abax*, where the last verse does not rime with any of the preceding, no melody is perceived at the end of the stanza, the musical phrase remains unfinished, and the last vowel is again perceived as a discord. The whole combination fails to satisfy our sense of tonality. In fact, such arrangements of lines into stanzas are extremely rare in the world's literature. They are occasionally experimented with in modern Russian poetry; but whenever they are applied they produce a dissonant impression of something unfinished, restless, and unmusical.

249

If the key introduced by the second line terminates the whole group, i.e., if the last verse rimes with the second, an ordinary quatrain obtains with alternating rimes. This form, which is now one of the commonest forms in poetry, was at one time felt as a great and remarkable discovery. Poetically so extraordinarily simple, it has a very puzzling musical structure, which can be explained only by assuming, as we have done, two keys simultaneously active. Musical tension produced by one of those keys is increased by the interference of the other. If again, in analyzing Gray's *Elegy*, we omit all vowels except those which terminate each line, i.e., if we musically represent only the system of keys in each stanza, we obtain the following scheme:

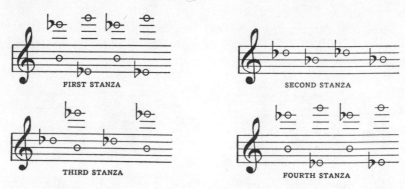

FIRST STANZA   SECOND STANZA

THIRD STANZA   FOURTH STANZA

The concept of poetic harmony.—Popular conception identifies musical harmony with the simultaneous coexistence of various tones which produce a pleasurable effect. This, however, is a very superficial definition. For technically the term "harmony" applies to the relation among various chords, rather than to a mere coexistence of sounds. A sequence of chords may be harmonious or disharmonious according to whether or not it follows certain rules of modulation, progression, and composition. If I take E♭ minor chord after C major and let both

250

be followed by a dominant seventh chord, say, in the key of
D, no harmonic progression results. The sequence is not perceived as a whole. In order to be perceived as a harmonious
whole the chords are supposed to stand in a certain definite
relation of affinity to each other. They must be related to each
other by means of a common center of reference. This common center of reference is, again, the key. The harmonic structure of a musical piece always follows a key. If it goes from
one key to another, it does this also according to certain rules.
In this latter sense, harmony is a systematic arrangement of
keys in a musical composition. As a rule every composition (if
it does not exceed the limits of a single movement) begins and
ends in the same key.

Let us call the arrangement of keys in a stanza its harmonic
form or structure, as distinguished from the melodic structure
of lines. The terminology is necessitated by the importance of
distinguishing a musical phrase in the sequence of vowels from
the progression of rimes, i.e., keys, in the composition of the
stanza; and it is justified by the analogy to musical forms,
where a regulated progression of chords is called harmony. In
poetry, as we know, rimes take the place of the key; by leading
our ear back to the original tone they transform the irregular
sequences of vowels into melodic phrases. Poetic melody is
horizontal; it follows the vowels of the verse lines. But we
know now that the solution of a melodic vowel phrase may be
temporarily suspended, i.e., postponed till the end of one or
more lines. The resulting discord, then, may be and as a matter
of fact generally and naturally is taken as the beginning of a
new musical phrase. Herewith another key is introduced into
the melodic composition of the vowel tones. The arrangement
of keys, which is variable from case to case, we call poetic harmony. It reads vertically. Thus in the opening stanza of
Gray's *Elegy* we distinguish two melodies in two different keys:
the first melody begins with "day" and ends with "way," while

251

the second, beginning with "lea," terminates in "me," reaching, so to speak, over the head of "way." The phonetic structure of the first melody is:

ā, ĕ, ō, ĭ, ēr, ĭ, ō, y̆, ō, ĕ, ēē, ĕ, ōū, ă, ō, ār, ŏ, ĭ, ēū, ĭ, ā

The second melody is expressed by the following series:

ēē, ĕ, ōū, ă, ō, ār, ŏ, ĭ, ēū, ĭ, ā, ă, ēū, ĕ, ēr, ōō, ār, ă, ōō, ēē

Both series are horizontal. If we, now, disregard those melodies, and follow only the development of the keys employed in the composition of this stanza, we obtain a series of four prominently emphasized chords:

representing the vertical series of rimes:

> day
> lea
> way
> me

or, in traditional notation, *abab*, which is a generalized expression of the harmonic form of all similar stanzas.

Complex poetic harmonies.—The principle of alternating keys, once introduced, opens theoretically an unlimited field of possibilities. Practically, however, the range of possible variations is limited by our inability to retain the image of a key over a distance exceeding four or five lines; we do not perceive a rime if it is placed too far away from its origin. But at a distance of two or even three lines, the "interlacing" is possible in many different forms. The quatrain itself allows only three different arrangements of rimes. Of these we have already discussed two: *aabb*, *"rimes suivies,"* or couplets; and *abab*, *"rimes croisées,"* or alternating rimes. There is still another arrangement possible: *abba*, called *"rimes embrassés,"* or inclosed rimes, as in Tennyson's:

> Ring out old shapes of foul disease;
>> Ring out the narrowing lust of gold;
>> Ring out the thousand wars of old;
> Ring in the thousand years of peace.

The harmonic structure of this stanza is, of course, different from that which corresponds to the alternating rimes. The key introduced by the word "disease" is not followed. The second line forms a total discord with the first, introducing in "gold" a new key, which, under the effect of a strong musical tension resulting from the preceding discord, is quite agreeably resolved at the end of the third verse. The original key is held in suspense till the end of the last verse. Expressed in musical signs the harmonic composition of this stanza is as follows:

The number of lines to be arranged in a stanza is not limited to four. While the quatrain has only three possible harmonic forms, the quintain allows ten different harmonic permutations: *aabbb, ababb, abbab, abbba, baabb, babab, babba, bbaab, bbaba, bbbaa.* Each of these has musically a different physiognomy. The harmonic form of Shelley's "To a Skylark":

> Hail to thee, blithe Spirit!
>> Bird thou never wert,
> That from heaven, or near it,
>> Pourest thy full heart
> In profuse strains of unpremeditated art.

253

is audibly different from Thomas Moore's "Echoes":

> How sweet the answer Echo makes
> To music at night,
> When, roused by lute or horn, she wakes,
> And far away o'er lawns and lakes
> Goes answering light!

The harmonic form of the first is:

The second has the following harmonic structure:

The specific character of each form is readily perceived by the ear, as the similarity between the different stanzas of the same poem is easily noticed even by inexperienced ears.

A stanza may, therefore, be defined as a specific system of melodic tensions and relaxations caused by some specific arrangement of the vowel-keys. Evidently each specific arrangement has its own emotional appeal. Reading and, especially, listening to a poem, we are rarely conscious of the form in which rimes are put together into stanzas; but we are definitely conscious of a rhythmical reappearance of certain harmonic groups which strike us as in some respect identical. We know now where the real source of identity lies. It lies in the identity of their harmonic structure.

Even considering the natural psychological limitations mentioned above, the number of clearly distinguishable harmonic groups is very large. Through centuries poetry was experimenting with various ways of arranging rimes, and new harmonic forms were constantly accumulating in the archives of literature. The simplest complication results from the reduplication of the quatrain. In medieval French poetry, this complication was successfully applied by Villon and Marot in the form: *ababbcbc*. In Marot's *"Epigrammes"* we find, for example:

> Plus ne suis ce que j'ai été,
> Et ne le saurais jamais être;
> Mon beau printemps et mon été
> On fait le saut par la fenêtre.
> Amour, tu as été mon maître:
> Je t'ai servi sur tous les dieux.
> Oh! si je pouvais deux fois naître,
> Comme je te servirais mieux!

This, both in its sense and in its harmonic structure, is only a double quatrain. The octet acquires an independent value only when the harmonic structure of each constituent quatrain is different from that of the other, as in this passage of Milton's:

> It was the winter wild,
> While the heaven-born Child
> All meanly wrapt in the rude manger lies;
> Nature in awe to Him
> Had doff'd her gaudy trim,
> With her great Master so to sympathize:
> It was no season then for her
> To wanton with the sun, her lusty paramour.

Represented in musical signs the harmonic structure of this stanza is:

255

Radically different in emotional appeal, though quite similar in harmonic appearance, is the seven-line stanza, such for instance as the English rime royal, *ababbcc*. This difficult form will be forever connected with the name of Chaucer; for he brought it to the point of unsurpassed perfection. Hardly in any language was it practiced with such success as in English; and among the English poets, hardly anyone applied it with greater taste and skill than Chaucer. However, the form seems to have originated in France. Ronsard was probably the first to employ the seven-line stanza in his frequently quoted little ode: *"Où allez-vous, filles de ciel."* In England this form made its first appearance in the well-known "Complaint unto Pity," which is believed by some to be a translation of a not yet identified French poem. "Here we have," writes Saintsbury, "beyond reasonable doubt, the first English piece in the great Rime-royal, ... which Chaucer afterwards brought to such perfection and which long held the premier place among our stanza forms. His pitching on it and his preference of it are fresh proofs of his instinctive genius for prosody. It is not indeed a stanza-of-all-work. But it can do several things well, and one thing, the expression of clamorous cry, it can do supremely. It is odd that, this being so, the very first example of it should be in so suitable a subject." It is interesting to note that in France the interest in this form of harmonic composition was revived under the English influence. Tristan employs *rime royale* in his *"Plaintes d'Acante"*:

> Un jour que le printemps entre les fleurs,
> Acante, qui n'a rien que des soucis dans l'âme,
> Pour fléchir ses destins faisait parler ses pleurs
>   Humides témoins de sa flamme;
> Et se représentant les rigueurs de sa Dame,
>   Semblait un morceau du rocher
> Sur lequele ses pensers le venaient d'attacher.

It is known that Tristan, then an officer of the guards, fought a duel, was obliged to leave France, and spent some time in England precisely at the time when rime royal under Chaucer's hand became extraordinarily popular. Probably ignorant of its French origin, Tristan brought it back to France as a novelty. The novelty, however, evidently did not appeal to the French sense of poetic harmony, for it was completely abandoned by classicists and moderns. The whole incident is interesting as an illustration of the inherent unity and compactness of certain harmonic forms which can be transmitted not merely from one generation to another but from one country to another. Once formulated, the harmonic forms live and multiply like living organisms. This indirectly shows that each form has its specific emotional appeal, which attracts, or repels, the poetic temperaments of different nationalities.

So unpopular in France, rime royal enjoyed a great popularity in England. Martinon explains this by reference to the English fondness for the terminal double rimes. He argues:

> C'est d'ailleurs une chose extraordinaire que la fortune de ce rythme en Angleterre. Non seulement le XVe et le XVIe siècles en sont encore pleins; mais on le trouve jusque chez les modernes. Nous avons vu déjà, à propos de chaque strophe, le goût qu'ont les Anglais pour la rime double finale: nulle part il ne s'est montré avec tant d'évidence.

Yet this observation, though probably correct, does not account for the popularity of rime royal; for there are many other combinations possible with two riming lines at the end. What seems extraordinary in this situation is, not that English poets are so fond of this form, but that in other languages it is so seldom used. This has, I think, its explanation in the highly developed sense of poetic harmony which is a natural consequence of the enormous wealth of vowels so characteristic of the English tongue. Musically unproductive and evidently dull, the Anglo-Saxons developed the most musical language

257

on earth in so far as the variety of its vowel sounds is concerned. The effects which are impossible on the basis of eight or nine French vowels fall easily within the reach of the English system with its large number of fundamental vowel sounds. The seven-line stanza is a difficult harmonic form. When read in French or in Russian, an effort is required to retain its image in mind; whereas in English the harmonic unity results of itself—probably owing to the complex melodic structure of each individual verse. In fact, the ease is remarkable with which the Anglo-American poets, even of the third and fourth magnitude, handle this difficult and fragile rhythm. We often find the seven-line rhythms in places where we should least expect them to appear—successfully practised by such minor poets as Charles E. Carryl, the author of the once so popular "Davy and the Goblin," or the exuberant Richard Hovey, the adventurous theologian of Illinois, whose famous "Stein Song" is included in Untermeyer's anthology:

> Give a rouse, then, in the Maytime
>> For a life that knows no fear!
> Turn night-time into daytime
>> With the sunlight of good cheer!
>>> For it's always fair weather
>>> When good fellows get together,
> With a stein on the table and a good song ringing clear.

Charles E. Carryl makes a daring and yet successful experiment in his "The Plaint of the Camel," introducing a dissonant line at the end of each stanza:

> Canary-birds feed on sugar and seed,
>> Parrots have crackers to crunch;
> And as for the poodles, they tell me the noodles
>> Have chickens and cream for their lunch.
>>> But there's never a question
>>> About my digestion—
>>> ANYTHING does for me!

The last line is rhythmically irregular (it is a trochaic verse in an iambic meter), and is melodically dissonant (for it has no rime); and yet, perhaps precisely for these two reasons, it is so forceful that the effect of the whole poem rests upon this peculiar ending.

Stanzas with a number of lines larger than eight are rather exceptional. The nine-line stanza falls easily apart into a series of tercets. Yet there are some harmonic forms which are possible only on the basis of nine lines, such as Spenser's: *ababbcbcc*, which he developed in *The Faerie Queene:*

> A gentle Knight was pricking on the plaine,
>> Ycladd in mightie armes and silver shielde,
> Wherein old dints of deepe woundes did remaine,
>> The cruell markes of many a bloody fielde;
>> Yet armes till that time did he never wield.
> His angry steede did chide his foming bitt,
>> As much disdayning to the curbe to yield:
> Full jolly knight he seemd, and faire did sitt,
> As one for knightly giusts and fierce encounters fitt.

Its harmonic structure judged by the standards of modern pronunciation is:

Ten-line rhythms are not very exceptional, but eleven-line stanzas occur but rarely. They were used in the so-called chant royal, which was a ballad form with five stanzas and an envoy, of the form *ababccddede + ddede*. This harmonic form, complicated though it is, is sometimes employed even in light verse. H. C. Bunner, a poet not of first rank, uses it in one of his satirical poems, "Behold the Deeds!" After telling the story of a certain Adolphe Culpepper Ferguson, a salesman of fancy notions, who was locked up in his room by his puritanically energetic landlady, Mrs. Jones, the author makes him exclaim in the last stanza:

> Thou, for whose fear the fugitive crow
> I eat, accursed be thou and all thy kin!
> Thee I will show up—yea, up I will show
> Thy too-thick buckwheats and thy tea too thin.
> Ay! here I dare thee, ready for the fray:
> Thou dost not "keep a first-class house" I say!
> It does not with the advertisements agree.
> Thou lodgest a Briton with a puggaree,
> And thou hast harbored Jacobses and Cohns,
> Also a Mulligan. Thus denounce I thee!
> Behold the deeds that are done of Mrs. Jones!

> ENVOY
> Boarders! the worst I have not told to ye:
> She hath stolen my trousers, that I may not flee
> Privily by the window. Hence these groans.
> There is no fleeing in a robe de nuit.
> Behold the deeds that are done of Mrs. Jones!

Longer harmonic forms, with one notable exception, are but rarely used. The exception is the sonnet, which is regarded by some prosodists as a stanza. In fact, it sometimes is used as a compositional unit out of which to construct larger poems. George E. Woodberry's "Ideal Passion," for example, consists of forty-two sonnets. Vyacheslav Ivanov, one of the most prominent Russian symbolists, made an interesting experiment by writing a poem in fifteen sonnets, of which the first contains the fourteen fundamental ideas to be developed by the succeeding sonnets; the first of these, i.e., the second sonnet in the poem, begins with the first line of the first, the so-called fundamental, sonnet, and ends with its second line, which, in turn, begins the next sonnet, and so on till the end. The reason why the sonnet form is so easily perceived as a whole lies probably in the fact that it is naturally divided into a "huitain" and a "sixain." It is a well-known fact that a sonnet seldom turns out successfully unless the ideas are arranged in accordance with this two-fold scheme.

Thirteen-line stanzas are scarce in modern English. Yet at the beginning of the history of English rime, this difficult and complicated harmonic form played a very prominent part. It is an interesting fact, and a curious one, that the early English rimers displayed such a strange curiosity with regard to the most tangled and intricate forms. At the time when rime had evidently just appeared and was struggling against indomitable alliteration, it was, according to Saintsbury, the thirteen-line stanza that was first crystallized out of "the seeming chaos of a not so much earlier time." In fact, we find thirteen-line stanzas in some of the Arthurian romances, for instance, *Awntyrs of Arthur*, and in the beautiful *Pistyl of Susan*, in both of which rime appears as an aid to alliteration. The patience with which this complicated scheme was followed by pioneers is remarkable. "The *Awntyrs* . . . . must have given the poet a great deal of trouble to write; for he had to work out a stanza as complicated as the most complicated in the mere metre-poets, and he had the burden of alliteration as well." Eight lines of "interlacing" rimes of the form *abababab* are followed by a ninth with a fresh rime-sound, *c*; this group of nine lines is then followed by the so-called "wheel" (*bbbc*), which all together make thirteen lines:

In the tyme of Arther thys antur be-tydde,
Be-syde the Tarnewathelan, as the boke tellus;
That he to Karlylle was comun, that conquerour kydde,
Wythe dukys, and with dosiperus, that with the deure dwellus,
For to hunte atte the herd, that lung hase bynne hydde;
Tyl on a day thay hom dyght into the depe dellus,

Fellun to tho femalus, in forest was fredde;
To the fayre by fermesones, by frythys, and felles
Wudde thay weyndun, these wlonkes in wedes;
  Bothe the kyng and the quene,
  And other doghti by-dene;
Syr Gawan, graythist on grene,
  Dame Gaynore he ledus.

The *Pistyl of Susan* is of generally similar composition; only instead of the ninth long line there appears an extremely short, single-footed verse, the so-called "bob":

Als this schaply thing, yede in hire yarde
  That was hir hosbobdus, and hire that holden with hende,
"Nou folk be faren from us, thar us not be ferde;
  Aftur myn oynement warliche ye weende;
Aspieth nou specialy the yates ben sperde,
  ffor we wol wassche us I-wis bi this welle strende."
ffor-thi the wif werp of hir wedes un-werde;
  Undur a lorere ful lowe that ladi gan leende
    So sone.
      By a wynliche welle,
      Susan caste of hir kelle;
      Bote feole ferlys hire bi-felle
    Bi Midday or none.

Terza rima.—There is one more harmonic form to be considered, the *terza rima*, which was, we are told, originally invented by Dante's teacher, Brunetto Latini, and employed by Dante himself as the harmonic scheme of his *Divine Comedy*. It naturally had its great success in Italy. Petrarca uses it in his *Triumphs* and Ariosto in his *Satires*. It links the verse lines together by "interlacing," constantly and regularly introducing fresh rime-sounds alternately at even and uneven lines, such as: *aba, bcb, cdc, ded,* etc. For example:

262

Make me thy lyre, even as the forest is:
What if my leaves are falling like its own!
The tumult of thy mighty harmonies

Will take from both a deep, autumnal tone,
Sweet though in sadness. Be thou, Spirit fierce,
My spirit! Be thou me, impetuous one!

Drive my dead thoughts over the universe
Like withered leaves to quicken a new birth!
And, by the incantation of this verse, ...

Its harmonic form is as follows:

Now the question arises which has been asked many times:
Why has this meter never really acclimated itself in the Eng-
lish-speaking world? Why did not Chaucer, for instance, at
a time when he was evidently under very strong Italian influence, make further experiments in this favorite meter of the
"great poet of Italy"? The answer that Saintsbury gives to this
question is, perhaps, satisfactory from the prosodic point of
view, but it is obviously incomplete and merely shifts the problem a little farther: Because Chaucer found, and because all
have found, that it would not do. But why? We know, of
course, that it "would not do" (because no one has done it
successfully), but do not see why it should not.

Harmonic analysis gives the key to an at least probable answer. From the harmonic representation of *terza rima* just
given we see that it lacks harmonic unity. Just compare its harmonic structure with that of a quatrain or a rime royal, and you
will see that each of these represents a whole that can be identi-

fied and indefinitely repeated as a whole, while the harmony of the *terza rima* flows forward in a continuous change. It is, therefore, very likely that precisely for this reason it is so repugnant to the Anglo-Saxon mind, which worships unity in everything. It is not a linguistic but a psychological failure.

In France the influence of the Italian *terza rima* begins to show itself only at the end of the Renaissance. Jean Lemaire in the beginning of the sixteenth century claimed the initiative in the matter of introducing this form into French poetry. Whether his claim is really justified or not, I am not in position to say. Ph. Martinon believes that *terza rima* originated in France at the time of the troubadours. But he fails to give any evidence for this view. In any event, we do not find this form employed by any of the prominent French poets prior to Lemaire. In the great mass of literary documents from Dante's time to the end of the Renaissance, I have found only two pieces in which *terza rima* appeared: Rutebeuf's *"Mariage"* and Adam de la Hale's *"Jeu de la Feuillée."* In view of this, Lemaire's *"Concorde des deux langues"* may in fact be regarded as the first experiment of this kind in French. Since that time it has been quite extensively used, even by the poets of the *"Pléiade"* (Tyard, Baif, Jodelle).

In Russia it was never employed till the arrival of symbolism. The first really successful experiment in *terza rima* in Russian was Balmont's "The Chimeras of Notre Dame," a beautiful piece of work which shows that this meter is by no means out of harmony with either the Russian language or Russian psychology. The comparatively late appearance of this form is explained not by any opposition to it but simply by the fact that Russian poetry is so young that it has had no time as yet to experiment with all the discoveries of Western poetic art, particularly in view of the fact that Russian poets have had to consider and bring to perfection many domestic forms entirely unknown to the West. The period of experimentation

264

that long ago passed for the West-European literatures, in Russia just began with the advent of symbolism.

Résumé.—Let us briefly recapitulate this chapter. With regard to rhythm, rime has two different functions to perform: (1) As the key in the melody of verse, it attracts our attention to the rhythmically important places, the most important place being the end of each line. Stressing the end-rimes rectifies the rhythm distorted by "interruptions." Such is the melodic function of rime with regard to rhythm. (2) As the chief principle of poetic harmony rime helps to arrange the verse lines into the larger, also rhythmically repeated, units called stanzas or strophes.

Neither of these achievements would be possible if rime had no emotional effect prior to its rhythmical function. If we were indifferent to its musical qualities, we should not be able to use it for rhythmic purposes. Its rhythmic value is not a primary and independent factor, but merely a function of its melodic value.

265

VII

THE LOGIC OF EMOTIONS

P SYCHOLOGISTS define emotions
as feelings of bodily changes which follow the perception of
some exciting fact.[1] Thus every emotion appears to have its
origin in the physical world. This does not mean, however, that
it consists entirely of physical elements. Every emotional process contains a residue that cannot be accounted for by purely
physical or physiological methods. This may be called its
"psychic residue." It is this residue that lies in the center of
our present interest. But before analyzing it psychologically we
must study its physical roots.

The bodily changes which form the physiological basis for
the rise of emotions are varied. The change of heart beats
and the tempo of breathing, visceral stirrings and the flushing
of the face, certain contractions of muscles, and, above all, many

---

[1] William James, *Psychology*, 2:449.

chemical changes that take place in various glands—these produce internal sensations accompanied by various shades of pleasant and unpleasant feeling which are summarily called emotions.[2]

The study of the physical side of emotional processes is facilitated by the fact that the physical factor can be directly observed and measured objectively. Modern behavioristic psychology has contributed a great deal to the study of the physical aspect of our emotional life.[3] A. Mosso found that even comparatively weak emotional variations are followed by visible physiological effects, such as enlargement of the brain vessels and contraction of the blood vessels of the extremities. He observed, on the Mossoan scales specially constructed by him for such experiments, that the slightest emotional excitement causes the blood of a recumbent man to stream toward his head, causing to sink that part of the scales where the head rests.[4] Lehman's and Weber's experiments have shown that "pleasant" emotions are accompanied by the enlargement of certain parts of the head and an appreciable retardation of the pulse, while unpleasant stimuli cause opposite effects.[5]

Taking into consideration a large number of similar experiments, Bechterev comes to the conclusion that the emotional process in its physiological aspect is an expression of the nutritive conditions in the brain, favorable conditions corresponding

[2] E. B. Tichener, *An Outline of Psychology*, pages 229 ff.

[3] Quite recently a brilliant representation of the behavioristic point of view with regard to emotions was given by K. Dunlap in his paper, "Emotion as a Dynamic Background," *Wittenberg Symposium on Feelings and Emotions* (Clark University Press, Worcester, Massachusetts, 1928), pages 156–161.

[4] A. Mosso, "Application de la balance a l'étude de la circulation chez l'homme," *Archive italien de Biologie*, 1884.

[5] W. Bechterev, *Objektive Psychologie*, page 110.

to the positive and unfavorable conditions to the negative emotional tone. He also noticed that emotional processes are usually accompanied by certain chemical changes in the organism, which are sometimes very violent and evident, as for instance those which manifest themselves in the cold sweat caused by fear.[6]

Thus, while sensations physically depend upon external stimuli, the so-called emotions depend largely upon internal changes in the organism itself: variations in the nutritive conditions of the brain, differences in the blood circulation, and, above all, numerous chemical changes caused by various secretory glands. Of course, the nutritive variations also belong to the group of chemical changes. Thus we may assume that our emotional life is a function of the chemical processes within our organism. Among various emotional reactions Bechterev also considers those which are connected with the visual and auditory impulses. He calls them aesthetic emotions.

Now, if this is true, i.e., if our emotional reactions depend largely upon the chemical conditions of the organism, especially of the brain, the field of emotional experience psychologically must be considerably wider than is commonly believed. For what does not cause a chemical change in our organism? Every perception, every slightest sensation must be accompanied by the processes of composition and decomposition of organic substances within certain cells. And indeed, it is a long-established fact in psychology that all our sensations, and possibly our perceptions as well, are accompanied by slight

[6] Bechterev, pages 107–123. There is still another possible way to account for the nature of emotions by identifying them with the useful (or useless) movements of the organism which is under the stress of emotion (J. Dewey, "The Theory of Emotion," *Psychological Review*, 1894–1895). Modern behavioristic conceptions are largely an outgrowth of that point of view. Yet it is evident that "behavior" itself is a function of physico-chemical conditions within the organism (see W. B. Cannon, "Neural Organization for Emotional Expression," *Wittenberg Symposium on Feelings and Emotions*).

emotional reactions, called by the Germans "Gefühlstöne."
Every sound, every hue, every shade of red or blue has its
specific emotional appeal, being either pleasant or unpleasant.
It is, however, impossible to believe that this appeal is adequately described by reference to such vague and general terms
as "pleasantness" or "unpleasantness."[7] Those reactions display
more specific differences. For sensations may be pleasant and
unpleasant in as many different ways as logical propositions
may be true or false. To say that some particular emotion is
"pleasant" means just as much as to say that the distinguishing
feature of a certain man is "blond hair"; for there are millions
of men with equally blond hair. Similarly, there are billions
of specific and distinctly different emotions which are equally
pleasant. Therefore the reference to pleasure does not adequately describe the innumerable differences in our emotional
response. The monotonous sound of a cricket on a still night
may be just as pleasant—or just as annoying, if you wish—
as prolonged practicing of the same musical phrase on the piano.
Yet the two are so totally different from each other that the
slight variation in the intensity of pleasure derived from them
is insufficient to express the difference. The two situations
involved, although equally pleasant, or equally annoying, display different emotional content.

Thus emotion is something more than mere pleasantness
or unpleasantness. It has its own content and speaks its own
language, the meaning of which goes far beyond the crude
material of pleasure or even the intricacies of rational meaning.[8] It is true that emotions are intimately associated with
pleasure and pain. But they display finer distinctions and in-

[7] Compare W. McDougall, "Emotion and Feeling Distinguished," *Wittenberg Symposium on Feelings and Emotions*, pages 200–206.

[8] With regard to the meaning or significance of emotions, see Ed.
Claparède, "Feelings and Emotions," in *Wittenberg Symposium on Feelings
and Emotions* (1928), pages 124 ff.

troduce us to a realm of qualitative differences which defy all our attempts at measuring them by what is more or less pleasant. Considering those differences, we are obliged to say that the range of emotions reaches considerably farther than our emotional vocabulary is able to follow. We have but few words referring to our emotional life. Love, hate, fear, hope, alarm, anxiety, and a few more, identify that portion of our emotional life which appears from the practical point of view important and is discussed in the textbooks of psychology. The bulk of our emotions remain forever nameless. And yet it is precisely this portion which supplies material for the domain of art.

It is the purpose of this chapter to introduce some evidence of the independence of our emotional content, both from the crudeness of pleasure and from the fineness of rational meaning. Without introducing any controversial matter from the domain of philosophy, we shall try to establish certain propositions which elucidate the nature of those emotional entities in general. And then, on the basis of those propositions—which do not properly belong to either psychology or aesthetics, but constitute the beginnings of a separate discipline that might be called the logic of emotions—we shall attempt the solution of the long-standing controversy with regard to the value and applicability of rime.

Melody once more.—Music affords a good illustration of what we intend to show. The independence of musical emotions both from pleasure and meaning has been amply discussed in musical literature. Therefore it is convenient to start again with musical considerations.

It is easy to show that melody is not an auditory sensation, but a form of emotional response. The tonal material that affects our ear is not yet melody. Hearing alone does not constitute what we call musical ear. Beethoven was deaf; never-

270

theless he remains the greatest master of music. But play one of his sonatas to a Bushman (who hears distinctly every single tone), and he will not be able to hear the melody. For, strictly speaking, one does not "hear" a melody. We are able or unable to follow it, which means that we either have or have not the ability to organize the tones into a higher unity. This organization is accomplished emotionally. It is what makes melody different from a mere succession of tones. Emotion is the cement that binds various parts of melody together.

The crucial test of the correctness of the assumption that melody is a form of emotional response lies in the psychophysical analysis of its origin given by Helmholtz. It has been already pointed out, in the first chapter of this work, that a melodic transition from one tone to another stimulates a desire to return to the original tone. We are, generally speaking, conscious of our desires only in so far as they are accompanied by emotions. In fact the peculiarity of each desire is known by and practically coincides with the characteristic features of its emotional accompaniment. Therefore a transition from one tone to another is, under normal conditions, invariably accompanied by emotional effects. Of course everybody knows by experience that even single notes affect us differently. A note played on an oboe has an emotional physiognomy different from one played on a violin. But succession of tones has a still stronger emotional stress. Every musical interval has a specific emotional appeal, a peculiar "Gefühlston," which associates itself with the sound of that particular interval in a manner similar to that in which pleasant or unpleasant emotions are associated with definite contrasts of colors. Only, as a rule, the tone combinations, both successive and simultaneous, are emotionally more effective than color combinations. Accumulation of a number of such emotional stimuli gives rise to what we call melody. It is evident that individual differences of such emotional clusters do not consist of various degrees of

271

pleasantness, for two melodies may be equally pleasant and yet totally different in their emotional content.

Emotions constituting a melody are not of a representative character, that is to say, they do not express the composer's state of mind, or his feelings, that somehow existed in his soul prior to and independently of the musical material. Musical emotions are those which are stimulated by tones, and by nothing else. They might be, in some cases, vaguely similar to the emotions of love, or freedom, or something else; but this similarity is wholly external to music, which is what it is without any reference to either love, or freedom, or anything else whatsoever. There are till now, and I am afraid there always will be, many dilettante enthusiasts of music who maintain that when they hear Beethoven's "Moonlight Sonata" they visualize some lonely landscape flooded with moonlight and covered with beautiful flowers or some other banalities. One would say that the landscape is lonely, another would insist that you are supposed to see angels moving along, etc. It is popularly believed that it belongs to the intelligent listening of musical compositions to have stories connected with them. And thus, forgetting music, people fabricate their stories. Romantic thinkers contributed much to this popular misunderstanding, bestowing upon it the air of philosophical profundity. Even Hegel, the sanest of all, believed that music is a form of expressing something else, namely, the inner truth of the soul. Schopenhauer defines music as the language of the universe. And, following Schopenhauer, Wagner, that protagonist of philosophical music, declared that music is of a feminine character because it conceives and bears what is given to it from the outside. This "outside" is drama, the inner conflict of passions and ambitions, which music is called upon to illustrate. In all these theories there was very little new. They are all but variations of an idea handed over to us from gray antiquity which, in the words of Plotinus, says that "music dealing with rhythms and harmonies is but a copy of the real music which, in the realm of spirit, deals with the ideal rhythm."[9]

In contrast to this romantic interpretation of music, Hanslick, a contemporary of Wagner, advanced his formal and realistic interpretation. In his *Vom Musikalisch-Schönen* he assumed that the principle of music must be "specifically musical," i.e., it lies exclusively in the relation and affinity of the tones involved and not in any ideas or emotions which, being foreign to the tonal material, are somehow expressed in it.[10] "If one asks," he says, "what is expressed in the tonal material of a melody, the answer is: musical ideas. And a wholly actualized musical idea is an independent manifestation of beauty, an end in itself, and not merely a means or material for expressing thoughts or feelings."[11] Under the stress of polemics regarding Wagnerian expressionism, Hanslick goes to the extreme of declaring that the content of music is purely "tonal." Now it is tonal in the sense that it is neither intellectual nor in any way representative. But it is not tonal in the sensuous sense. It does not consist wholly of tones but includes emotions also. Yet those emotions form a specific group of emotional contents which, strictly speaking, do not find their expression in music, but simply exist as music.

Carefully perusing *Vom Musikalisch-Schönen*, one comes to the conclusion that the author anticipates the neo-realistic point of view in aesthetics. He objects to "feeling," not because he wishes to defend the sensualistic position by reducing melody to acoustic sensations, but rather because he finds in it something more definite and more permanent than both sensations and feelings. He demands for beauty the same thing that Bolzano demanded for logical truth: an existence *an sich*,

[9] Plotinus, *Enneades*, 5 : 9, 11.
[10] Ed. Hanslick, *Vom Musikalisch-Schönen*, page 64.
[11] *Ibid.*, page 65. Compare *ibid.*, pages 73, 149–150, 185.

an objective validity that would be independent of our consciousness. Quite in accordance with the modern phenomenological and neo-realistic movement, Hanslick declares: "What is beautiful remains beautiful even if it does not produce any feeling whatsoever, nay if there is no one to behold or to enjoy it." There is no doubt an element of truth in this exaggerated opinion. Melody is a specific relation of affinity among tones which is not idealistically dependent on mental phenomena. That this affinity cannot be comprehended by means of rational concepts, but has to be felt, does not change anything in its objective value. For is everything that exists accessible to us only through the medium of rational ideas? Is not feeling also a valuable instrument of awareness? If melody were nothing but feeling, then it would be a psychological fact, a piece of consciousness; then it would have no other existence except within our mind at the moment of its performance. But, to be sure, it does not spring into existence every time it is performed, and does not dwindle into nothingness every time a performer ends his program. As a beautiful form it is valid all the time. For at this particular moment it is very likely that Beethoven's "Ninth Symphony" is not being produced anywhere. Does this mean that Beethoven's symphony does not exist? And if by chance it is simultaneously performed in two different places, does this mean that there are two "Ninth Symphonies" in existence?

Thus with regard to music we may consider as established the following propositions: (1) Music is independent of the pleasure it affords to those who listen to it. It is independent, that is, in the sense that it cannot be adequately described by reference to various degrees of pleasure derived from it. Its content is much more complicated than the sheer banality of pleasure. Two melodies may be equally pleasurable and yet entirely different. (2) It is independent of intellectual interpretations. It is not an intellectual relation, not a variety of

274

knowledge, but one of feeling or emotion. It is also important to bear in mind that musical emotions do not intend to represent various forms of emotional responses that grow out of the conflicts of life, such as love, hate, will to power, or what not. They are emotions that grow out of the affinity of tones and out of nothing else. (3) And yet being emotions they do not depend on the momentary state of our mind, are not psychological entities—which proves that at least certain kinds of emotions have certain a-psychological or neutral nuclei which remain relatively constant and can be with fair approximation transmitted from one individual to another. Now we cannot unreservedly indorse Hanslick's philosophy of music. Yet the foregoing propositions will prove of service to us in our further discussion. For what he says about music applies, with certain modifications and restrictions, to other groups of aesthetic emotions. With those other groups, however, the truth is more obscure. Reference to music may therefore clarify many dark points in the nature of other emotional contents.

Descriptive content of emotions.—It is necessary at this stage of our inquiry to mention certain discoveries of modern philosophical science.

For the purpose of practical knowledge it is important to analyze ideas not according to what they are as psychic entities born in our fancy, but according to what they mean, or are able to accomplish for the system of knowledge. Failure to discriminate between ideas as mental entities and ideas as logical or artistic operations has had many deplorable consequences. Under the effect of this confusion reality was finally submerged in subjective sensations, apriori intuitions, mystical categories, or pragmatic instrumentalities. It seems to be the privilege of our day to rediscover ancient platitudes which have been sometimes for centuries obscured by scholastic folly. One of those pseudo-discoveries is the realization of the fact, well known to the ancients, that although our ideas are most certainly born within our mind they possess a meaning which can by no means be interpreted as a psychological entity. As to their substance they may very well be mental, although in view of the enormous diversity of psychological schools it is difficult to see what it means. But as to their function, i.e., its way of participating in an objective context, the word "mental" is unintelligible. For any mathematical or logical proof, for the success of any scientific experiment or value of an argument, it is entirely irrelevant, whether our ideas are "mental entities," or "accumulations of physical energy," or "material aggregates of moving atoms." Neither spiritualistic nor materialistic nor even pragmatic interpretations are of any consequence if we wish to consider their work within a given context. An idea will do what it does regardless of whether it is philosophically regarded as "mental" or "material," which are both equally discreditable categories.

But if such a radical change of philosophic interpretation (going from extreme mentalism to extreme materialism) does not affect the work done by the ideas, if it is possible for different thinkers, or even for the same thinker at different times, to regard an idea as "mental," or as "material," or as "purely symbolic" or what not, then there must be something in it that is above and beyond any and all of these interpretative characteristics, something that every idea does regardless of whether it is "mental" or "material." This something which is left behind when we suspend all philosophic theories concerning the essence of ideas—this empirical and purely descriptive residuum that enables us to distinguish one idea from another—is what the modern philosophers refer to when they speak of "neutral entities."

The term "entity" is badly selected. For they are not entities, but rather operations or functions. But disregarding this inaccuracy of expression we can depend upon the value of the

276

experience indicated by it. We prefer to call those functions "neutral nuclei." It is important to bear in mind that no mystical implications or absolutistic tendencies are allowed to obscure the issue. Each such nucleus is neither a new substance nor an eternal, immutable particle, but merely an operation, which exists only in its performance. Far from being platonically immutable, it is rather to be regarded as variable. For meaning depends upon the context in which it functions. "Man" can variously be defined as a "rational animal," or "featherless biped" or "ζῷον πολιτικόν." A zoölogist will define "man" in terms totally different from those employed by the historian and perhaps even unintelligible to the latter. And yet the intention of every definition is to identify, not a part or aspect of "man," such as his brains or his nose, but the whole "man" as such. Similarly every other idea has a variety of defining concepts which assume different values for every particular frame of reference. "My house is worth seven thousand dollars" and "my house is small" are two statements about "my house." But it is merely a grammatical illusion that the words "my house" mean identically the same thing in both sentences. In the first case "my house" is an economic object with all the teleological implications of a negotiable good. In the second case it is a mathematical magnitude comparable to some conventional unit of measure. The frames of reference are different, and the concepts are different. Thus the idea changes its meaning from context to context.[12]

---

[12] The word "change" is admittedly unprecise. The "change" that we here have in mind must not be confused with either psychological or biological variability in time. It has nothing to do with either time or evolution. Time itself is a variable whose value depends upon the choice of reference coordinates. But it would be absurd to say that time varies in time; for there cannot be any other time in which it can change its value from moment to moment. Thus logical variability is not to be understood as a continuous alteration. It is nearer in meaning to the concept of a variable in mathematics where

Similarly, for the purposes of art it is important to demonstrate that emotions, too, like ideas, have neutral nuclei; that these nuclei are not constants but variables, which change their value from one situation to another and yet can be identically transmitted from one individual to another if the situations are sufficiently alike; that those nuclei do not under any circumstances define anybody's mind or consciousness, but represent an independent and specific system of relations that cannot be otherwise defined or grasped; and that it is in the same sense illegitimate to regard the world of art as a product of our mind as it is illegitimate to regard nature as a product of science. It is very important to realize that these neutral nuclei, being wholly determinate and descriptively complete, are not immutable entities. Like ideas they exist only in a flux. Their nature is fundamentally heraclitic.

Music supplies a convenient illustration. The same melody may delight us or annoy us or leave us entirely indifferent, according to what we call our "mood," i.e., a set of other emotional contents with which the musical emotion has to associate. A given interval has one value in one melodic phrase, and an entirely different value in another phrase. And yet, like the idea of "man" in its various definitions, it is the same interval, not merely acoustically, but aesthetically determined as such. Under similar conditions it is always nearly the same. Moreover, whether it is "mental" in one sense or another, or "material" is entirely irrelevant with respect to what this interval "means" for the musician. A musician may be wholly ignorant

it simply means a quantity to which an unlimited number of values can be assigned. Similarly a concept P can be assigned a set of values $P, P, P, P, \ldots$ $P, \ldots,$ depending upon the context in which the idea stands. Thus in one context "man" means as much as "political animal," in another "rational animal"; but in most practical cases it simply means a certain familiar figure that we see daily in the streets. Only from co-ordination of all these concepts arises "man" as such.

278

as to what a modern psychologist means by "mental," and yet may have a perfectly clear grasp of the interval and its possible significance for any phrase he may eventually produce. This "grasp" is not an intellectual understanding but a specific feeling of its musical value. The musician symbolically indicates this meaning by notes, which he is able to "read," not as words but as musical relations. This emotional neutrality, which is the foundation of every intelligible theory of art, may be formulated in the following propositions:

Proposition I (Declaration of Independence).—*Although the content of emotions is given to us through mental processes, it is not dependent on those processes for its specific quality or structure.*

This proposition may be supported by the following argument. It is axiomatically, and without reservations, assumed in psychology that "fear," "love," etc., are mental processes, or manifestations of consciousness. Yet what is consciousness? Psychologists till now cannot agree as to the meaning of the term. Every psychological school—and psychological schools are very numerous—has its own conception of how mental process or consciousness should be defined. Behaviorists refuse to admit that consciousness exists at all. An average man knows nothing about mental processes. And yet everyone knows what fear is and knows it very definitely without the inherent vagueness of psychological theories. We have the testimony of an ancient fairy tale that a man who knows not what fear is is but a fool. Nobody in the days of fairy tales would have regarded a man as particularly foolish for not knowing what "mental process" meant.

Many psychologists still maintain that our mental processes are "immediately given to us." There is revealed in this assertion a remarkable inability of philosophical minds to draw a line between facts and theories—remarkable especially in view of their incessant argument about this very distinction. There is nothing surprising in the fact that men of science grow suspicious whenever a philosopher begins to speak of "facts." It is quite possible, to be sure, that men of science commit the same fallacy; but there is nothing surprising in this, since it is not their business to give an epistemological account of the distinction. A philosopher ought to be more cautious. Speaking of mental processes he ought to remember that they appeared comparatively late in the history of human knowledge, that the ancient Greeks knew nearly nothing about those "facts," and that there was a great deal of thinking necessary to grasp the distinction between the inner and the outer world. Even now the distinction is very far from being clear, and every psychological school, nearly every individual psychologist, has a different conception of what inner life, consciousness, or mental process is. That shows that consciousness is not an immediately given fact but a doctrine, a theory obtainable only through learning, and a great deal of learning. It is not a "sensation" that is immediately given to us, but "red" and "blue," "rough" or "smooth," "loud" or "soft." "Sensation" represents a psychological theory that is superimposed upon those immediate facts. Consciousness is a giver that in itself is never given.

For similar reasons the content of an emotion must be different from its psychological nature—different precisely in the same sense in which "red" is different from "sensation." Strictly speaking, it is not an "emotion" that is directly given to us in experience, but "fear" or "love," "courage" or "hate," "hope" or "despair." In experience we are aware of those things emotionally in the same way as we are of red and white visually. Musicians who invent melodies do not exactly create them but merely discover them in a manner similar to that by which thinkers discover truth. Through the medium of sound they discover a whole world of specific qualities and relations which otherwise would have remained closed to us.

It might be objected, however, that "fear," "love," etc., are

280

nevertheless emotions. Of course, we shall reply. But it is also true that space, in so far as it is given to us, is a perception. And yet this proposition, though true, does not prove a single item in the system of geometry. For mathematicians dealing with space "take consciousness in parentheses," and forget all about their perceptions, which never appear in their arguments or proofs. Similarly a man who is in love can hardly derive anything from his knowledge of psychology that would have any bearing upon his prospective happiness or pain. Yet he can derive a great deal of practical and useful insight into the matter from literature and poetry, which deal largely with the content and genuine structure of love and not at all with its "psychology."

Proposition II.—*The content of emotions, although a legitimate subject for theoretical analysis, cannot be intellectually comprehended. It can be logically discussed, but can never be grasped by intellect alone.*

One who says "fear," attaches a certain meaning to the word. Referring to this meaning, i.e., discussing fear, one is not supposed, at the moment of discussion, to live through an actual experience of fear. One may intelligently discuss fear without being actually afraid of anything or anybody. This is a purely theoretical situation in which nothing but meanings are involved. From this situation the actual experience of fear is totally different, and whoever lives through this experience knows that he not merely means but feels fear. There is something present in his experience that goes beyond logic, something that cannot be logically or intellectually accounted for. One who loves and enjoys music knows that no logical terms, in fact no theory whatsoever, can "explain" melody. One must actually feel melody in order to grasp it. No logical terms can possibly give it to us. It is true that one who says "Sigfried melody" attaches a definite, intelligible meaning to his words. Those are not merely words, but words with a definite logical meaning capable of being grasped by the intellect. And in the territory of logical concepts there is a concept that corresponds to these words. Yet that concept itself is merely a symbol. To indicate the "Sigfried melody" itself, words and concepts are not sufficient. We need musical signs. And one who reads those signs reads directly the melody itself.

Value of emotional independence in art.—Now let us briefly discuss the application of these propositions to the general problems of aesthetics. The value of the first proposition concerning independence of emotional contents from consciousness lies in establishing a kind of home rule, so to speak, for a large realm of phenomena which otherwise appear in constant danger of being misjudged by a foreign tribunal. How often, under the effect of psychological fallacy, art is regarded as a revelation of the artist's soul! It is almost pathetic to read discussions usually printed on symphonic programs pretending to explain to the ignorant public all the joys and grievances which the composer condescended to pour into various movements of his composition. And many people naïvely believe that the value of listening to good music lies in the opportunity of getting intimately acquainted with the soul of a good man who composed it. Why in the world I should be particularly interested in contemplating other people's souls, has never been properly explained. But it is generally taken for granted that it is a highly interesting and above all a profitable occupation. To read the mind of a great artist—isn't it indeed a glorious aim?

It is. But those who recommend it to us seem to forget two very important things. One is that when I go to a concert or to an exhibition of paintings I am not in the least interested in reading anybody's mind but simply and plainly in listening to music or seeing pictures. On the other hand it is to be remembered that the "souls" of many artists are by no means as glorious as their art. As a Polish poet, Zigmunt Krasinski, says: "In thy veins flows the stream of Beauty; but thou art not beautiful thyself."

The public at large in this respect just repeats the error committed by learned psychologists. Instead of analyzing the structure of what is actually given to us in our artistic experience or otherwise, they insist on analyzing the process of experience itself. This leads to grave misunderstandings and substitutions. Elements of consciousness are substituted for objects. Real, objective relations are changed to mental reactions. And those reactions are then erroneously identified with objects. In philosophical discussions this is a very common error. But, especially harmful because almost universal, this blunder appears to be in the domain of aesthetics and art criticism. How often beauty is measured by the amount of personal satisfaction it affords to the spectators! How often the aesthetic pleasure derived from dramatic art is believed to originate from relaxation that one finds in plays; it is thereby completely forgotten that the pleasure of relaxation from life's worries that people really find in the theater does not in any way constitute the pleasure derived from the excellence of the play itself. That music is almost regularly misinterpreted as the "innerest revelation of inner life" has been, I believe, sufficiently shown in the preceding paragraphs. To avoid this error it is well to have the truth of the first of our propositions constantly in mind. It is important to remember that artistic emotions are not merely mental states or spiritual entities, but primarily neutral complexes which show us a whole world of independent relations and specific qualities not otherwise brought to consciousness; that their physiological and psychological nature, as processes, are merely instrumental, and that their artistic value lies not in how they approach that world but in what they help us to see and feel in it.

The second proposition opposing intellectualism in art

guarantees a correct method of dealing with numerous objects of art. There are three ways of enjoying artistic work. The first is illustrated when we simply and naïvely enjoy an artistic production without trying to "understand" anything beyond what is immediately given to us in the form of enjoyment. This is perhaps the most adequate and, I am inclined to say, the most sympathetic way of approaching art. For that is precisely what the artist expects us to do. There is another, a professional, way of approaching an artistic work, which is based on training, on the study of technique and history. This professional way by no means interferes with the naïve enjoyment. It only discloses for enjoyment new points which otherwise may escape our attention and makes our appreciation of the work more thorough and profitable. There is, however, a middle way between those two which is neither naïve nor professional and consequently does not at all belong to the proper territory of art. It consists of "understanding" reached through "philosophy" and based on "profound interpretations." People who are dull and inartistic and unable to feel the content immediately given to them in music or poetry often wish to prove their "intelligent" reaction by what they claim to be mystical revelations. They substitute symbols and images for the genuine content of great works. And thus the tragic harmonies of Beethoven's "Sonata, Opus 27" are brought down to the level of a pictorial moonlight melodrama that may be successfully utilized for advertising Ivory soap or Packard cars. To avoid such illegitimate mutilations it is highly important to realize that emotions cannot be properly "understood," but can merely be "emoved," or felt.

Poetry and poets.—Now let us see how our propositions can be applied to the study of poetry. It is commonly believed that poets express in their work their moods and emotions. The fundamental assumption here made is that the poet knows what he wishes to express; he cultivates and carries in his heart his sentiments and when they are fully ripe he expresses them in words. In other words, his sentiments are growing within his soul and independently of expression; and when they are sufficiently grown he "transmits" them to others.[13] Let us see if the facts really corroborate this belief.

Words affect us emotionally in four different ways: by what they mean; by what they convey through association; by sound; and by rhythm. The first two, meaning and association, are generally considered the most important ones. Transmission of meaning is, of course, the chief function of words. Yet there are emotional concomitants connected even with the most abstract ideas. Every logical form throws its shadow into the land of emotions. It is these shadows that make our driest abstractions appear beautiful. Even geometrical theorems are not entirely deprived of this subtle beauty. For do not mathematicians often speak of the intrinsic elegance of their proofs and the beauty of their geometrical constructions? Possibly it is even the purest, the "barest," form of beauty that made a modern poet, in humble resignation, exclaim:

Euclid alone has looked on Beauty bare.

Great mathematicians are great artists even in spite of themselves. But there are emotions associated with any form of abstract thinking, and sometimes, no doubt, very strong emotions. These are not "love" or "hate," "fear" or "anxiety," but, as Croce puts it, "the effort of the thought itself," which may be painful to the point of torture or joyful to the extent of ecstasy.

Yet meaning remains the chief business of words, even in

---

[13] This belief has been carefully elaborated into doctrine by M. Grammont who in his capital work, *"Le Vers français,"* endeavors to formulate various means by which different emotions may be rhythmically and phonetically "expressed."

poetry. And it is the business of business to be unemotional. For the large part emotions stimulated by words are derived not from meaning but from association. An idea may be expressed in a businesslike form, in which only those words are used that are necessary to convey the meaning desired; or it may be expressed in what we call a poetic form, which appeals, to use Liddell's phrase, to our "human interest," bringing it into association with our previous experiences in other fields of life.

Those two forms of emotional content often do exist in the poet's mind prior to expression. In expressing infatuation for an abstract idea or bringing in, in a roundabout way, connections with some previous experiences, the poet expresses feelings which must be there in his "soul" before he expresses them. But in spite of the general belief to the contrary, those contents are very vague and utterly unprecise. They are incapable of correct transmission, because the same situation is seldom experienced by two different individuals in precisely the same way. What causes in the poet's mind a definite emotional response on the basis of his experience may cause a different response or no response at all in his reader's mind, because the latter had not had his experience or because he had it in a different form. It is true, when Macbeth reflects:

> Duncan is in his grave;
> After life's fitful fever he sleeps well;
> Treason has done his worst: nor steel, nor poison,
> Malice domestic, foreign levy, nothing,
> Can touch him further.

every single phrase, even every individual word is saturated with emotion. Of course, there is a difference between the two statements: "Duncan is in his grave" and "The life of Duncan is extinct"; the latter is a mere statement of fact, while the former suggests melancholy associations with "my mother's grave," or "my father's grave," or "his son's grave." It is true that such associations necessarily modify the plain statement of fact. But it is doubtful whether for all individuals it is identically modified. The poet cannot identically transmit his feelings to me because I am differently prepared for their reception.[14] Therefore even in this case the poet does not exactly express what is going on in his soul, but merely stimulates in others an emotional reaction of some sort relying on the relative similarity of human experience. If he really desires to communicate exactly what he feels, he finds himself in the rather pathetic situation of almost fatal incongruity between his thought and his expression. Expression in this respect appears to be an unattainable ideal. As a Russian poet, Tiutchev, puts it, "A thought expressed is falsehood."

Yet with regard to those emotional contents which are caused by meanings and associations the word "expression" has significance. There is at least an ideal possibility that emotions experienced by the poet are identically transmitted to the reader. In any event, there is something in the poet's soul that he strives to transmit to others; and this he can do with various degrees of success. In order to appeal to us intellectually, he must have something to say. In order to touch us emotionally, he must have some emotional experiences before he sets to work. But there are other kinds of emotions—those properly called poetical—which are attached organically to the expressions themselves and do not exist apart from them. The poet cannot "cultivate" those emotions in his "heart" prior to their expression, because they are properly an attribute of expression and do not exist apart from it.

The emotional contents derived from meaning and association are not sufficient to describe all emotional contents asso-

[14] Compare M. H. Liddell, *An Introduction to the Scientific Study of English Poetry* (1902), pages 37–38.

ciated with human speech. There are emotions which are caused only by words, as physical sounds, without any reference to either meaning or associations.[15] "It is true," says Santayana, "that language is a symbol for intelligence rather than a stimulus to sense, and accordingly the beauties of discourse which commonly attract attention are merely the beauties of the objects and ideas signified; yet the symbols have a sensible reality of their own, a euphony which appeals to our senses if we keep them open." Words, just like tones and colors, also have their emotional physiognomies; their acoustic personalities are varied. With every uttered phrase are connected, not merely those emotions which are produced by association and remembered from our previous experience but also those subtle and transient emotional fragments which are connected with the sound, rhythm, and physignomy of words:

> Reason has moons, but moons not hers
> Lie mirrored on her sea,
> Confounding her astronomers.

Every verse, every phrase, has such satellites of a-logical formation which revolve around the meaning and the sound of words. In our everyday conversation, where meaning stays in the foreground, those emotional satellites are ordinarily small and too far removed from the center of attention to be noticed. "The words of most men kiss with satiated familiarity," says the poet in Bodenheim's *Impulsive Dialogue*. In poetical language they are, on the contrary, deliberately cultivated. Poetry, according to Santayana, is the speech in which the instrument counts as well as the meaning. "So, while the purest

[15] It is possible, as Jespersen conjectures (*Language*, page 437), that it is precisely in this meaningless aspect of language that its origin lies. "It is possible," he says, "that speech has developed from something which had no other purpose than that of exercising the muscles of the mouth and of amusing one's self and others by the production of pleasant or possibly only strange sounds."

prose is a mere vehicle of thought, verse, like stained glass, arrests attention in its own intricacies, confuses it in its own glories, and is even at times allowed to darken and puzzle in the hope of casting over us a supernatural spell."[16]

There are two means of making speech emotionally more effective: rhythm and rime. We have seen how the distribution of accents affects the acoustic physiognomy of verse. An iambic verse with a trochee in the first foot has a different emotional appeal from that associated with one which has the trochee in the second foot. Those emotional differences do not "express" any human passions or sentiments previously cultivated in the poet's heart. The poet does not "know" them until he succeeds in actually producing the effect. It is true that he often feels the rhythmic effect before he actually puts it into words.[17] But this does not mean that he finds in his soul a ready-made emotion that is to be expressed by the coming rhythm. For what he feels is nothing other than the vague image of the emerging rhythm, and not any passion or sentiment previously known to him. This does not in any way injure poetical emotions associated with rhythm nor make them less powerful and effective. The fact that they do not "express" any passions received from the heart of the poet is no argument against their strength or beauty. Does it in any way injure musical emotions that they originate from the affinity of tones? Are they less effective because they are independent of the practical conflict of passions? What reason do we have to believe that only those emotions are strong and valuable and worthy of cultivation which have some rational task to perform, or have some practical significance? Musical emotions are very strong and worthy of cultivation without being just a copy or imitation

[16] G. Santayana, *Interpretations of Poetry and Religion*, page 256.

[17] This feeling testifies to the existence of what Mr. Scott terms "rhythmical instinct" (*Rhythmic Verse*, pages 212 ff.).

of any practical sentiments. Why do we assume that in order to be aesthetically effective an emotion must "imitate" or represent some such things as "love" or "hate," passion of "worship" or humiliation of "repentance"? Are Miltonian rhythms less powerful just because they do not imitate or represent any passions that slept in Milton's heart? Does it make them more "empty" if they are filled with emotions otherwise unknown and nameless? Milton had other means of expressing his passionate personality than either rhythm or rime. Of course his rhythms are unique, i.e., just his own, displaying certain idiosyncrasies that are not found in the rhythms of anybody else. But this does not prove that they "express" necessarily his peculiar way of loving or hating, his "tristesse" or his "indignation."[18] They express nothing but precisely his rhythmical preferences. It is also true that he might have preferred certain rhythms because of his emotional character; but this does not prove that his rhythms represent just those emotional qualities that he otherwise displayed in loving or worshiping. They might be independent qualities and yet remain his own and nobody else's. Those who insist on calling rhythmical emotions "empty" just because they are not representative of anything else either arbitrarily assume that only those emotions are not empty which have some biological significance or else lack the organ for appreciating and feeling rhythm in its own specific element.

Rhythm has a hypnotic power apart from anything that sentimental souls imagine it to represent. Why not take and

[18] See M. Grammont, *Le Vers français*, 1913. Grammont gives a whole list of emotions that may be variously expressed by varying rhythms and rimes. He never proves, however—in fact, that would be impossible—that different rhythmic and acoustic effects that he so carefully analyzes are really identical with the emotions assigned to them. They may be just vaguely similar. His analysis is highly valuable, but only as analogy, not as an expression of actual fact.

290

enjoy it at its face value? We know that primitive people rouse themselves to the point of exaltation by the monotonous rhythm of often senseless incantations. We are told by travelers that certain oriental tribes have festivals during which processions with music and burning torches are organized; in the middle of the procession, surrounded by musicians, goes a group of men carrying vessels with burning oil on their shoulders; they dance as they move along and the burning oil comes down in streams on their naked bodies. Of course religious convictions enable us to stand a great deal of pain; but I doubt if religion alone without the assistance of music and poetry would be able to produce a state obviously approaching anaesthesia. Such is the power of rhythm. It is evident that in such cases rhythm achieves its effect not because it represents a profound religious sentiment or any rational conviction but because it creates by itself a highly emotional state of mind. No matter how irrational, its effect is organically profound. The poetry of civilized nations is nothing but the evolution of this primitive effect. A stealthy sob that one often suppresses when reading good poetry, the feeling of joy and ecstasy that one derives from reading the familiar lines of one's favorite poems, the peculiar infatuation with certain expressions and passages which when expressed more prosaically do not contain any profound ideas or feelings—in a word, all those things that Tolstoy describes as the "tears of imagination" are very often but a distant echo of the primitive oriental drum reflected by the cliffs of centuries. They are emotions, and very powerful, profound emotions, which arise from rhythmical, not metrical, repetition of uttered syllables. Their undignified and apparently superficial origin does not prevent them from being highly dignified and profound in their effect. Rhythm, according to T. H. Scott, is the "shaper and form-giver of language."[19]

[19] T. H. Scott, *Rhythmic Prose.*

Thus the poet does not express himself in rhythm but, rather, rhythm expresses itself through the medium of the poet. The latter appears to be just a spectator who discovers new and often vast terrains of emotional vision. But his vision —and this is contrary to the general belief—is not a reduplication of anything that he previously cultivated within his soul. For the form of the discovered emotional contents depends on the physical appearance of rhythm, which, as we know, can be graphically represented; while rhythm as a rule does not depend on any previous emotion. This becomes still more evident if we consider the emotional effect produced by rime.

The poet and his rimes.—Another group of emotional contents associated with words are introduced by rime. We know that rime is based largely on the music of vowels. Even if there are some other factors that render it pleasing to the ear, such as the rhythmical effect of alliteration, those factors are negligible in view of the powerful effect of vowels. Rime is that technical device by means of which a succession of vowel sounds becomes a melody. We know that this melody is not merely a *façon de parler,* but an actual fact with a physical foundation. Our emotional response to a musical phrase evidently depends on that phrase as a physical reality and cannot be formed and molded according to our wishes. Therefore, even if the poet wishes to "express" in his rime a certain feeling or mood that happens to be in his mind, he will not be able to do it through the medium of rime, because the quality of rime emotion depends on the sound of vowels and not on his inner feelings. The poet is free to produce any melody of vowels; but he is not free to associate ad libitum any emotion with a given melody. He is bound by the physical structure of rime.

This, again, is by no means an argument in favor of the superficiality of the rime effect or against its power. For, being

292

purely musical and depending entirely on sound, the effect is nevertheless very strong and often absorbingly intense. In view of this effect we often forget the emptiness of intellectual content and the vagueness of emotional associations. The beauty of the melody of vowels is forced into the center of attention. The logical sense retreats into the background.

Rime is one of those irrational satellites that revolve around reason. It is concerned not with the meaning of verse but only with its form, which is emotional. It lies within the plane of the a-logical .cross-section of verse. For this reason the effect of rime often appears "mysterious," a work of "genius," which is too "dazzling" for our intellect to follow. The fact is, however, that being itself not intellectual, it is not at all unreasonable. It belongs to the form, to the external appearance—poets call it the "dress"—of a poem which is at the same time the inherent substance of poetry. Deprived of this charming dress, the poem often becomes ugly and ridiculous, a direct contrast to what one would call poetic. In any event, even if not completely distorted, the general tone of a poem deprived of rime becomes quite different from the original. Here, for instance, is what a poet says on poetry:

> And most of all, the pure ethereal fire,
> Which seems to radiate from the poet's lyre
> Is to the world a mystery and a charm,
> An Aegis wielded on a mortal's arm,
> While reason turns her dazzled eye away,
> And bows her scepter to her subjects' sway;
> And thus the poet clothed with godlike state,
> Usurped his Maker's title—to create;
> He, whose thoughts differing not in shape, but dress,
> What others feel more fitly can express.

Now take off the riming "dress" from this charming fragment! I shall ask my reader to have the patience to read the same lines once more without rime:

And most of all the pure ethereal flame
Which seems to radiate from the poet's lyre
Is to the world a mystery and a lure,
An Aegis wielded on a mortal's arm,
While reason turns away her dazzled eyes,
And bows her scepter to her subjects' sway;
He, whose thought differing not in shape, but attire
What others feel more fitly can express.

I have changed only three words in the passage, substituting for them words which are equally poetic or even more so— "flame" for "fire," "lure" for "charm," and "attire" for "dress." And yet it sounds almost like a caricature of Holmes' poetic eulogy.

Criticism of the Romantic theories of rime.—Poetry, like all professions, has its superstitions. As we have just seen, one of those superstitions, widely believed in, indeed, almost universally accepted, is that poets through their rhythms and rimes express the deepest moods and the loftiest sentiments of their souls. This belief was impressed upon us by the romantic school. Hegel was its most profound exponent.

We have seen that, according to his doctrine, rime "leads us back to our inner self." It brings forth and represents the emotional appeal of poetry in so far as the latter depends on the beauty of words as plain physical sounds. In the music of rime one hears "the vivid tones of the soul itself." It is hereby tacitly assumed that those "tones" originally exist in the soul of the poet in the form of a feeling (emotion), and that he brings this feeling to expression through a skillful arrangement of words. "The desire of the soul to perceive itself" finds, therefore, in the identity of rime "a real source of satisfaction."

We are led, hereby, to believe that rime is not merely pleasing in itself but pleasing also because it represents some-

294

thing else which is of far greater importance—the moods and feelings of the poet. The similarly intoned words at the end of the verse lines appear to be "somehow mysteriously related to each other," as Tieck puts it; and the mystery of their relation leads us deep into the poet's soul. We are further led to believe that the creative impulse in poetry consists of inspiration, which is a peculiar state of mind that distinguishes the poet from an ordinary mortal and gives him the ability to mold his feelings into sounds. Under the effect of inspiration, rhythms and rimes appear to be symbolic; they express what is going on in the soul of one who has inspiration. In other words, poetry requires an ecstatic state of mind, a peculiar "rapture," which precedes creative work; and the poet—to use Wordsworth's phrase—"gives to that rapture an accordant rime." Into the music of words he puts his inner feelings. In this process he does not follow the logic of ideas; for his words are "mysteriously" related, not to what he says but to what he feels. In expressing his feelings he follows largely the logic of sound. For the sound of words, as Shelley explained, has its own "peculiar order."

Yet this "peculiar order" that constitutes the music of words does not represent or express any emotions beyond those which are caused by the sound. For those emotions do not exist apart from the sound. We have seen, in the preceding paragraphs, that a given melodic transition, say, from *fa* to *si-bémol*, is pleasing to the ear, and pleasing in a specific way that is characteristic of this particular interval. It is an established fact in psychology that specific emotional contents are associated with different intervals in a way similar to that in which specific emotional responses are associated with different colors. It is evident that those emotional contents do not exist without either colors or intervals as the case may be. They are satellites of sensations. It would be absurd to believe that they represent or express some other moods or sentiments, because they are

295

chained to given sensations, and do not exist apart from them. Similarly, we know that the vowels of human speech consist of peculiar arrangements of overtones. Therefore, a change of voice from *e* to *o* is in fact a melodic transition from one specific chord to another. With this transition, too, is associated a specific emotion. This emotion, again, does not express or represent anything beyond itself. It does not pre-exist in the poet's soul, for he is unconscious of it until he actually utters the sound or at least feels it coming.

There is, however, a grain of truth in the Romantic doctrine. Classical aesthetics emphasized largely the external or objective factors in the constitution of beauty, such as "measure," "perfection," "form," in a word, all those things that Irving Babbitt sums up in the term "decorum." For ancient thought, beauty was a matter of external form, something to be discovered, not created; something to be intellectually contemplated in the world of perfect ideas, "beyond the orbit of the sun." It was left to the Romantic school to discover the human factor, the element of subjectivity in art. It was a valuable and permanent discovery; and no one at present, I think, will deny that there is a great deal of truth in it. Yet, correct in one sense, it was wrong in another.

In so far as rime is concerned, it is quite true that it conveys emotions. It greatly intensifies the emotional appeal derived from poetry by rendering it more musical in the direct sense of the word. It not merely assists rhythm by means of regular beats at the end of each verse, but it adds a new wealth of emotional material by introducing unity of key into the melody of vowels. Strong "feeling" is associated with rime. It is also true, of course, that feeling is a subjective factor and has its origin in our "soul." But it is by no means true that the feeling associated with a given rime is just an echo, or a symbol, or an "expression," of some other feelings that were previously growing in the poet's heart. This romantic reduplication is senseless, for we have no idea as to how one feeling may be regarded as a symbol or "expression" of another feeling.

But will not poetry be rendered "empty" if we deprive rhythm and rime of their symbolic value as expressions of the poet's moods? Is the mere jingling of sound an object worthy of poetic cultivation? But it is not a mere jingling of sound. Poetry does not express emotions, it is true; but it does something infinitely more important: it creates emotions. What difference does it make that those emotions originate in sound and not in the "heart"? Their physical origin is not in any way injurious to their poetic dignity. They are not rendered any weaker or less effective. Their content and their intensity are not changed. On what basis should we consider them "empty"? Is music empty because it grows out of sound? Does not sound make us cry? Combinations and successions of tones are creative of emotions. Those emotions do not swim in the poet's heart as ready-made entities that he in some mysterious way puts into rimes, rhythms, and melodies. He produces them. Experimenting with tones, vowels, and words he is able to find and transmit entirely new emotions which have never been in anybody's "heart" before; but he certainly is unable to cultivate those emotions independently of the physical material with which he works.

The conception of the poet as a precious vessel for the cultivation of refined and beautiful emotions is deeply rooted in our modern thinking. That poets often do that, and do it very successfully, we do not deny. They have legitimate ways and means of doing it through the perfectly natural application of description and suggestion, i.e., by meaning and association. But this is not what people generally mean by saying that the poet "expresses himself" in poetry. What is meant by this phrase is far from ordinary. It is commonly believed that the poet "expresses himself" not as everybody else does by using words as conventional signs but largely by using rhythms and rimes. For these are the distinguishing marks of poetry: "the moment . . . . verse ceases to be felt as rhythmical, it ceases to be felt as poetry."[20] And it is almost universally believed that the poet, not merely constructs rhythms and rimes, producing thereby emotions which he never had before, but that he fills up his rhythms and rimes with emotions that he had previously cultivated in his heart. "The desire to quintessentialize, to heat-up an emotion until it burns white-hot, seems to be an integral part of the modern temper," declares Amy Lowell in the Preface to *Sword Blades and Poppy Seed*. And of course it is to be understood that the "quintessence" of poetic emotion is to be found in the rhythm of words. Ezra Pound expresses himself still more clearly on the subject. "I believe," he says, "that every emotion and every phase of emotion has some toneless phrase, some rhythm-phrase to express it."[21]

Thus we see that not only critics and laymen but also the poets themselves believe the story of "expression." This is the strangest of all. For, granted that these statements are really sincere, it is strange to see great minds live and work under the effect of so obvious an illusion. They ought to know by experience that the emotions and moods which they produce with their rhythms are not, and cannot possibly be, representations of other emotional contents which they had in their minds prior to the creation of some particular rhythm. It is true, of course, that every rhythm creates an emotional response. But it does not follow logically from this that every emotion is expressible in rhythm. It could not be, precisely for the reason that rhythm *creates* emotions. Therefore, those emotions which are created by rhythm do not exist before rhythm created them. It is almost mathematically evident that, since every particular rhythm has its specific emotion, therefore that emotion which

[20] Bliss Perry, *A Study of Poetry* (New York, 1920).

[21] Ezra Pound, "Vorticism," *Fortnightly Review* (1914), 71:461.

298

is not produced by rhythm is *eo ipso*, not expressible by rhythm; for, if it were, it would be, *ex hypothesi*, one of those which are produced by rhythm.

A similar consideration applies to rime. Our analysis has shown that rime has a physical basis in the melody of vowels. These melodies produce strong emotional responses. The contents associated with those responses can never be conveyed to us in any other way except through the medium of rime. Being attached to the sound of words or, more precisely, to the melodic phrases that accompany the uttered words, those emotional fragments accumulating energy from line to line ultimately produce a highly emotional state of mind. It is therefore true that every rime creates an emotional response. But it does not follow that any emotion can be expressed in rime except emotions which are born together with rime. The latter are unique, and are untranslatable into the language of other emotions. We cannot interpret the enthusiasm derived from a beautiful rime as an expression of "love" or "hatred" that was burning in the poet's heart. We cannot interpret it; we cannot properly "understand" or "grasp" it except by repeating the phrase. Neither can it be controlled or modified by any intellectual considerations. It follows exclusively its own logic.

Thus rime is a specific emotional response associated exclusively with certain physical situations. Moreover, it belongs to the class of "satisfying" emotions. One may object to this particular kind of satisfaction, perhaps, may regard it as "vulgar" and "barbarous." This objection will be carefully considered in the next chapter. But, vulgar or not, rime is a kind of satisfaction, which belongs to its phenomenological content and is characteristic of the essence of this content—this, of course, only on the subjective side, i.e., in so far as it is an emotion.

On the basis of our physical analysis we can more precisely describe the nature of the satisfaction here involved. We know that riming lines constitute a musical phrase. The tension characteristic of every melodic motion is in a verse resolved by the riming vowel. Thus each rime is a solution of a musical problem. It gives us a relief from tension. As a solution of some specific musical problem each individual rime is unique and absolutely irreproducible. It grows out of the unique musical situation presented by each given sequence of vowels. Consonants, as drum-beats, also belong to the coloring of the phrase. Every change, therefore, of either vowels or consonants causes some change, however insignificant, in the musical structure of the verse. The same pair of riming words used for two different verse couples are musically different entities. For they are "reposes," or harmonic "resting places" (solutions) for two different sets of musical chords. Each rime, like each human being, has a unique and unalienable face. It is not an abstraction but an individual. It is for this reason that we consider it impossible to define rime as a pair of words with identical endings. Properly speaking "rapping ... tapping" do not constitute a rime, but only a riming word couple. They become a rime only in a concrete poetic situation of a given verse. Each rime physically is an absolutely unique and individual situation. To this situation corresponds phenomenologically a certain ideal function, which we called neutral nucleus, and which constitutes what the poet has in view when he speaks of a "given rime." It is a generalized emotional content.

It is questionable whether such emotional contents can be identically transmitted from one person to another. Our perception of a given rime may each time be different. For each time we have only an incomplete view of its ideal content—a view which is subjectively colored and variously modified by our incidental moods. These momentary glimpses are what psychologists call emotional responses. Now, psychologically, i.e., as a response to a certain physical situation, a given content depends, not merely upon that situation, but also upon the conditions of the responding organism. The same musical phrase sounds "elevating" when played at a concert, and merely "annoying" when repeated over and over again by a practicing student. Even if it is repeated identically, our response is slightly different, perhaps, each time. The artistic effect of a rondeau is based on this fact. Every time the main theme is heard it appears, like phoenix, newly born and with an increased glory. And yet we call it the same theme. The sameness lies on the physical and phenomenological side; it is identically constructed. But the meaning of this structure for us each time is, or at least may be, quite different. The same consideration applies to rime. Rime is heraclitic. It moves. It has no absolute identity. For us it constantly changes its face. The same rime that seemed interesting and stimulating a moment ago may appear dull and flat when we are not in the mood for it. A rime that sounds beautiful to the average man may seem quite banal to the supporter of free verse. It is protean. What are the conditions determining its subjective value? This question will be the theme of our last chapter.

VIII

THE CONTROVERSY CONCERNING
THE VALUE OF RIME

IN our day there may be observed in the literature of various countries a considerable decrease in the enthusiasm for riming which, in some cases, takes the form of a deliberate protest against rime.

The nature of the controversy.—The modern emphasis on rhythm renders rime "in most cases undesirable," as it hinders rather than assists the proper appreciation of rhythmical nuances. Therefore, free verse, based on cadence, is bound to avoid rime in order not to distract the attention of the reader from the subtleties of rhythm. Those subtleties and nuances "are designed largely to take the place of rime."

On the whole, the argument against rime may be summed up under the following three categories:

First, rime appears as a handicap in the logical construction of verse. The poet's thinking is hampered and hindered by his

302

obligation to follow the chosen rime scheme. Without rime he would possibly express his ideas in a briefer and better way. He often has to strain the sense in order to keep rime. Therefore both blank verse and, later, free verse appear to the modern mind as a deliverance from an intellectual bondage. "Vers libre," writes Harriet Monroe, "whose rhythmic subtleties may be only at the beginning of their development, is a demand for greater freedom of movement within the bar and the line."

Second, rime is often felt to be a superficial and unnecessary ornament. It absorbs a great deal of the reader's attention, taking it away from the ideas and emotions expressed. It creates within a poem a superficial and external beauty at the expense of its spiritual beauty. Occasionally rime "may be necessary to stress some complex variation, or to hold together the patterns of the poem"; but on the whole it is not merely unnecessary but harmful, because its annoying sweetness often eclipses the effect of finer details. As a beautiful face on a portrait often conceals the neglectful brush of the painter, so the superficial jingling of rime often serves merely to cover poor composition. Indeed, how many poems appear daily which are accepted by the public as poetry only because they rime. How many old-fashioned trivialities are covered by the powder and rouge of dilettante rime. No wonder that many a sincere poet comes to regard rime as a painted prostitute of poetry, a dissolute sister of rhythm.

Third, rime appears as an easy and cheap method of keeping time—a sort of mechanical device to escape from the difficulties of creating real rhythm. It seems to relieve the poet from the difficulties and responsibilities of unrimed rhythms. It is rhythmically annoying in its drum-like effect. Fletcher finds that the bondage of rime produces an effect similar to that of "monotonous rag-time." Is not this a modern variety of the Miltonian reaction against rime?

And yet all these objections, however true, are powerless

303

to discredit rime, and poetry still remains largely rimed verse. The theoretical advocates of rime find a defense with which to meet every one of the stated objections. Against the logical or, rather, intellectual criticism maintaining that rime is a handicap to the expression of ideas, it is pointed out that it is by no means easier to write verses without rime. In favor of this argument we have the testimony of such an authority as Lessing, who said that it was more difficult for him to avoid rime than to observe it. Instead of delivering us from a bondage the advocates of blank verse impose upon us the heavier bondage of unrimed rhythms. Against the second, the aesthetic, objection it is argued that the reproach of "cheapness" does not affect riming in general but only bad riming. Indeed, the fact that the world is flooded with cheap poetry and miserable rimes does not logically prove that there is not any good poetry nor any excellent riming. Naturally, the same objection can be applied to unrimed poetry. The modern poetry magazines abound in very poor free verse experiments. These do not prove that there are no excellent poems written in free verse. That rime makes even a good poet deviate from the natural flow of thought and rhythm is also untrue, for "the necessity of rhyme," says Dryden, "never forces any but bad and lazy writers to say what they would not otherwise." And we know that Pope called bad riming a "disease." As to the third argument, saying that rime creates "lame meter," we have plenty of authoritative testimony from equally great minds claiming that rime helps meter and creates beautiful rhythm.

History of the controversy.—Opposition to rime as a "vulgar" and "barbarous" device dates from the sixteenth century, the age of momentous events and colorful episodes, pregnant with great theories and intense conflicts, the historical time-home of Ariosto and Torquato Tasso, of Shakespeare and Cervantes, Copernicus, Leonardo da Vinci, Raphael, Michael

Angelo, Albrecht Dürer, Martin Luther, Henry the Eighth. It has, perhaps, the longest list of heroes, and villains. All of them, including Ivan the Terrible, are historical stars of the first magnitude. It was the time when our fundamental types of cultural reaction were produced, when the main artistic and scientific categories were coined, and great conflicts were planted into the soul of the modern man. It was predominantly an age of controversies. No end of arguments and disputes. Among the minor controversies of the century we find that of rime versus blank verse.

It was by no means a mere chance that the controversy originated at that time. The sixteenth century was not merely producing art, but trying to comprehend its substance and analyze its rules. It became in full sense art-conscious. Numerous "Poetics," "Rhetorics," and "Defenses" undertake to explain the significance of poetry and the importance of the poet. These discussions and disputes reach as far as the Balkan Peninsula, where in the city of Raguza on the Dalmatian coast a national Serbian school of poetry was founded by Marulić (1457–1527); and still farther east beyond the eastern frontiers of Prussia as far as Poland, where Rey devotes page after page of his *Mirror or Life of an Honest Man* to discussion of the value and nature of poetry, and where Kochanowski (1530–1584), though a disciple of Ronsard, writes an experimental tragedy in blank verse, *The Dismissal of the Grecian Envoy*. Art and literature are no longer ashamed of serving the purpose of purely aesthetic enjoyment, and their numerous apologists endeavor to convince the pedantic moralists of the Old School by quoting the well-known platitude from Horace that poetry has educational importance and is reasonably "useful." The brilliant court circle of Margaret of Navarre (1492–1549), the gifted poet-sister of Francis I, including such men as Clément Marot (1495–1544), François Rabelais (1490–1553), and the founder of "free-thinking," the secretary of the Queen,

De Perrier, laid the foundation for that style of thinking and system of "good taste" which later on was codified by the Academy.

It is not surprising that under the influence of this all-European enthusiasm for poetry, and "good taste" in poetry, the question arose whether the poets should strictly follow the ancient classical forms, or be allowed to deviate from those forms in favor of modern "inventions" and "innovations." The chief difference between ancient and new poetry lay in the fact that the former knew no rime. Thus rime became the center of a new controversy. Those who were inclined to regard Greek and Latin as an ideal and accepted their forms as the only ones worthy of cultivation, or even those who, like Milton, wished to guard poetry against vulgarisms of a barbarian origin, advocated the use of blank verse. Whereas those who trusted more their linguistic instinct than any tradition, however old and learned, accepted rime as a powerful means of creating new emotions.

The campaign against rime began in Italy. The country where rime achieved its first great success in Dante's *Divine Comedy* became the cradle of the anti-rime reaction. The reaction followed immediately after the new amazing success achieved by rime in the epics of Ariosto (1474–1533). In the beginning of the sixteenth century there appeared in Italy a group of poets, with the learned G. Giorgio Trissino at their head,[1] who both in theory and in practice advocated the return

[1] There was much talk among the humanists at the end of the fifteenth century about the contrast between Homer and Virgil. Homer was regarded as a crude, somewhat vulgar representative of the spontaneous folk-poetry, resembling the contemporary street singers. Virgil on the contrary was deemed incomparably superior. He was highly valued as the originator of the "classical" epos—classical now in the sense of law-abiding, correct, artificially faultless composition. Trissino led the reaction. He imitated the *Aeneid* in his pompous, stilted "Italy Liberated from Goths." The anti-rime movement was a part of this "liberation."

to ancient meter, and endeavored to discredit rime as a vulgar and barbarous device, not suited for the "educated taste" of those who were acquainted with the poetry of the ancients. Trissino, whose *Sofonisba* is commonly regarded as the first tragedy in modern literature, opened the crusade. "A dignified and serious scholar,"[2] he wrote *Italia Liberata* in imitation of the classical hexameter in blank verse expressedly in opposition to Ariosto, whom he considered to be "pleasing only for the common folk." For the "educated taste" he offered rimeless hexameters, which he proceeded to fabricate with the same scholarly seriousness with which he worked hard to effect a formal union between classical mythology and the Christian point of view, arriving with his "Angel Neptune" and especially with his "Angel Venerio," at a strange and naïve combination of uncombinables. In his theoretical attack on rime Trissino was preceded by Leon Battista Alberti (1404–1472) and followed by Bernardo Tasso, the father of Torquato. Thus the idea of blank verse, as a reaction against rimed verse, appeared on the horizon of European literature.

It took about one hundred years for this idea to travel to England, where at the close of the sixteenth century under the influence of the Italian Renaissance there appeared a number of poets and critics who conducted a bitter and highly spirited attack on rime. "It is glory enough for Henry Howard, Earl of Surrey—the greatest poet from Chaucer's day to his own—to say that he was the pioneer, and a successful one, in the use of blank verse in English. . . . . The Italians were at that time beginning their movement to remand rhyme into the suburbs of their good pleasure, as a modern and rather discreditable thing, in comparison with unrhymed quantitative verse after

[2] Trail, *History of Italian Literature*, page 184. Compare also K. Borinski's discussion of Trissino's poetics in *Die Antike in Poetik und Kunst-theorie*, 1:212 ff.

the classical Latin model. . . . . Just how far Surrey, a constant student of Italian models, was influenced by them in his use of blank verse is difficult to say; but so sonorous and majestic a vehicle for poetic thought—dramatic, philosophical, and even narrative—was bound to come. . . . . At this period of almost universal curiosity, novelties in verse were appearing on every hand: now imported from Italy, and now invented—Nash's pretty poem—by the very prodigality of freshly singing genius."[3] The movement prepared the ground for the splendid success of blank verse in England under Milton.

In 1570 Roger Ascham's *The Schoolmaster* appeared. Ascham was evidently the first to introduce into England the theory of the late Italian humanists concerning the origin of rime from the "Goths and Huns," a theory that was repeated later on so many times in England and Germany. He believes it to be a historical fact that our "rude and beggarly" art of riming was "brought first into Italy by Goths and Huns, when all good learning too was destroyed by them, and after carried into France and Germany, and at last received in England by men of excellent wit indeed, but of small learning and less judgement in that behalf. . . . ." Thus rime was for the first time, in England, proclaimed to be an "invention of a barbarous age." It needed centuries of thinking on the subject to see nothing compromising in such origin. For Hegel it was indeed possible to accept rime as an advantage and a conquest even from the hands of Goths and Huns. But in the sixteenth century when ancient learning, art, and culture were still in the process of reviving from the terrible disaster of the barbarian invasion, the effect of which lasted for a whole thousand years, it was still quite impossible to believe that anything that originated from "Goths and Huns" could possess any cultural value whatsoever. Therefore rime appeared as a child of ignorance and

[3] C. F. Richardson, *A Study of English Rhyme*, page 110.

idleness. Its "barbarous" origin seemed to be sufficient reason for its artistic condemnation.

Ascham's Goth-and-Hun theory was so universally accepted that it appeared even in poetry:

> Of many faults rhyme is perhaps the cause;
> Too strict to Rhyme, we slight more useful Laws;
> For that in Greece or Rome was never known,
> Till by Barbarian Deluge o'erflown,
> Subdued, undone, they did at last obey,
> And changed their own for their Invader's way.

It evidently became customary and fashionable to regard rime as "vulgar art," even though the critics were to use rime to say so:

> Numbers and Rhyme, and that harmonious Sound,
> Which not the nicest Ear with Harshness wound
> Are necessary, yet but vulgar Arts.[4]

The theory that was rather modestly advanced by the Italian humanists, and that never became popular in Italy, produced in England a whole revolution, and was repeated by English critics with much gesticulation and in highly abusive language. William Webbe — "Graduate" — calls riming "brutish poetry" of barbarous origin and vulgar use. And with remarkable consistency for a modern, "educated" man (one should never forget that he is a "graduate"), having thus abused the "bald art of riming," he proceeds to make rules for this very art.[5] Thomas Campion speaks of rime as a "childish titilation" and advocates the use of unrimed iambics, sapphics, odes, and anacreontics, illustrating those "numbers" with his

---

[4] John Sheffield, *Essay on Poetry*, 1682.

[5] *A Discourse of English Poetry. Together with the author's judgement touching the re-formation of our English verse*, by William Webbe, Graduate, 1586 (Arber's Edition, pages 57–72). Webbe's codification of rime—in his

own original compositions, "of which many are clever and even musical."[6] "Some ears," he says, "accustomed altogether to the Fatness of Rhyme, may perhaps except against the cadences of these numbers: but let any man judicially examine them, and he shall find they close of themselves so perfectly that the help of rhyme were not only in them superfluous, but also absurd." The opposing party was hardly more moderate in its expressions. The dramatist Thomas Nash, "the most violent of all the controversialists," speaking for the defense, goes into a violent polemic against those "idiot art masters" who believe to be able to surpass the best poets with the "swelling bumbast of a bragging blank verse."[7] Poets preserved a better sense of humor in the controversy. At the end of Jonson's much-quoted *A Fit of Rhyme Against Rhyme* most dreadful and cruel wishes are hurled against the inventor of rime:

> He that first invented thee
> May his joints tormented be,
>   Cramped forever;
> Still may syllables jar with time,
> Still may reason war with rhyme,
>   Resting never!
> May his sense when it would meet
> The cold tumor of his feet
>   Grow unsounder;
> And his title be long Fool,
> That in rearing such a School
>   Was the founder.

scheme of English prosody rime for the first time is established as a "rule"—would be entirely inconsistent with his bitter attacks on the art of riming, if it were not for a remark that "in our English tongue it beareth as good grace, or rather better, than in any other." Thus the English language is regarded as being peculiarly adapted for riming purposes and therefore in a way diminishes the barbarism of this otherwise disreputable device.

[6] C. F. Richardson, *A Study of English Rhyme*, page 139.

[7] Quoted from Richardson, *ibid.*, page 133.

310

Although, as we see, highly picturesque epithets were hurled against the inventor of rime, yet on the whole the above fragment lacks the bitterness of those "graduates" who were leading the attack in prose. The whole poem is so amusingly humorous that, if we had no further knowledge concerning the literary idiosyncrasies of its author, we could easily mistake his purpose as implying a subtle defense of rime.

The seventeenth century is much calmer. The controversy continues. In fact, in the middle of the century, with the entrance of Milton and Dryden into the struggle, it reaches its climax. But it takes now the form of a scholarly and academic, though sometimes passionate, dispute. Its tone becomes milder; it reminds one at times of a casual exchange of academic politenesses. The adherents of blank verse laid stress upon the freedom of thought and the importance of the intellectual content. Rime for them appeared as an unnecessary ornament which hampered the free development of ideas by forcing upon the poet the duty of imposing "the jingling sound of like endings" upon his earnest thought. It was felt as a "hindrance and constraint." The opponents of blank verse, on the contrary, emphasized the "refinement of poetic form," and considered restraint as essential to excellence. Our luxurious imagination, they argued, might lead us too far, "did not the labor which is required to well-tuned and polished rhyme, set bounds to it." "For the one," so Professor J. W. Good formulates the substance of the controversy, "restraint was essential to excellence. For the other, all real excellence was conditioned upon liberty of thought and expression, such as was afforded by blank verse and exemplified in *Paradise Lost*. Upon this liberty depends the possibility of attaining the excellence of the Ancients."[8]

It seems that Milton was the first who had the courage, in

[8] J. W. Good, "Studies in the Milton Tradition," *University of Illinois Studies in Language and Literature*, 1915, 1:164.

the name of all the poets, to confess that rime often makes them express many things in a more strained way, and "for the most part worse," than they would have expressed them without rime. This courageous confession, all the more valuable because of the greatness of the poet who made it, caused some defenders of rime to take an unfair advantage of the frankness of a great mind. Milton was accused of "slender sophistry."[9] And even Dryden, answering this particular point in Milton's argument, is almost insultingly polite when he says: "And now having laid this as a foundation, ... I must crave leave to tell him, that some of his arguments against rhyme reach no farther than, from the faults or defects of ill rhyme, to conclude against the use of it in general. . . . . A good poet never establishes the first line till he has sought out such a rhyme as may fit the sense, already prepared to heighten the second." Therefore, "the necessity of a rhyme never forces any but bad or lazy writers to say what they would not otherwise."[10]

A clear echo of this controversy one perceives a hundred years later in Germany. The arguments on both sides repeat themselves with such remarkable precision that no doubt is left as to the influence which the rime controversy in England exercised upon the poetical parties in Germany. Even in poetry we hear practically the same objections and almost the identical complaints. Compare, for example, Rabener's satire dedicated to "lovers of rime" with Jonson's *A Fit of Rhyme Against Rhyme*.

> Der Reim? Wie? Dieser Zwang, der das Gedicht entselet?
>   . . . . Ein Henker, der uns quälet,

[9] Thomas Rymer, *Tragedies of the Last Age*, 1678.

[10] In his *Essay on the Origin and Progress of Satire* Dryden remarks that the main reason why Milton advocated the abolishment of rime was "plainly this, that rhyme was not his talent."

312

Der Ordnung und Verstand auf seine Folter streckt
Der Wörter radebrecht, dem Dicter Angst erweckt,
Der Warheit und Natur in schwere Fesseln Schmiedet.

It sounds almost like a free translation of Jonson's "not un-
kindly satire," the end of which was quoted above. Here is the
beginning of it:

> Rhyme, the rack of finest wits,
> That expresseth by fits
> True conceit,
> Spoiling senses of their treasure,
> Cozening judgement with a measure,
> But false weight;
> Wresting words from their true calling,
> Propping verse from fear of falling
> To the ground;
> Jointing syllables, drawing letters,
> Fastening vowels, as with fetters
> They were bound!

Klopstock led the attack in Germany (1724–1803). He believed rime to be altogether superfluous, and even "contrary
to the spirit of our tongue." Speech is melody; speech is
rhythm. "But what is rime," he asks, "with its drum-like
rattle? What is the meaning of its harangue?" And he replies:
"an evil spirit" (*"ein böser Geist"*). The meaning of rime is to
produce "verbal noise" (*"Wörtergepolter"*). Quite in the spirit
of the Goth-and-Hun theory he accuses modern poetry of
abandoning the path of classic rhythms, and substituting "awkward" (*"plump"*) rime instead:

> Die spätern Sprachen haben des Klangs noch wohl;
> Doch auch des Silbenmasses? Statt dessen ist
> In sie ein böser Geist, mit plumpem
> Wörtergepolter, der Reim, gefahren.

313

Red' ist der Wohlklang, Rede das Silbenmass;
Allein des Reimes schmetternder Trommelschlag,
Was der? Was sagt uns sein Gewirbel,
Lärmend und lärmend mit Gleichgetöne?

Herder seems to have taken Milton's words too literally and dogmatically. In the same frequently quoted and still more frequently misunderstood preface to *Paradise Lost*—seeming to consist of quotations, which, like golden coins, have entered so many books, and so many minds—Milton casually remarks that modern poets in applying rime were "carried away by custom," and evidently by false custom. Herder evidently concludes therefrom that English poetry is controlled exclusively by convention and is, from the nature of the language, indifferent to form. With a purely "Siegfriedian" patriotism he declares: "Our language commands form more than any other. Compared with German the French and English languages are formless in poetry; for only arbitrariness and custom (*'Willkür und Uebereikunft'*) established there the art of riming and rules of good taste which did not lie in the nature of their language (*'die der Sprache selbst nach unbestimmt waren'*). Whereas our language tends toward the most difficult, but at the same time most beautiful . . . . form, that of the ancients."[11] This sweet linguistic patriotism leads Herder to believe that German poetry is naturally adapted to the imitation of ancient meters, and consequently for the abandonment of rime. Through Herder it became, for a while at least, quite fashionable in Germany to cultivate exotic rhythms and to regard rime as unworthy of cultivation. In consequence Herder's school regards rime largely as an unnecessary constraint which tends "to deprive the poem of its soul."

[11] Herder, *Wiederaufhebung der Alten, Briefe zu Beförderung der Humanität, Achte Sammlung,* 1796.

314

Lessing very convincingly, and with a charming simplicity of argument, assumed the defense of rime. His apology is worthy of being quoted in full:

It seems to me that those who are mercilessly antagonistic to rime are, perhaps, only wishing to avenge themselves for their own failure to master it. With a haughty mien they call rime a jingling sound. As though the sensually pleasing repetition of sound were the only reason why one should wish to retain it. Don't you consider at all the pleasure that arises from overcoming a difficulty? Is there no achievement in not letting one be carried away by rime but through skilful arrangement of words to produce the impression that no other word can possibly stand in its place? Those who doubt the possibility of such arrangements reveal thereby their own weakness in the command of language and a lack of adequate (grammatical) transformation in their mind. Haller, Hagedorn, Gellert, Utz, have sufficiently demonstrated that a poet can have a complete control over his rimes and that it is in his power to give them a perfectly natural appearance. The difficulty is rather a commendation for it than a reason for discarding it. And yet, dear sir, do not conclude from this that I am entirely against those who advocate blank verse.

And then he proceeds to explain that in the matter of rime he is an advocate of the same principle of "republican freedom" that he would be happy to introduce everywhere if he only could. He adds:

To proclaim rime an indispensable part of German poesy would imply displaying a thoroughly Gothic taste. Yet to deny the aesthetic advantage of rime, and that only for the reason that Greeks and Romans had not had it, would mean to misuse the example of the ancients. Let the poet have the choice. Is his enthusiasm sufficiently persistent to survive the difficulties of riming, let him rime. But if his inspiration subsides in the process of developing the theme, let him then better discard rime. It is difficult to say which method is of greater merit.

315

The French reaction against rime develops more independently, and therefore adds some new and original points to the controversy. The chief contribution of the French discussion in this matter lies not so much in clearing up the relation between rime and rhythm as in that between rime as an emotional vehicle and the intellectual content of poetry. At the time when in Italy and in England we meet with a growing sentiment against rime, in France we find established the classical tradition which made rime obligatory. Occasional and isolated French experiments in quantitative or blank verse met with contempt and ridicule. The only authoritative voice that was raised in favor of blank verse in the middle of the sixteenth century was that of Joachim du Bellay, the French Ovid, who declared the unrimed verse of Signor Luigi Alemanni to be pleasant and worthy of cultivation.[12] The only admittedly successful blank verse experiment of the time belongs to Blaise de Vigénère in his translations of the *Psalms of David*. But he himself is apparently inclined to regard his literary form as measured prose rather than as verse, pointing out that measured prose has certain advantages in religious writings over the unmetrical variety.[13] In view of these advantages he proposes "to hold to a middle way between the two, not giving up entirely the measure, cadence, and numbers, but at the same time not following strictly all the rules and laws established for poetry," i.e., in a way between ordinary prose and verse.

Those were the chief voices that were raised in favor of *"vers blanc"*—a rather weak and timid defense. From the very end of the Middle Ages, after the abandonment of asso-

[12] Du Bellay, *Deffense et illustration*, in *Les Œvres Grançoises* (1569), 2:7.

[13] Blaise de Vigénère, *Le Psautier de David*. The author "s'etait bien apperçu que les vers tissus de nombres et cadences sont assez plus delectables a oyr, plus commodes à réciter, plus facile à ... les retenir ... qu'un simple prose ... , qui ne peut avoir le mesme air, ni si bonne grâce."

316

nance, French prosody surrendered itself to the unconditional authority of rime. It was felt that it was something in the nature of the language that prevented unrimed verse from being beautiful or appealing in any way to the ear. Quite contrary to the English feeling, it was precisely the unrimed verse that was regarded as ignorant and vulgar. Already at the close of the fifteenth century Henry de Croy, criticizing certain unrimed versicles of the time, declared that they are good only for "provincial and ignorant people" (*"laquelle n'est approuvée que entre ruraulx et ygnorans"*). After the sixteenth century, rime was not merely admitted by French poets and prosodists as an additional ornament, as it was in England, but actually canonized as an essential element of French verse without which it ceases to be verse.

The French mind seems to have a special predilection for "rules." It has manufactured "rules" for the whole of Europe. After the sixteenth century rime was also treated as one of these "rules." In a treatise on the poetic art that was intended "for the instruction of young students" in 1548,[14] we read that unrimed verse is just as unnatural for "our French poetry" as would be for Latin and Greek a verse that did not observe the divisions into long and short syllables. There are, in fact, very few French poets, the author of the treatise explains, who write verses without rime; and if they do, they print them in the form of prose "without the customary distinction of lines, as though wishing to suggest that they did not consider them worthy of the name Poem." Even the forerunners of the Academy (1634), Jean Antoine de Baif (1532–1589) and his group, advocates as they were of the ancient quantitative versification, were finally led to introduce rime as an additional canon. The first to attempt this experiment was Claude de Buttel (in 1586). During the seventeenth century, in spite of

[14] Sibillet, *Art poétique français*, Paris, 1548.

317

Fénelon's authoritative opposition, rime was definitely and permanently canonized.[15] In Deimier's widely read *L'Academie de l'art poétique* (1610) we read:

> Just as every nation is ruled by laws and customs suitable and necessary for it; as every kingdom and every republic has a specific kind of humor and manner of speech . . . .; similarly every language possesses its own sweetness and elegance of expression which is natural and agreeable to it. It must therefore be left to Greeks and Latins to retain the feet and measures of their verse, because this exactly fits their language; but for us who are French, there must be retained, following the nature and usage of our tongue, a definite number of syllables to form the line, a true pause in the middle of the verse [caesura], and rime that crowns the verse and supplies it with the sweetest harmony.

The tradition concerning versification appears to be at this time completely formed: (1) an equal fixed number of syllables in each line; (2) caesura; and (3) rime.[16] Boileau, the "enlightened" dictator of good taste, could add to it only the more or less plausible requisite of good sense, saying that

> Quelque sujet qu'on traite, ou plaisant, ou sublime
> Que toujours le bon sens s'accorde avec la rime.[17]

Voltaire finally comes to the conclusion that, in French, "blank verse is nothing but prose." "It cannot be distinguished

---

[15] "Lorsque les Poetes connurent que les vers mesurez ne plaisoient point, il les rimerent" (P. Richelet, *La Versification française* [Paris, 1672], page 90).

[16] L. Quicherat, in his *Traité de versification française* (1850), regards rime, on Voltaire's authority, as absolutely indispensable for French poetry: "La rime est le fondement et la condition de notre poésie. ... Ceux qui ont attaqué notre rime prouvaient qu'ils n'avaient aucun sentiment de l'harmonie" (pages 46–47).

[17] "Art of Poetry," from *The Poetical Treatises*, edited by A. S. Cook, page 159 (Canto II, lines 27–28).

318

from prose except by a certain number of equal and monotonous syllables in each line that make it possible to call them verse." And farther on he declares that those who write in blank verse do so only because they don't know how to rime. To write a poem consisting of blank verse, he says in the Introduction to his translation of *Julius Caesar*, "is not any more difficult than to write a letter." It is, therefore, merely a way of avoiding the difficulties of rime, and, consequently, those of poetry. He writes in a letter to Marquis Maffei:

J'aurai souhaité pour voir, à l'exemple des Italiens et des Anglais, employer l'heureuse facilité des vers blancs ... mais je me suis aperçu et j'ai dit, il y a longtemps, qu'une telle tentative n'aurait jamais de succès en France, et qu'il y aurait plus de faiblesse que de force à éluder un joug qu'ont porté les auteurs de tant d'ouvrages, qui dureront autant que la nation française.

Herewith he said much, for a Frenchman; for, no doubt, in his opinion "la nation française" is to last forever, and, if it perish, down goes the world with it. For rime this is a great compliment, for the passage quoted leaves us under the impression that civilization will last as long as rime lasts, and vice versa.

We see that until the close of the eighteenth century blank verse was never seriously considered nor much practiced in France. At the end of the eighteenth century, however, there appeared on the literary horizon of France a man who must be regarded as the most serious and enthusiastic advocate of unrimed verse that the country has ever produced: Fabre d'Olivet. Putting aside the question of his merits as a poet, and the value of his "eumolphic" verse, we shall discuss him merely as an experimental prosodist who really succeeded in adding a new point to the controversy. He does not discard rime altogether. He knows it is not an invention of a barbarous age. He admits that it has brought forth thousands of beautiful verses. "God forbid that I should pretend to separate it from French verse of which it is a charm." Rime he considers necessary and indispensable, but only to romantic poetry and to all that is derived from it. "It adds an infinite grace to all that is sung or recited with chivalrous sentiment. The lyric style receives from it a romantic harmony which accords with it. . . . . It can, up to a certain point, embellish descriptive verse, soften didactic poems, add to the melancholy of the elegy, to the grace of the idyl; it can at last become the ornament of dramatic art such as we possess, that is to say, chivalrous and impassioned." But rime does not agree with intellectual poetry. Where rational content prevails, rime is only an obstacle. Olivet distinguishes two kinds of intellectual poetry, epic and eumolpic. The first is intellectual and passionate, originating from Homer and exemplified in the *Iliad* and the *Odyssey*. The other type is intellectual and rational, going back to the legendary times of Orpheus, and exemplified in the archaic theogonies and cosmological systems in hymns and oracles, in treatises on nature and moral apologues, which in ancient Greece had no relation to epopoeia, and which Greek hierophants and philosophers continued to write long after Homer and Hesiod. Only the ruins of this art have reached us: fragments of the great Parmenidian poem on Being, and the Golden Verses of Pythagoras, fragments from Heraclites and Democritos, belong to this genre. The art itself has long been forgotten, and even the memory of it has been almost completely lost among the moderns. Olivet makes an attempt to revive the "eumolpic" verse by translating into French the philosophical poems of Pythagoras. To do justice to the original he had to devise a special form of verse which he calls "*vers eumolphique*," which consists of measured cadences with alternate feminine and masculine endings but without rime. In defense of this form he wrote a whole treatise. Rime, according to him, has something melancholy and soporific in it; something that causes the soul to dream, and lures it in spite of itself, not into the sublime region of thought

320

and allegory but into the vague spaces of imagination, where under a thousand whimsical forms the romantic mind evaporates. Therefore it is quite proper to employ rime wherever imagination and sentiment are involved. "But as to real Eumolpoeia and Epos, that is to say, as to what concerns intellectual and rational poetry, ... prophetic verses or hymns, emanated from the divinity or destined to be raised to it, philosophical verse adapted to the nature of things and developing the diverse moral and physical systems, epical verses uniting talent to allegorical genius and joining together the intelligible world to the empirical world—with all these, rime is incompatible. . . . . Imagination harmonizes with it; allegory is opposed to it. It is chivalrous and not heroic; agreeable, brilliant, clever, melancholy, sentimental; but it could never be either profound or sublime." In one word, rime as an emotional vehicle interferes with the intellectual content of poetry, and must therefore be avoided wherever logic, sense, and meaning come to the fore.[18]

Walt Whitman.—A similar feeling of inadequacy of rime for themes of momentous import seems to have guided Walt Whitman (1819–1892) through his revolutionary career in poetry. His verse and his attitude toward life are thoroughly eumolphic. In the attempt "to comprehend the size of the

[18] Among the modern prosodists Grasserie defends the possibility of blank verse in French without advocating it as a better kind: "La possibilité du vers blanc en français nous paraît d'abord évidente, la rime seule ne constitue pas notre rythme. La meilleure preuve en est qu'on cité souvent un vers isolé, que ce vers ne rime pas. . . . . En effet, il se compose de deux hémistiches égaux dont chacun a le même nombre de syllabes et qui se trouvent separés par la césure, ces deux hémistiches sont, en réalité, deux petits vers ne rimant pas entre eux. Eh bien! ce qui se passe entre deux hémistiches peut avoir lieu entre deux vers formant un distique et même entre un plus grand nombre" (*Des Principes scientifiques de la versification française,* page 141).

whole people, ... the modern, the busy nineteenth century
. . . . with steamships, railroads, factories, electric telegraphs,
cylinder press, ... the practical labor of farms, factories, work-
shops, mines," he feels that rime would be an improper, almost
cynical coquetry. Rime would block the momentous task of intellectual self-analysis in the one who was the first in poetry to
"utter the word Democratic, the word En-Masse." A man who
says:

Distant and dead resuscitate,
They show as the dial or move as the hands of me, I am the clock myself.

A man who feels that he is called to be the "clock" of his time,
is too much of a philosopher to sing in rime.

Walt Whitman's condemnation of rime is well known from
a passage frequently quoted from the *Notes:*

In my opinion, the time has arrived to essentially break down the
barriers of form between prose and poetry. I say the latter is hence-
forth to win and maintain its character regardless of rhyme, and the
measurement rules of iambic, spondee, dactyl, etc., and that even if
rhyme and those measurements continue to furnish the medium for
inferior writers and themes (especially for persiflage and the comic,
as there seems henceforward, to the perfect taste, something inevitably
comic in rhyme, merely in itself, and anyhow), the truest and greatest
poetry . . . . can never again, in the English language, be expressed in
arbitrary and rhyming meter, any more than the greatest eloquence,
of the truest power and passion. While admitting that the venerable
and heavenly forms of chiming versification have in their time play'd
great and fitting parts,—that the pensive complaint, the ballads, wars,
amours, legends of Europe, etc., have, many of them, been inimitably
render'd in rhyming verse,—that there have been very illustrious poets
whose shapes the mantle of such verse has beautifully and appropriately
enveloped—and though the mantle has fallen, with perhaps added
beauty, on some of our own age—it is, notwithstanding, certain to me,
that the day of such conventional rhyme is ended. In America, at any
rate, and as a medium of highest esthetic practice or spiritual expression,

present or future, it palpably fails, and must fail, to serve. The Muse of the Prairies, of California, Canada, Texas, and of peaks of Colorado, dismissing the literary, as well as social etiquette of over-sea feudalism and caste, joyfully enlarging, adapting itself to comprehend the size of the whole people . . . . resumes that other medium of expression, more flexible, more eligible—soars to the freer, vast, diviner heaven of prose.[19]

Thus we see that the main point of Whitman's argument against rime is based upon its inability to express a "eumolphic" situation.

Free verse.—The controversy has never been settled. It persists till our day and is now perhaps felt more acutely than at any previous time. It forms a part, and it seems to me an essential part, of the issue between the adherents of traditional verse and those of the vers libre.

Free verse does not necessarily exclude rime. La Fontaine's *Fables,* for instance, make extensive use of rime with very irregular rhythms. The contrast to rimed verse is afforded by blank verse. But in poems written in vers libre, rime may be very well and quite successfully employed.[20] And yet the modern followers of this movement scarcely make any use of terminal assonance, producing the impression that they deliberately avoid it. "Though free verse," writes Louis Unter-

[19] Walt Whitman, *Complete Works,* 5:272 ff.

[20] Even in Medieval Latin we find combinations of free verse with rime. As an example one may quote the hymn known as *"Planctus Beatae Mariae,"* one of the numerous paraphrases of the *Stabat Mater*:

Moestae parentis Christi Mariae lacrymas eia nunc recita, plebs. Agni mitis cruore
   redempta.
Qui generis humani collapsi maculas purpurea lavavit in cruce vulnera passus cruenta:
Sputa, clavos atque ludibria, spinas tulit et saeva vertebra.
Mater cernens tanta supplicia flet discrepens pectus et ubera . . . .
Sic stat mater desolata
Iam non mater ded orbata
Dulci suo filio . . . .

meyer, "dispenses with any decided meter, it employs all other assets of poetry: assonance, alliteration, balance, even, though not always, rime." With this "even" Untermeyer reveals a characteristic feature of the new movement. Other ornamental assets of poetry are allowed to be used without the limitations imposed by an "even" or a "but," whereas rime is almost unwillingly admitted, evidently with a feeling of condescending superiority similar to that with which an exclusive, intellectual group might occasionally admit and tolerate a Babbitt in their company. It is no more than tolerated by the moderns, and is treated nowadays as a poor and distant relation of poetry. And we are told why: because it interferes with freedom of expression and imposes chains upon the imagination of the poet.

But there is, perhaps, a deeper reason for this. Free verse is still in the experimental stage. It reveals thousands of new resources, thousands of effects that are new and unknown to traditional verse.[21] The whole movement constitutes a vast but confused technical experiment, where each language, and each author even, applies individual methods and seeks individual effects. And it is difficult to experiment with subtle effects while listening at the same time to the incessant music of rime. Its effect, whether good or bad, is so strong that it kills finer nuances. It appears therefore "in most cases undesirable." The organism of free verse is too delicate and sensitive to operate with rime.

Besides, it appears more than natural, psychologically, that when tradition is broken in one respect, for instance with regard to conventional rhythm and meter, the rupture should tend to affect the whole system. "I think," writes Mr. Alding-

[21] Wherever traditional, classic verse made use of free rhythms it invariably introduced new emotional contrasts and effects. "Dans tous les cas," remarks Grammont, "il faut que le changement de mètre soit justifié par le sens; mais les effets qu'il produit peuvent être extrêmement nombreus et variés" (Le Vers français, page 114).

ton, "that five centuries of intense production have somewhat exhausted the possibilities of our prosody. If our poetry is to be anything but a pastiche of masterpieces, we must get back to the essential qualities of poetry which may develop new methods of expression. Vers libre . . . . may be a move in the right direction. It forces man to create his own rhythms instead of imitating other people's."[22] In the search for new possibilities of expression and presentation the poets come to distrust all the old methods. Thus the anarchism of free verse quite naturally results in an implied protest against rime.

This protest, however, appears to be one of the passions of a transitional epoch. It is already on the decline.[23] The anarchism of free verse (vers libre), results in France in the discipline of "freed verse" ("vers libèré"). The direct disciples of Walt Whitman and Gustave Kahn seem to have already accomplished their historical mission. The epigons are of small experimental value. In the newest technique of the French "Unanimists," represented chiefly by René Arcos, G. Duhamel, Jean Hytier, G. Chenneviére, and Jules Romains, rime emerges again from the temporary disrepute into which it was thrown by the first advocates of free verse. But it emerges in a new experimental form that allows free play for terminal assonances and dissonances. Another body of experiments that was suggested and made possible only after the emancipation of verse from the bonds of traditional technique is to be found in the Russian "imperfect rimes," which extended tremendously the possibilities of riming and delivered traditional rime from its objectionable monotony.

[22] R. Aldington, "The Art of Poetry," *Dial*, 1920, pages 166–180.

[23] "Les verslibristes se font de plus en plus rares. Il n'est pas indifférent de noter que parmi les adeptes les plus fervents et les plus remarquables du verslibrisme d'il y a vingt ans la plupart de ceux qui ont survéçu et continué à produire sont revenus peu à peu au mode classique ou à quelque chose d'approchant" (Grammont, *Le Vers français*, page 168).

The controversy proved fertile in discoveries. Within a number of linguistic groups it resulted in important technical reforms.[24]

Meaning of the controversy from the physical point of view.—What is there physically in the nature of rime that appears to be pleasing to one person, and objectionable to another? We have seen that physically rime is a specific case of succession of tones in which the latter appear to be organized into vowel melodies. It sets the key for every line, and produces a great deal of artistic satisfaction by bringing the melody of the verse back to the original tonic. Therefore, apart from the rhythmical construction of the poem, apart even from its logical sense and meaning, rime is beautiful in itself as a musical phrase. It produces specific emotions totally independent of those suggested by the meaning or created by the rhythm of words.[25] In other words, physically, rime is a complex stimulus for a specific kind of emotions. In search of these emotional effects poets will always continue to rime.

Yet under certain circumstances these emotions resulting from rime may seem undesirable. For they may interfere disagreeably with other features of the poem, such as its rhythm or its meaning, and may appear superfluous and even annoying. Owing to the musical nature of rime the emotions produced by it are largely "satisfying," "pleasant," "graceful," and "winsome." They all have a certain soothing and even soporific musical quality that may strongly conflict with the emotions which are produced by the meaning of the poem. How

[24] Compare Jean Hytier, *Les Techniques modernes du vers français*, 1923.

[25] Grasserie describes this emotional character in the following manner: "Un sentiment profond, mélancolique, s'attache à l'emploi de la rime et en même temps elle donne au vers une vivacité, une vie que le dessin rythmique seul ne peu lui communiquer" (*Des Principes scientifiques de la versification française*, page 94).

326

much the following realistic lines from Edgar Lee Masters would lose through rime!

> Do you know what makes life a terror
> And a torture, Spoon River?
> It is due to the conflict between the little minds
> Who think life is real,
> And who therefore work, save, make laws,
> Prosecute and levy wars—
> Between these and the big minds
> Who know that life is a dream,
> And that much of the world's activity
> Is a pure folly, and the chattering of idiots.

The seriousness of the conviction here expressed would be spoiled by the introduction of either rime or regular meter. Where a sincere conviction is at stake, rime is really superfluous.

Being itself an emotional element, rime has the power of modifying other emotions. To anger it lends an element of graceful elegance at the expense of passion and force. To melancholy it lends more strength but deprives it of its real poignancy. Even to a tragedy it adds an air of emotional consolation, making it rather sad than grave. Indeed, a tragic situation may gain by the introduction of a dissonant line, as is done, for instance, very skillfully, in Siegfried Sassoon's "Does It Matter?":

> Does it matter—losing your legs? . . . .
> For people will always be kind,
> And you need not show that you mind
> When the others come in after hunting
> To gobble their muffins and eggs.
>
> Does it matter—losing your sight? . . . .
> There's such splendid work for the blind;

And people will always be kind,
As you sit on the terrace remembering
And turning your face to the light.

Do they matter—those dreams from the pit?
You can drink and forget and be glad,
And people won't say that you're mad;
For they'll know that you've fought for your country,
And no one will worry a bit.

The fourth line in every stanza forms a dissonance; for it does not rime with any of the others, and we know that an unriming line among a group of riming ones is immediately detected by the ear as a dissonance. This dissonance no doubt contributes to the quality of our emotional protest aroused by the tragic situation depicted by the poet. At the same time all other lines do rime, thereby musically tranquillizing and soothing our emotional response, making us feel rather melancholy than actually angry. The conflict between these two reactions produces the effect evidently desired by the author, that of nervous dissatisfaction with ourselves, of a restless sense of inconsistency in our hearts.

It can be seen from this example that the music of words may be applied to produce highly variegated and complex effects. But one can very well imagine poetic situations in which any additional stimulus that stirs up our emotions to a higher pitch is ruinous. By the magic of rime any given emotion is instantly transformed into something more soothing and accommodating than it appears to be in the mind of its creator. And this may profoundly vex the poet; for he often finds his emotions modified by rime in a direction contrary to his intentions. The same physical effect that makes rime beautiful may serve as an objection against it; for in addition to the logical and rhythmical content of a poem, rime introduces a new element of verse melody which, being beautiful and attractive in

328

itself, absorbs a great deal of our attention and offers too much enjoyment. In this sense rime is a rival of both meaning and rhythm. If one or both of those factors are intended by the poet to play an exclusive part, rime will appear as a hindrance. Therefore, intellectual poetry saturated with ideas and forceful images, philosophical or "eumolphic" poetry, as Fabre d'Olivet used to call it, other things being equal, will be inclined to avoid rime. Similarly those poets who are interested primarily in producing and elaborating rhythmical effects will also be inclined to disregard and even to belittle rime. For the assistance offered by rime to rhythm is so obvious, and in a way so cheap, that it often appears trivial and vulgar. It cannot be disputed that rime helps rhythm. The theory of the physical nature of rime gives a reasonable explanation of its rhythm-assisting function: producing pleasurable sensations at the end of each verse it helps us to keep time within the stanza and to organize lines into larger rhythmic units. But this assistance is so obvious that to many a modern poet it appears beneath his dignity to create rhythmic effects by so easy a method. Whoever has tried to write poetry knows that it is very much more difficult to create rhythm without rime's assistance. And we have Lessing's testimony that it is easier to find rime than to avoid it. Thus, though rime is rhythmically effective, its effect is not always desirable. Quite on the contrary, it is perhaps for the most part undesirable. If the function of rime were merely to produce rhythm, it would have been abandoned long ago.

But rime is not merely rhythmically important. It has a charm that is totally independent of its rhythmical implications. This charm lies in its melodic quality, in its ability to produce melodious vowel-phrases. It is based on the characteristic overtones of human speech. Poetry does not consist merely of rhythm. Its musical quality is equally important. And it is rime that makes poetry musical, for it is only through rime that melodic unity is brought into the music of vowels. It actually makes musical phrases of the successive vowel sounds. Every such phrase, like every musical theme, is associated with a specific emotion. There is an infinite variety of such phrases, and consequently an infinite variety of nameless emotions associated with them. In search of those emotions poets will never cease riming. Why should they? Just because other poets prefer to hunt after the emotional values which are associated with rhythms? But what is the difference? Both are equally strong, equally effective. To discard one in favor of the other would be just as absurd as to discard one branch of art in favor of another. Should musicians stop producing music just because painters find it more to their liking to extract emotions from the play of colors? Musical emotions may appear trivial and vulgar when a painter or a sculptor conceives the absurd idea of expressing them by means of color schemes, just as dramatic ideas often appear unbearably naïve when "expressed" in the pseudo-imitative chords of program music. A great deal of Wagner's vulgarity and theatrical affectation depends on his resolution to express one value by another. Similarly, when rime assumes rhythmical functions, it appears superfluous and annoying, although quite effective. But it does not lie in the essential nature of rime merely to assist rhythm. It may eventually do that too. But primarily it has quite a different function, namely, to create the melody of verse. To be sure, as is quite evident, the poet is not absolutely obliged to present those emotions which are associated with the music of words. But, as is equally evident, one is not obliged to go to a concert when one wishes to visit an exhibition of paintings. One situation gives no rule for the other.

On the basis of the foregoing analysis how and in favor of which side shall the old controversy be ended? Shall we use rime, or shall we try to avoid it? We can easily see now that in such a general form the question has no meaning. Technically rime is an apparatus for producing specific emotions.

330

Therefore if one has the desire, and the talent, to create such emotional contents, nothing but a prejudice can prevent him from doing so. If, on the other hand, one feels that this type of emotions interferes too strongly with other things that one wishes to express, he is at liberty to avoid them. The decision rests entirely with the poet. The thing that every individual poet must bear in mind when deciding this question for himself, the thing that we believe we have made sufficiently clear in the foregoing analysis, is that rime, far from being a mere vehicle for expressing some given emotion, actually creates emotions of an entirely specific kind. These emotions cannot be better or worse expressed by other means for they cannot be expressed by any other means at all. Those who are interested in producing them (a perfectly legitimate desire!) will have to use rime, in the same way that musicians will always be obliged to use tones (for they cannot write silent music!). Those who are not interested in those emotions are at liberty to apply other methods of expression and presentation. But they must bear in mind that they are omitting something for which nothing else can be substituted. When using blank rhythms they do not express the same thing in better or worse fashion. They present, as far as the ornamental emotions are concerned, an entirely different thing.

By-ways of the controversy.—Parallel to the general controversy concerning the value of rime a number of subordinate controversies run through the history of poetry concerning the applicability of rime to various forms of poetic composition. Thus it is often maintained that rime is incompatible with the epic (Poggel, Fabre d'Olivet, Milton). It is pointed out that epic calmness and clearness, the rationalistic objectivity of the epos, are inconsistent with the emotional character of rime. For this reason rime is held responsible for the absence of epic poems in modern times (Fabre d'Olivet). This, as a matter of

331

fact, is not true. Modern Europe is in possession of a highly successful epic that was produced right in the middle of the nineteenth century: Adam Mickiewicz's *Pan Thadeusz*, which quite recently was beautifully translated into English by Professor G. R. Noyes. As to the high qualities of this poem, we have the authority of Brandes, who calls it "the only successful epic of modern times." It seems that in this poem, though it is fundamentally epic in its character, rime is not merely an artistic but a historical necessity. Mickiewicz wrote it at a highly dramatic and for him an actually tragic time (1831), when his nation, Poland, had lost her last battle, when a civilization that had lasted for over a thousand years was shattered and his country was just about to disappear. He confessed that he had no strength to be an echo of events. When grief becomes too intense it cannot be employed as a material for art. There is a limit beyond which art appears a sacrilege. Thus in the midst of clashing arms and falling centuries Mickiewicz turns to the reminiscences of his happy childhood. "Today," he writes, "for us, the unbidden guests of the world, there is but one region in which there is a crumb of happiness for a Pole: the land of childhood. . . . . This one consolation remains: when in the evening's twilight you sit by the fireside with a few of your friends, and lock the door against the uproar of Europe, and escape in thought to happier times, to the days of your childhood, and muse and dream of your own land. . . . . That land will ever remain holy and pure as the first love; undisturbed by the remembrance of errors, not undermined by deceitful hopes, it stays there forever, unchanged by the stream of events." Under such circumstances rime becomes indispensable. With its tender musical accompaniment it serves as substitute for the ancient lute. It throws a veil of reminiscence over the stream of events, isolates them from reality into a frame, and helps the author to "lock the door against the uproar of Europe." From the physical point of view I can see no objection to the employment of rime in the epic. The basis of rime is music. And why an epic poet whose chief urge, according to the fitting words of Harriet Monroe, is to tell the tale of the tribe, should have no right to be musical is more than I can see. We know that the ancient epic was intimately associated with music. Epic poetry is an art thoroughly saturated with and even partly based upon musical emotion. Rime is a powerful, and perfectly legitimate, substitute for music. And, as a matter of fact, be it in the form of lyre or lute, or in the form of rime, music has always been used for the accompaniment of epic poems. Not to cite a certain version of the *Niebelungen Lied* which ran in rime, it is sufficient to name Dante and Ariosto to show that successful epics certainly were written in rimed verse.

Somewhat different is the situation in the drama. For here the music of words may interfere too violently with the realism of action. And we actually know but few dramatic plays that have made a successful use of rime.[26] The best illustration of this kind is, of course, Goethe's *Faust*. But in this particular case the application of rime is justified by the unusual lyrico-philosophical character of the play. Who thinks of *Faust* as being merely a play? It is a dramatic play merely in form; in its substance and spirit it is a synthesis of nearly all literary forms. It is as much a play as it is a novel in verse, and it is as much a novel as it is a lyric poem. The action in *Faust* is not an objective one, but is seen through the magic glass of Goethe's own intensely subjective personality. The whole play has a certain lyric overtone. Even the most tragic scenes, such as Valentin's death or Margucrite's insanity, are shrouded with an easily perceptible mist of subjectivity. With such a dramatic composition rime is not at all inconsistent. This in a smaller

[26] Except in French, where rime is almost universally considered indispensable for any verse. The best tragedies of Racine are those which display the most careful art of riming.

333

degree may be verified by other dramas. Whenever a dramatic play takes a fantastic turn, rime at once appears, as, for instance, in Shakespeare's *Macbeth* or Byron's *Manfred*.

The chief objection against using rime in drama is based on its unnaturalness. Rime appears to be in conflict with the realism of action. No one formulated it better than Dryden, although he never believed in the validity of his argument. "A play," he says, "is the imitation of nature; and since no man, without premeditation, speaks in rhyme, neither ought he to do it on the stage. . . . . It will appear that your actors hold intelligence together; that they perform their tricks like fortune-tellers, by confederacy. . . . . Thus you see, your rhyme is incapable of expressing the greatest thoughts naturally. . . . . For what is more unbefitting the majesty of verse, than to call a servant, or bid a door be shut in rhyme?" This objection is relatively true. But Dryden was wholly aware of the element of relativity in this criticism when he asked in return: does any man in real life ever speak in blank verse, or in measured prose?

There is, however, I think, a more pertinent objection to the use of rime in dramatic plays, especially in tragedies. Rime, being a special form of music, would produce throughout the play an independent set of aesthetic emotions, which in the long run would act soothingly, "musically," causing in the mind of the audience a certain vaguely pleasant mood, which, though not consciously perceived, would nevertheless unconsciously modify other emotions essential to the play. In connection with the tragic action such a mood is bound to produce an element of vaguely sentimental sadness which is not in harmony with the intellectual seriousness of tragedy.

In comedies, on the other hand, rime is quite in the right place and is very frequently used. It is particularly important for such analytical comedies as Griboyedov's *Misfortune from Intelligence*, which aim at sharp and brief characterizations and

334

consist largely of lines having a proverbial character. It is well known that at least half of the *Misfortune* has entered the Russian language in proverbial form. *Uriel Acosta* may serve as a more familiar illustration of a similar use of rime. It is an unrimed play which, however, makes an extensive use of rimes scattered throughout the work in the form of sententious remarks. In such cases rime helps to bind lines together into compact rhythmical and melodic wholes, which, to recall Herder's expression, carry in their rimes the "seal of eternal truth."

I think it quite safe to say that no literary form absolutely excludes rime; as, on the other hand, there is no literary form that absolutely commands rime. There are unrimed poems, and there are rimed novels, such as Byron's *Don Juan* and Pushkin's *Eugene Onegin*. There are short stories written in rime (*Beppo*), and ballads without rime (Serbian ballads). No rules can be established apriori for all cases. One is obliged to agree with Debussy that "no fixed rule should guide the creative artist; rules are made *by* works of art, not *for* works of art."

Rime and history.—Is it an accident that periodic revivals of protest against rime historically coincide with great social upheavals? The Miltonian controversy took place right in the middle of the English revolution, when an intense puritanic fermentation took possession of the whole country. It was a typically "eumolphic" period, in the sense in which Fabre d'Olivet uses the word, indicating a predominance of intellectual and religious interests, "a revolt against a licence that had become unbearable," as Amy Lowell aptly defines it. Hardly can we regard Milton's protest as a matter of personal preference or individual taste. There was something in the nature of the epoch that was hostile to "the jingling sound of like endings." The intense seriousness of the puritanic outlook on life, the vitality of the social, political, and religious issues under

335

discussion made many people feel that excessive emotional ornamentation was simply a waste of time unworthy of a serious mind. It is highly significant that the other ardent advocate of blank verse in Europe, Fabre d'Olivet (1768–1825), lived at the time of the great revolution in France.

Contemporary Russian poetry may perhaps throw some light on this at first sight somewhat mysterious connection between blank verse and revolutions. Together with the growing practice of imperfect rimes that we have already discussed at some length, we find among the modern Russian poets a profound interest in free verse. In free and unrimed verse Ilya Erenburg writes his "Prayers," uttered by a tortured soul in an ecstasy of all-forgiveness. Here is an extract from his "prayer for Russia":

> For our native land
> Let us pray to the Lord.
> For our fields vast and cold,
> For our unloving hearts,
> For those who have no strength to pray,
> And those who murder children;
> For those who sing the songs of sorrow,
> And those who are roaming around with knives and clubs;
> For all tombs let us pray to the Lord;
> For those which have neither cross nor tombstone;
> For the ruins where our churches stood,
> And sacred lamps of our altars, now extinguished,
> For all the desolation of our native land—
> Again and again let us pray to the Lord.

Revolution is a torrent of the most unexpected discords. Like war, it reveals the worst and the best in man. It is not merely cruelty and disorder. It is not a change of government either. It is not a rational change at all. Ideas, programs, resolutions, new institutions (for which no one cares and before which everyone trembles), new laws (hastily made), all these are on the surface. Down deep at the bottom, revolutionary life is a huge tangle of instincts and theories, of bare necessities and mad projects. To an outsider it may appear a terrible mess or—perhaps—a great social experiment, depending on one's political views. To the average participant it appears primarily as a tragedy. Now, sweetening tragedy with rime means that one does not take it very seriously, but rather sentimentally, as Goethe or Byron did, enjoying the conflict in an Epicurean manner comfortably seated in an armchair, or as Titus Lucrecius Carus did, watching battles from a safe distance. But if a poet is profoundly and vitally interested in a tragic matter, if he really lives amidst the tragedy that he describes, he either rimes in dissonances or he does not rime at all. For what is the effect of "like endings"? We know now that the effect is musical. It modifies our emotions by introducing new ones, those which are associated with the melody of vowels. By creating within the poem this new emotional material the poet intentionally modifies his emotional response, suppressing bitterness in favor of a rather vague musicality and turning the whole emotional current in a direction of lower ethical resistance. Some emotions are thereby intensified, others are dampened or even altogether suppressed. On the whole, our emotional energy is thus given a false outlet. Therefore a poet who is vitally interested in his subject-matter, who wishes to present his ideas and feelings in their original and undistorted form, must feel that rime is his enemy. If a poet grows "eumolphic" at heart and yet feels that he is unable to renounce rime, he will create under the sway of two conflicting tendencies that in the long run may destroy his poetic genius and even crush his life. Such tragedies are not exceptional in revolutionary periods. Rime and revolution seem mutually to repel each other.

The life and work of Adam Mickiewicz affords perhaps the most striking illustration of this curious incompatibility. It always was a mystery to me how a poet of Mickiewicz's rank,

337

admittedly the greatest poetic genius among Slavs, could have lived for over twenty years without producing any poetic work. We hear from his biographers that his genius was probably exhausted, that he lived through a religious crisis, similar to that of Tolstoy's, which made him renounce poetic activity as "empty" and "trifling." And yet how could such a man as he, a veritable poet by God's grace, for whom rimes were just as natural and easy as words are for ordinary mortals, whose poems read with the facility and naturalness of a beautiful prose—how could such a man be so absurdly conscientious and so fanatically loyal to his painful resolution "never to use his pen for trifles"? There seems to be only one reasonable explanation of this. He felt that the type of poetry to which he was accustomed, and which alone he regarded as poetry, i.e., rimed and measured verse, was not an adequate vehicle for expressing what after 1831 he really cared to express—the profound suffering and dying agonies of his destroyed fatherland. It is highly significant that he deliberately renounced his poetic activity after the Polish uprising in 1831. With *Pan Thaddeusz*, which appeared in 1833, his poetic life closes. As a matter of fact he continued writing. But neither he himself nor his critics regard his work as "poetry." He writes in measured prose. It evidently was not caprice, exhaustion, or conviction that prevented him from further poetic activity. It was the incompetence of rime to deal with a "eumolphic" situation that revealed itself in his personal life. The problem he presents cannot be solved by reference to individual circumstances, inborn Slavic mysticism, or similar generalities. That the conflict was not confined to his individual poetic career can be seen from the fact that Mickiewicz's immediate successor, Zigmund Krasinski, also writes his deeply philosophical, thoroughly "eumolphic" plays in measured prose. A temporary reaction against rime was evidently one of the effects of the revolution.

338

That there were other poets, of no less talent, who at the same time continued riming, is not a point to be used against our argument. I do not mean to suggest that some mathematical connection exists between blank verse and revolutions which makes it impossible or even undesirable to rime in periods of social upheaval. Every poet reacts differently to contemporary events. I venture to suggest only that social unrest appears to be productive of conditions which are unfavorable to riming and that there emerge in revolutionary periods certain things and situations which are better expressed in blank verse. This does not imply, however, that the riming spirit can ever be entirely extinct.

Knowing that rime and revolution mutually repel each other, one begins to understand better the character and the message of Fabre d'Olivet, as well as the unrimed tragedies of Alfieri. Our generation can perhaps understand the connection still better and more deeply. The modern poet lives and works, like all of us, under the effect of the strenuous readjustment of life that was inaugurated by the Great War. Amy Lowell begins her *Tendencies in Modern American Poetry* with an apology for commencing a book of poetical essays with a reference to the war. "In fact," she writes, "the war and the subject of this volume are not so far apart as might at first appear. The so-called 'new movement' in American poetry is evidence of the rise of a native school. The welding together of the whole country which the war has brought about, the mobilization of our whole population into a single, strenuous endeavor has produced a more poignant sense of nationality than has recently been the case in this country of enormous spaces and heterogeneous population. Hyphens are submerged in the solid overprinting of the word 'America.' We are no more colonies of this or that other land, but ourselves, different from all other peoples whatsoever." Knowing that the author (d. 1925) of these lines was the acknowledged leader of this "new movement," and that this movement is for the most part in favor of free verse, we see that such a beginning suddenly acquires a greater significance than the author evidently meant to imply. It is a direct acknowledgment of the connection that we have tried to establish between rime and revolutions. By revolution we do not mean necessarily a violent and armed uprising against the existing form of government. What Amy Lowell describes in the lines above as "the welding together of the whole country . . . . into a single strenuous endeavor" is much more "revolutionary" than a dozen South American revolutions which do not produce any permanent change except in the personnel of the government. But the creation of "a more poignant sense of nationality" is a phenomenon of vital importance. In this molding and shaping of national self-consciousness, of a new type of national self-consciousness that has never been witnessed before, poetry has much to say, many things to learn, and many sentiments to teach. And the poets of our days justly feel that to the monotonous accompaniment of rime such a momentous task can never be accomplished. Under such circumstances rime must temporarily retire. A generation that has much to say cannot rime.

But such a reaction is only temporary. The time will come —and the symptoms of it are already in sight—when rime will regain its full prestige. The world cannot live in permanent unrest. The quieter and happier ages will always be inclined to regard rime as indispensable. One such happy interval in the history of mankind was the late nineteenth century. This is perhaps the reason why free verse meets with so much opposition on the part of the older academic minds. It is not an ordinary conflict between fathers and sons. It is a collision of historic epochs. For the serene academism of the nineteenth-century poetry was comfort and encouragement. It belonged more to the inner soul and less to action. It concealed more

340

than it revealed. It was a mystery and a miracle. And rime was then properly identical with poetry. Our poetry of today, to use Untermeyer's happy formulation, "is less a narcotic and more of a nourishment." And it prefers free verse. The task of the coming generation is to find again not a mechanical combination but an organic synthesis of both free verse and rime.

Summary and conclusion.—We have attempted to approach the problem of rime, not with the traditional mystico-romantic categories, but from the scientific point of view, armed with the exact results of physical science and experimental control. We have seen that in the light of the science of acoustics human speech resolves itself into a succession of musical sounds, vowels, rhythmically separated from each other by various kinds of faint noises which we call consonants. Thus we have found in our speech two essential ingredients of melodic composition: musical sounds and rhythm. But a mere succession of musical sounds even though rhythmically arranged does not constitute a melody. To become melodious the sound elements must be organized into musical phrases. This, in music, is usually done by means of tonality, or key, which introduces a common point of reference dominating the whole phrase. It has been found by experience that the greatest amount of emotional satisfaction is associated with sequences which begin and end in the keynote (Lipps-Meyer Law). Thus the simplest and most unpretentious form of musical organization is a plain return to the original tone. Similarly, in speech, the raw material of vowel sounds rhythmically uttered may be left to follow its own haphazard flow without much musical organization and control. This is prose. Or it may be organized, by means of "returns," into a well-ordered series of melodic phrases. This results in rimed verse. Hence rime may be properly regarded as the organizing factor in the melody of verse which elevates a mere succession of uttered sounds to the value of a musical phrase.

We have also seen in chapter vi that rime, owing to the strong musical appeal associated with it, can be profitably utilized to attract attention to the rhythmically important places. Since, in our measured speech, meter is ordinarily distorted by "interruptions," rime can be employed to restore the damaged meter. The association of melody and rhythm makes rime a strictly musical phenomenon. We have further shown in chapter vii that physical tones, especially if they are well ordered into phrases, are usually associated with emotional reactions. Hence rime, as a factor actually creative of a subtle melodic accompaniment to our measured speech, possesses an enormous power of stimulating our emotions.

Considering the subtlety and evanescent character of this accompaniment, its power is indeed enormous. It has been justly said that rime is a cultural factor of incalculable value and of equally incalculable harm. It was for more than a thousand years the moving force of poetry. It assisted man in his religious cults. It helped to develop his language. It fomented revolutions. It was, and still is, a powerful means of propaganda, sex-expression, education. Throughout the centuries of our cultural growth it was continually used in schools to assist memory, in churches to produce religious exaltation, on the stage to intensify dramatic effects. It was often a source of the greatest happiness, as of most excruciating pain. For many a man was cruelly put to death for a "daring rime"—the early Christians with their "outrageous" hymns, John Ball with his "vulgar" couplets, André Chénier. Rime is a great historical force. It is an additional triumph of modern science that, instead of marveling at the mystery of this force, we can "dissect it as a corpse" and study it in our physical and psychophysical laboratories.

342

APPENDIX I

～～～～～～～～～～～～～～～～～～～～～～～～

THE foundation of sound-recording technique was laid by Koenig and Scott.[1] Their apparatus was provided with a soap-film diaphragm from which a beam of light was reflected upon a screen indicating the movements of the film that followed the condensations and rarefactions in the air produced by the sound-wave. The same investigators succeeded in producing a fairly representative picture of the sound-wave by producing the sound within the atmosphere of the burning gas, the form of the wave being then clearly indicated by the shape of the flame.[2] On the basis of this technique M. Rap developed an apparatus for sound photography. His apparatus was perfected and experiments with it were continued in America by J. Blake and R. Cross of Boston. The most highly developed successor to Koenig's recording apparatus is an instrument devised by D. C. Miller and called by him the "phonodeik." The principle of the phonodeik the reader may find discussed at length in D. C. Miller's *Science of Musical Sounds*, or in Harvey Fletcher's *Speech and Hearing*. The principle of the phonodeik was commercialized by Dorsey, who devised a convenient instrument for acoustic demonstrations called the phonelescope, widely used for classroom work.[3]

My first experiments in rhythmic photography were conducted with Dorsey's phonelescope in Professor J. G. Brown's (Stanford University) laboratory. The results obtained, however, were unreliable because

[1] *Cosmos* (1859), 14:314.

[2] Rousselot, *Principes de phonetique experimentale*, pages 194 ff.

[3] Direct recording methods (i.e., non-photographic) have been used by Georges Lote, in his experimental study of the French *alexandrin* (*Études sur le vers français*, Paris, 1913. Two volumes).

the phonelescope's mirror has vibration-frequencies of its own which tend to intensify certain partials. Moreover, the diaphragm of the instrument is not sufficiently protected from the air currents caused by the speaking voice, and intensified the effect of certain consonants.[4]

To correct those defects an apparatus was set up in the electrical engineering laboratory of Stanford University under the direction of Professor F. E. Terman.[5] The pick-up used in this work was an ordinary Jensen dynamic loud-speaker. It was mounted on a large baffle board of three-ply wood. The whole was screwed to a table which had soft rubber pads between its legs and the floor. This was to eliminate floor vibrations, for the equipment was very sensitive. The field of this particular speaker was wound for twelve volts, but sufficient sensitivity was obtained by using six volts. A better pick-up such as could be obtained from a condenser microphone was not necessary, for our purpose was not a correct reproduction of the wave-form but the distribution of loudness of sound over the space of two and one-half or three seconds. The moving coil of the loud-speaker was connected directly to the amplifier. Thus the loud-speaker in this experiment was used in an inverted sense, as a source of electrical energy rather than sound energy, which is its usual function.

The amplifier used was built in the laboratory. It is a three-stage transformer coupled amplifier. The diagram of its connections is shown in the accompanying sketch. The first two stages using 301-A tubes are arranged for voltage amplification, and the last stage with a

[4] The records obtained from the phonelescope, however, for some particular verse lines, where explosive consonants had not been employed, showed even better results than those which are here communicated. But this applies only to masculine voices. The soprano pitch was evidently in the region of the instrument's own vibration-frequencies, and the accented syllables were enormous in size. On the whole, however, the distribution of accent-energy could be easily traced from syllable to syllable.

[5] The author of this essay, not possessing sufficient training in electrical engineering, depended much upon the courteous co-operation of Professor Terman and his assistant in this matter, Mr. Douglas Ring, who are largely responsible for the data contained in this report. All drawings are executed by Mr. Ring.

344

171-A tube furnishes the necessary power. The input from the loud-speaker is connected across a 2,000-ohm resistance. This is for the purpose of balancing the impedance on the input to the first tube. Amplification is controlled by an 18,000-ohm rheostat connected across the primary of the first transformer. The plate-voltage on the first tube is reduced somewhat by a series resistance. The transformers used were exceptionally high quality Ferranti transformers for the interstage coupling, and a General Radio push-pull transformer for the output. This was built to operate a dynamic speaker which has about 10 ohms impedance. The oscillograph element to which it was connected had about this impedance also, so that there was a good balance. The first two tubes were operated on the same C-battery, but a separate battery was used for the power stage.

AMPLIFIER CIRCUIT

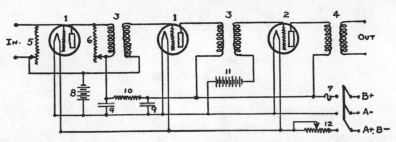

1. 301-A vacuum tube
2. 171-A vacuum tube
3. Ferranti transformer, Type AF3
4. General Radio transformer, Type 541C
5. 2,000-ohm rheostat
6. 18,000-ohm rheostat

7. Fuse
8. 9-volt C battery
9. 4-microfarad Dubilier condenser
10. 1,000-ohm Vitrohm resistor
11. 22-volt C battery
12. Filament rheostat, B battery, 135 volts

The loud-speaker pick-up and the amplifier were tested by connecting a second loud-speaker to the output of the amplifier and talking into the first speaker. The reproduction was excellent. The amplifier alone was also tested by applying a known voltage at various frequencies and measuring the current output.

The output of the amplifier was directly connected to the vibrator of the oscillograph. This oscillograph was the General Electric Company's Type EM, Form C, three-element instrument. This instrument enabled us to obtain photographs of the sound-waves, which were converted into electric currents and amplified to the proper strength by the apparatus.

The theory of the operation of the oscillograph is quite simple. When a loop of wire carrying an electric current is suspended in an electromagnetic field, it is subjected to a mechanical force tending to twist it at right angles to the field. If the current is reversed, this force is reversed in direction. The voice currents are passed through a loop of wire, which is suspended in a strong magnetic field produced by field coils provided for this purpose. A very tiny mirror is cemented to this loop of wire. The whole is submerged in oil, so that there will be no vibration except when currents are flowing. The voice currents are alternating. That is, they flow back and forth in the loop with a frequency that is the same as that of the sound producing them. Hence, the mirror is caused to turn back and forth or vibrate at the frequency of the sound-waves. The amount that it turns each time depends on the loudness of the sound.

An arc light is used to furnish a very intense beam of light which is focused by an optical system of lenses and prisms upon the tiny mirror on the vibrating loop of wire. The beam is reflected from the mirror and sweeps back and forth as it vibrates. This sweeping beam of light is allowed to fall on a moving photographic film. In this way the vibrations are spread out so that a record of each wave is obtained. The record may be crowded close together or may be spread out so that every detail is visible by varying the speed at which the film is moved.

Wherever we have mechanical parts driven by forces of an alternating nature, the movement of the mechanical parts may not correspond exactly to that of the forces acting because the mechanical system has a natural period of vibration of its own at which it would prefer to move. Thus, when we strike a piano string, it vibrates at a definite frequency. In this sound-recording apparatus the moving coil carrying the mirror constitutes a vibrating mechanical system, and as such has its own natural frequency of vibration. It is 5,000 cycles, according to the manufacturer. Owing to the damping effect of the oil we shall obtain accurate response from this system for practically all frequencies below 5,000, but not above this frequency. This gives us practically perfect response for voice work, for 5,000 cycles is the highest frequency to reach us on a chain broadcast program.

The complete layout for taking the pictures is shown in the accompanying sketch. It was desirable to mark the pictures when certain words or syllables were spoken, so that they might be easily identified. This was arranged for by connecting a battery and telegraph key to one of the other elements of the oscillograph. This element produced a straight line on the film when the key was open. When the key was closed the line was offset about an eighth of an inch, thus marking the time when the key was opened and closed.

LAYOUT OF EQUIPMENT

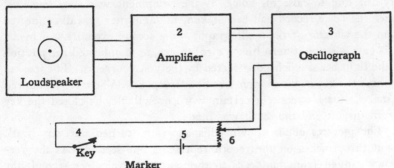

1. Jensen Dynamic Speaker, Type D4
2. 3-stage vacuum tube amplifier
3. General Electric oscillograph, Type EM, Form C
4. Telegraph key
5. 1.5-volt dry cell
6. 6-ohm potentiometer

We have seen something of the operation of each unit of the equipment. We shall now see how it was operated as a whole. Connections were made as shown in the layout diagram. Instead of using photographic film, it was found that satisfactory records could be obtained by letting the light beam fall on Bromide paper. Eastman Bromide Paper P.M.C. No. 1, White Glossy paper was used. Strips of this paper 12 inches long and 3.5 inches wide were placed on a drum. This drum was placed in a container and fastened to the oscillograph so that the light beam could move across the paper. The drum was rotated by a variable speed motor. For the records taken the speed was adjusted so that the drum made one revolution in 3.5 seconds.

347

The oscillograph is equipped with a shutter which is operated electrically by a timing device connected to the shaft of the drum. This was arranged so that the operator could pull a string when he was ready to take a picture. After he had pulled the string, the shutter opened automatically when the revolving film was in the correct position for the start of the record. The same contact that opened the shutter also operated a telegraph sounder, producing a loud click, which indicated that the record had started and that the speaker should commence speaking.

The speaker whose voice was to be recorded sat three or four feet from the loud-speaker and talked in a normal voice. It was not necessary for him to raise his voice, as the equipment was very sensitive. After the voice record had been taken, the amplifier was disconnected from the vibrator of the oscillograph, and a second exposure was made. This gave a straight zero line for reference, as it indicated the position of the light beam when not affected by the voice currents. The speaker operated the key in the marker circuit as he spoke. Whenever he desired to make a mark opposite a certain word or syllable, he closed the key for an instant and the mark was made.

The pictures obtained with this apparatus turned out very well. About three inches on the record represents one second. As the frequency ranged from hundreds to thousands of cycles per second, the individual waves on the records are crowded close together and in some cases make almost a solid pattern. The amplitude of the waves, or the amount of displacement from the center line, depends on the volume of the sound. Thus, an accented syllable will show waves of greater deflection than an unaccented syllable. The spacing between individual waves of course depends on the frequency.

It is especially notable that the pictures of any one person's voice show a predominant frequency represented by a great number of waves at the same distance apart. All of the speaking seems to have this frequency as a basis, with higher frequencies interposed according to the words spoken. This basic frequency for my voice was about 100 cycles. It is the fundamental tone produced by the vocal cords, and the higher frequencies which give the various sounds their distinctive quality are harmonics, or multiple frequencies, produced by the position of the mouth and tongue.

348

The pictures show that there are relatively long pauses between words and syllables in ordinary speech. On the records we see heavy marks of very small amplitude in these quiet spots. These heavy markings are due to room noises and vibrations that were not audible to the ear, but were picked up by the apparatus. When taking records it was necessary to wait until everything was very quiet and no automobiles were passing outside, so that these noises were reduced to a minimum.

In concluding this discussion of these sound pictures I can say that we have every reason to believe that they represent very fairly the voice waves that produce them. This reproduction of the actual sound in pictures lends itself to much more rigid and exacting analysis than would be possible by any method that depended on judging sound by ear. It must be remembered that these records are not to be taken as instances of how the respective verse lines ought to be read; they are records of facts, not norms. I am not in the least interested in, and am in no position for, giving advice to the dramatic reader. I am only making records of the work done by some trustworthy dramatic readers. Of course, I could simply have listened to their reading and noted the results. But then those results would depend not merely upon their reading but also upon my hearing; and no one has means to convince anybody that his hearing is correct. Moreover, it has often been pointed out that accent is not exclusively a matter of loudness. But rhythm cannot be heterogeneous. At any event it is important to study some one particular type of rhythm, in this case that of loudness. Which syllables are actually louder than others? This question cannot be accurately decided on the basis of plain hearing. Objective data are necessary. Our experiments furnish some such data.

Only a very small part of the results thus obtained are here communicated. We are here primarily concerned with rime, not rhythm. The nature and the limits of our theme do not allow us to print all the material we have at hand. It would be quite expensive, and of interest only to a small group of objective rhythmologists. Of course, I have not made records of every verse line used in my statistical tables. But I have prepared repeated records of the most important and widely repeated rhythmical figures. Some of them are discussed in Appendix II.

349

APPENDIX II

~~~~~~

To illustrate the contrast discussed on pages 231 f. between the symmetrical and the asymmetrical distribution of accents in iambic pentameter it may suffice to compare the following two verse lines:

> I weep for Adonais—he is dead.

and

> In charnels and on coffins where black death

The first is a symmetrical figure with two interruptions in the second and third feet (secondary accents). The adjoining photograph shows clearly three maxima of energy in the wave-train carrying the verse. In the second line the symmetry is violated by a spondee in the last foot. This can be seen on the second photograph. Reading from right to left, we observe two patches of equal size at the end of the line. The accents are not imaginary. They are actually there, are registered in an objective way. The verse in consequence of this specific asymmetry is heavy and slow, with a noticeable *ritardando* at the end.

Another symmetrical arrangement that frequently occurs in Shelley may be illustrated by the following fragment photographed in the third illustration on the plate:

> The gray grass and bare boughs . . . .

It is also a part of an iambic pentameter with a trochee in the second and a spondee in the third foot. The reader will find numerous illustrations of this figure in our statistical tables given on pages 229, 230. A spondee is often preceded by a trochee. The reason for this is obvious. An iambic foot followed by a spondee would result in a sequence of three accented syllables, which is too heavy for ordinary purposes. A

350

I weep for Adonais—he is dead.

In charnels and on coffins where black death
(This picture is taken at a very slow rate)

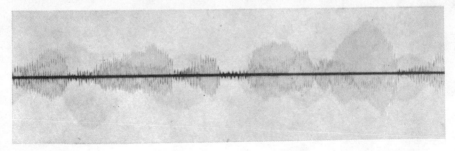

The gray grass and bare boughs . . . .

Humanity is needless . . . .

Suspended in a solitary dome
(Read from right to left)

trochee, by reversing the accents, destroys this heavy sequence, and by attaching an extra accent to the preceding foot makes the whole arrangement symmetrical.

In conclusion let us show a photographic record of a fragment from Robinson Jeffers:

Humanity is needless . . . .

The fragment is highly interesting, both intellectually and rhythmically. The intellectual aspect does not concern us here. Rhythmically it is interesting to see the effect of unusual consonantal environment, consisting largely of *m, n,* and *l,* upon the unaccented vowels. Such environment evidently tends to equalize the distribution of energy among the syllables. A vowel enveloped in *m, n, l,* and *r* absorbs much more energy than one which is surrounded by explosives or gutturals. This circumstance must be taken into consideration for the quantitative analysis of the photographic records.

A good example of a symmetrical verse line similar to that represented by the first record, shown on plate facing page 350, is given in the last recorded:

Suspended in a solitary dome

In our symbolic notation it corresponds to the "ideal" figure:

BIBLIOGRAPHY

ALDINGTON, A. E., "Is Rhyme Indispensable?" *Westminster Review,* 1908

AUERBACH, F., "Untersuchungen über die Natur des Vokalklanges," *Annalen der Physik und Chemie,* Ergänzungsband, 1876

AUERBACH, F., "Die Physikalischen Grundlagen der Phonetik," *Zeitschrift für französische Sprache und Literatur* (1894), 16: 117–171

BARTSCH, K., *Der Innere Reim in der Hofischen Lyrik* (Germania, 1867), pp. 129–194

BAUERMEISTER, K., *Zur Sprache Spensers auf Grund der Reime in der Fairie Queen,* Dissertation, 1896

BAUM, P. F., *The Principles of English Versification,* Cambridge, Massachusetts, 1922

BEATTIE, J., *Theory of Language,* 1783

BEHNKE, E., *The Mechanism of the Human Voice,* London, 1881

BELL, A., *Speech Tones,* Washington, 1893 (The Volta Bureau)

BELL, A., "Phonetics," *Science* (1890), 15: 5–7

BELL, A., *A Popular Manual of Vocal Physiology and Visible Speech,* New York, 1881

BELLANGER, L., *Études historiques et philologiques sur la rime française,* 1876

BERNHARDI, A. F., *Sprachlehre, 1801–1803*

BERNSTEIN, S. J., *Methodological Value of the Phonetical Study of Rime,* Pushkinsky Sbornik, 1922. (In Russian.)

BESHORNER, F., "Verbale Reime bei Chaucer," *Morsbach's Studien,* p. 59

BEVIER, L., "The Acoustic Analysis of the Vowels," *Physical Review,* 1900

BLAIR, H., *Lectures on Rhetoric and Belles Lettres,* 1801

BRAUNE, W., *Reim und Vers, Eine Wortgeschichtliche Untersuchung,* 1916

BROWN, A. C. L., "On the Origin of Stanza Linking in English Alliterative Verse," *Romanic Review,* 7: 271–283

BRUSOV, VALERIJ, *Science of Verse,* 1919. (In Russian.)

CHERVIN, A., *Analyse physiologique des éléments de la parole,* Paris, 1878

CRANDALL, I. B., "The Sounds of Speech," *Bell System Technical Journal,* 1925

DABNEY, J. P., *The Musical Basis of Verse,* 1901

DANIEL, S., *A Defence of Ryme,* 1603

DELAPORTE, P., *De la rime française,* 1876

DEWEY, G., *Relative Frequency of English Speech Sounds,* Harvard University Press, 1923

DINGELDEIN, O., *Der Reim bei den Griechen und Römern,* Leipzig, 1892

EHRENFELD, A., *Studien zur Theorie des Reims,* Zürich, 1897–1904

ELLIS, A. I., *On the Physical Constituents of Accent and Emphasis,* Transactions of Philological Society, 1873–1874

FAUCHET, C., *Origine de la langue et poesie françoise, ryme, et romans,* 1581

FISCHLI, A., "Ueber Klangmittel im Vers-Innern," *Sprache und Dichtung,* 1920

FLETCHER, H., "Physical Measurements of Audition and Their Bearing on the Theory of Hearing," *Journal of the Franklin Institute,* 1923, p. 196

FLETCHER, H., *Speech and Hearing,* New York, 1929

FOSTER, B. O., "On Certain Euphonic Embellishments in the Verse of Propertius," *Transactions of the American Philological Association,* Vol. XL, 1910.

FOUQUIÈRES, L. BECQ DE, *Traité général de versification française,* 1879

FOWLER, T. H., *Study of Suffix Rime in Otfried's Evangelienbuch,* Baltimore, 1905

FREYTAG, —, *Darstellung der arabischen Verskunst*, Bonn, 1831

GARTEN, S., und KLEINKNECHT, F., *Beiträge zur Vokallehre*, Abhandlungen der mathematisch-physikalischen Klasse der Sächsischen Akademie der Wissenschaften (1921), Vol. 38, Nos. 7–9

GASCOIGNE, G., *Certayne Notes of Instructions*, 1575

GINGUENÉ, —, *Histoire littéraire de l'Italie*, 1811, pp. 250 ff.

GLÖDE, C., *Die Reimbrechung in Gottfrieds von Strassburg Tristan*, Germania, 1888

GODDARD, P. E., "Mechanical Aids to the Study and Recording of Language," *American Anthropologist* (1905), 7: 613–619.

GOLDSCHMIDT, V., *Ueber Harmonie und Komplikation*, Berlin, 1901

GRAMMONT, M., *Le Vers français, ses moyens d'expression, son harmonie* (1913), pp. 347–375, 475–479

GRANDGENT, C. H., *Vowel Measurements, Publications of Modern Language Association of America* (Supplement, 1890), pp. 148–174

GRASSERIE, R. DE LA, *Des Principes scientifiques de la versification française*, 1900

GRASSMANN, H., "Ueber die Physikalische Natur der Sprachlaute," *Annalen der Physik und Chemie*, 1877

GRIMM, W., *Zur Geschichte des Reims* (Berlin, 1881–1884, Kleiner Schriften), 4: 125–336.

GRINDROD, C. F., *Studies of Rhyme and Rhythm*, 1905

GUENTERT, "Ueber Reimwortbildungen im Arischen und Altgriechischen," *Indo-Germanische Bibliothek*, 1914

GUEST, E., *A History of English Rhythms*, London, 1838 (new ed., 1882)

GUMMING, TH. P., "The Larynx the Source of the Vowel Sounds," *American Journal of Dental Science*, 1874

HAID, K., *Der Spaltreim in der Englischen Literatur des 19 Jahrhunderts*, Heidelberg, Archiv

HELMHOLTZ, H., *Die Lehre von den Tonempfindungen*, 1863

HENSEN, V., "Die Harmonie in den Vokalen," *Zeitschrift für Biologie*, 1891

HEUSLER, A., *Deutsche Versgeschichte mit Einschluss des Altenglischen und Altnordischen Stabreimverses*, Berlin und Leipzig, 1927 (*Grudriss der Germanischen Philologie*)

HILMER, W. C., *Rhyme in Schiller's Poems,* 1911

HOLMES, G., *A Treatise on Vocal Physiology,* 2d ed., London, 1880

HYTIER, J., *Les Techniques modernes du vers français,* 1926

JENKIN, FLEEMING, and EWING, *On the Harmonic Analysis of Certain Vowel Sounds, Transactions of Royal Society of Edinburgh* (1878), 28: 745–777

JESPERSEN, O., *Lehrbuch der Phonetik,* 3 Auflage, 1920

JESPERSEN, *A Modern English Grammar,* 1909

JOHANNESEN, F., *Zur Lehre vom französischen Reim,* Berlin, 1897

JOHNSTON, O. M., "Repetition of Words and Phrases at the Beginning of Tercets in Dante's Divine Comedy," *Publications of Modern Language Association of America,* 537–549

KINGSLEY, N. W., "Some Investigations into the Mechanism of Speech," *New York Medical Journal* (1879), 30: 28–65

KLUGE, F., "Zur Geschichte des Reimes im Altgermanischen" (*Beiträge zur Geschichte der deutschen Sprache und Literatur*), P.B.B. 9: 422

LAHR, I., "Die Grassmanische Vokaltheorie im Lichte des Experiments," *Annalen der Physik und Chemie* (1886), 27: 94–119

LANIER, SIDNEY, *Music and Poetry,* New York, 1898 (2d ed., 1914)

LIDDELL, MARK, *An Introduction to the Scientific Study of English Poetry,* 1902

LIDDELL, MARK, *The Physical Characteristics of Speech Sound* (Published by Purdue University), 1924–1927

LLOYD, R. I., "Speech Sounds, Their Nature and Causation," *Phonetische Studien* (1890–1897), 3: 251–278; 4: 37–67, 183–214, 275–306; 5: 1–32, 129–141, 263–271; 11: 1–24

LLOYD, R. I., *Some Researches into the Nature of Vowel Sounds,* University of London thesis, 1890

MARMONTEL, *Éléments de litterature. Oeuvres* (1819), 15: 280

MARSH, G. P., *Lectures on the English Language,* New York, 1887

MASING, W., *Ueber Ursprung und Verbreitung des Reimes,* Dorp, 1866

MASING, W., *Sprachliche Musik in Goethe's Lyrik,* 1910

MEHRING, S., *Der Reim in Seiner Entwickelung und Fortbildung*

MELODIA, G., *Studî sulle rime del Petrarca,* 1909

355

MEYER, G. H. VON, *Unsere Sprachwerkzeuge und ihre Verwendung zur Bildung der Sprachlaute*

MICHAELIS, G., "Ueber die Anordnung der Vokale," *Archiv* (1881–1884), 65: 403–460; 66: 77–96; 71: 73–96

MINOR, J., *Neuhochdeutsche Metrik* (Strassburg, 1902), pp. 369–416

MITFORD, *Inquiry into the Principles of Harmony in Language* (2d ed., 1864)

MURATORI, —, *Antiquitates italianae medii aevi*, 1738

NEUMAN, FR., *Geschichte des Neuhochdeutschen Reimes, von Opitz bis Wieland*, Berlin, 1920

OLOVSON, H., *Étude sur les rimes de trois poétes romantiques*

PAGET, R. A. S., "The Production of Artificial Vowel Sounds," *Proceedings of the Royal Society*, London, 1923

PAGET, R. A. S., *Vowel Resonances*, International Phonetic Association, 1922

PAGET, R. A. S., *Human Speech; Some Observations, Experiments, and Conclusions as to the Nature, Origin, Purpose, and Possible Improvement of Human Speech*, 1930

PETERS, W. E., "A New and Accurate Method of Photographing Speech," *Vox* (Berlin, 1913), 23: 131–135

PIPPING, H., "Zur Lehre von der Vokalklängen," *Zeitschrift für Biologie* (1815), 31: 524–583

PIPPING, H., "Ueber die Theorie der Vokale," *Acta Societatis Scientiarum Fennicae* (1894), 20, No. 11

PIPPING, H., "Zur Klangfarbe der Gezungenen Vokale," *Zeitschrift für Biologie* (1890), 27: 1–80, 433–499

POGGEL, C., *Grundzüge einer Theorie des Reimes und Gleichklänge*, 1836

PORTER, N., "The Vowel Elements in Speech," *American Journal of Science and Arts* (1866), 92: 167–183, 303–319

POUND, EZRA, "The Wisdom of Poetry," *Forum* (1912), pp. 497–501

PREECE, WILLIAM H., and A. STROH, "Studies in Acoustics. I. On the Synthetical Examination of Vowel Sounds," *Proceedings of the Royal Society of London* (1879), 28: 358–367

PUTTENHAM, GEORGE, *The Art of English Poesie* (Arber's edition), 1589

356

QUICHERAT, L., *Traité de versification française* (Paris, 1850, 2d ed.). Rime, pp. 20–50, 332–386

RANKIN, T. W., *Rime and Reason*. Publications of Modern Language Association of America, December, 1929

RAPP, K. M., *Versuch einer Physiologie der Sprache*, Stuttgart, 1836–1841

Report on the Construction of a Vowel Organ, Smithsonian Miscellaneous Collections (1905), 47 : 360–364

RICHARDSON, CHARLES F., *A Study of English Rime*, Hanover, 1909

ROUSSELOT, P. I., *Principes de phonétique expérimental*, Paris, 1924

SAINTSBURY, G. E. B., *History of English Prosody*, three volumes, Macmillan, 1923

SCHENK, A., *Étude sur la rime dans Cyrano de Bergerac de M. Rostand*, Kiel, 1900

SCHILLING, FELIX, *Poetic and Verse Criticism of the Reign of Elisabeth*, 1891

SCHÜTZE, J. S., *Versuch einer Theorie des Reimes nach Inhalt und Form*, 1802

SCRIPTURE, E. W., *The Study of English Speech by New Methods of Phonetic Investigation*, Proceedings of the British Academy, 1921–1923

SCRIPTURE, E. W., *Researches in Experimental Phonetics*, Carnegie Institute of Washington Publications N44, 1906

SCRIPTURE, E. W., "Nature of Vowel Sounds," *Nature* (1921), 106 : 632–634, 664–666; 107 : 2; 108 : 82–83

SCRIPTURE, E. W., *Untersuchungen über die Vokale*, Munich, 1906

SCRIPTURE, E. W., "On the Nature of Vowels," *American Journal of Science* (1901), 161 : 302–309

SHAKHMATOV, A. A., *Outline of the Modern Russian Language*, Petersburg, University Publications, 1913. (In Russian.)

SHULGOVSKI, N. N., *Theory and Practice of Poetic Art* (1913), pp. 291–403

SIDNEY, SIR PHILIP, *The Defence of Poesie*, 1595

SIEVERS, ED., *Gründzuge der Lautphysiologie, Bibliothek der Indogermanischen Grammatiken*, Band I, Leipzig, 1876 (subsequent edition under the title, *Grundzüge der Phonetik*)

357

SIEVERS, ED., *Zur Rhythmik und Melodik des Neuhochdeutschen Sprechverses (Verhandlungen der Philologie)*, Leipzig, 1894

SMITH, C. A., *Repetition and Parallelism in English Verse*

STARR, M. A., "Speech, Its Mental and Physical Elements," *New Princeton Review* (1886), 1: 320–341

STEDMAN, E. C., *The Nature and Elements of Poetry*, New York, 1892

TECHMER, FR., "Naturwissenschaftliche Analyse und Synthese der Hörbaren Sprache," *Internationale Zeitschrift* (1884), 1: 69–170

TECHMER, FR., *Zur Veranschaulichung der Lautbildung*, Leipzig, 1885

WACKERNAGEL, W., *Geschichte des deutschen Hexameters und Pentameters*, 1831 (Kleinere Schriften, Band II, 1873)

WACKERNAGEL, W., *Brief an W. Grimm* (Grimm's Kleinere Schriften, Band IV, pp. 339 ff.)

WEBER, F., "On Melody in Speech," *Longman's Magazine* (1887), 9: 399–410

WILLIS, R., *On the Vowel Sounds and on Reed-Organ Pipes, Transactions of the Cambridge Philosophical Society* (1830), 3: 231–262. Also published in German.

WILLIS, R., "Ueber Vokaltone Zungenpfeifen," *Annalen der Physik und Chemie* (1832), 24: 397–437

WÖLFFLIN, —, *Der Reim im Lateinischen, Archiv für lateinische Lexikographie und Grammatik*, 1884, pages 352 ff.

WYLD, H. C., *English Rhyme from Surrey to Pope*, 1923

ZHIRMUNSKI, V., *Composition of Lyric Verse*, 1921. (In Russian.)

ZHIRMUNSKI, V., *Rime, Its History and Theory*, Petersburg, 1923. (In Russian.)

ZIEHEN, TH., *Vorlesungen über Aesthetik*, 1: 245–268; 2: 386–388

358

INDEX